Bogged Down
in
County Lyric

About the Author

Peter Kinsley is an Anglo-Irish novelist, born in Avoca House in Stanley, Co. Durham. He was educated at St Cuthbert's grammar school, Benwell, Northumberland. After service in the British Army in Fontainbleu, France, 1953-55, he was a sub-editor on the *Daily Mirror*, Fleet Street, aged 21. Later he was a crime reporter on the *Daily Mail* and the *Daily Express*, and wrote the William Hickey column before resigning to freelance as a foreign correspondent in the south of France and Rome for the BBC and fourteen British newspapers, which is where he met the great characters in these books.

NOTE: The author thanks the Society of Authors and the Royal Literary Fund, London, for their generous assistance, enabling him to complete these memoirs.

Bogged Down
in
County Lyric

Peter Kinsley

AMHERST

A CIP catalogue record for this book is available
from the British Library.

ISBN 1 903637 06 6

Printed in Great Britain

First published in 2002

Amherst Publishing Limited
Longmore House, High Street, Otford, Sevenoaks, Kent TN14 5PQ

The Emperor of Ethiopia (The Lion of Judah), Haile Selassie, meeting again Tristan Jones who had skippered an anti-slave gunboat in the Ethiopian navy: 'Ah, Mister Jones. You know I've often wondered what makes a man like you tick.'

Tristan Jones: 'And I've often wondered what makes a man like *you* tick.'

* * *

Stephen Seley, in Ibiza: 'We're bogged down in County Lyric. All I ever wanted to do was write something that would sing down the centuries, to confirm what Louis Zukofsky, a New York poet and a gazelle, said: "It's a sad world anyway. Not many of us will get out of it alive." That's what he said to Ezra Pound when he visited him in the asylum.'

Peter McGinn: 'There are two last frontiers: the exploration of the Universe and the exploration of our inner selves: what makes us dream, why do we fall in love? What makes one man a poisoner and another a saint? The *real* mystery is within us.'

* * *

By the same author

What they said about Volume I

Loved the book — it made me laugh and cry. — **Neal Ascherson**, (author of *The King Incorporated* and a columnist on *The Observer*).

A lovingly detailed record of a World War II childhood and a threadbare, innocent world that is now as lost as Ur of the Chaldees - **Al Alvarez** (author of *The Savage God*, formerly the poetry editor of *The Observer*).

A fascinating record of young lives in the Second World War - **Penny Ritchie Calder**, Curator, Imperial War Museum, London.

A wartime story that took forty years to tell... now to be used in a major exhibition 'Children At War' at the Imperial War Museum, London - **Matthew McKenzie**, *Sunday Sun*, Newcastle Upon Tyne.

What they said about Volume II

This is the most vivid and entertaining account written of the 'Last Age' of Fleet Street - the era when the basic irreverence and humanity of journalists finally broke through into the pages of their own newspapers. Peter Kinsley, who worked on papers in northern England and as a self employed British correspondent on the French Riviera, belonged to the great period of the tabloid and popular 'diaries': the gossip columns which ostensibly chronicled the high life of the Establishment, but which did so with an increasingly radical ferocity that discredited and punctured the high-and-mighty. Nobody reading Kinsley will go on believing that the 1950s were a dull decade The procession of laughing , outrageous reprobates in his pages (some journalists, some their victims)shows very clearly how the way was being opened for the 'Satire Boom' of London in the 1960s. These two books of memoir are a wonderfully comic read but they are also infallible source material for anyone studying the 'end of deference' in Britain and the prelude to the head-on political and social challenges in the next period - **Neal Ascherson.**

A nostalgic walk down memory lane for those who recall the halcyon days of Fleet Street. Peter recounts with humour many stories concerning himself and the Greats who bestrode the Street in those times. He also reminds us of what great fun it could be, an element that seems sadly missing in today's newspaper world
This is the second part of four volumes. The first, All The Fields Are Covered with Snow, is a lyrical and deeply moving account of his wartime evacuation to a depressed coalmining village, incongruously named No Place - **Alfred Draper**, (author of The Amritsar Massacre)..

PREFACE

WHEN I published volume one and volume two of my memoirs, the first at the end of the year 2000 and the second as the millennium began, I looked over the manuscript of what was to be volume three, and it came as quite a shock to realise that most of the wonderful characters I had met over the years in London, the South of France, Dublin, New York and on the island of Ibiza had passed on, so that in some cases I could now use their real names instead of fictitious ones.

The character called Steve Primero was actually Stephen Seley. In the Calle de la Virgen, where he lived, on the island of Ibiza, he slid down a shop doorway, his face turned purple and he was rushed to Can Misses clinic, where he awoke at 3 a.m. looked up at the young Spanish doctor, and said: 'I'll have a gin and a cigarette,' and died. Another character whom I had christened Treasure Evans was, in fact, that intrepid sailor Tristan Jones, who got his one-way ticket to Fiddlers Green while teaching limbless children to sail in Phucket, Thailand. Tristan had taught me to sail off Ibiza, and one of his many sayings was (he was a born philosopher) : 'A sailor doesn't need legs. If he can pull up a sail, an anchor and make a meal for himself then he's in business.'

In New York, the Irish-American nurse, having ascertained that he was a Welshman, said that the British Army was getting a bad beating in the Falklands war, and added that his fellow countryman, Dylan Thomas had died in the very bed he was in at that moment.

Tristan said: 'Oh yes, and have you any other good news?'

'Yeah, we took your leg off last night,' she replied with

9

menopausal charm.

It was some years later, in Thailand, that his other leg was amputated, and he discarded his whalebone false leg for a little motor-scooter.

A New York publisher was about to bring out my first novel, a comedy set in London about a young con-man who lived inside the big blue whale in the Kensington Natural History museum to avoid paying rent, and they had booked me into the Chelsea Hotel, home of Arthur Miller, Tennessee Williams, Arthur C. Clarke, Jack Kerouac, Allen Ginsberg , Tom Wolfe, Brendan Behan and Dylan Thomas in his day. And that is where my story opens.

Peter Kinsley
London, 2002

CHAPTER 1

America

T HE first thing McGinn noticed about America when coming
out of the airport was the size of the gravestones, enormous granite
crosses and the occasional huge Celtic cross where some Irish citizen
had been laid to rest, and within a couple of days of settling into the
Chelsea Hotel he was headlong into Irish America, in the New York
Athletic Club, Jim Downey's bar drinking with the New York Giants,
P.J. Clarke's bar on Third Avenue, and the row of eateries on that famous
street where he asked one white-aproned server for a turkey dinner and
when he pointed at the bird set ready for carving the apron said: 'That's
not a toikey, buddy, it's a chicken.'

So here he was, in a country where the chickens were as big as
English turkeys and the headstones the size of small apartment blocks
and everyone in New York seemed to be snapping at each other. If you
said : 'thank you' to a waiter or waitress, they snapped: 'O.K., wiseguy'
and if two customers spoke together in a foreign language, the server or
bartender or cashier or cabby would snap: 'Hey — youse two — speak
English will ya? You're in Amurca now.'

The owner of the Chelsea hotel asked McGinn for a signed copy of
his comedy novel, to add to his collection of signed works by Dylan
Thomas, William Burroughs, Tennessee Williams and Arthur Miller,
and when McGinn wrote his own name and that of the owner on the
fly-leaf, he snapped: 'Hey, that's not good enough. Write something
more in there.' McGinn wrote: 'Best Wishes' which was ungraciously
accepted. Then Stanley, the owner, unbent a little and said: 'Hey', (funny
how everyone seemed to say 'Hey' before speaking) 'We're putting a

plaque up on the outside wall saying the Welsh bard was here before he croaked. You wanna come to the ceremony? There'll be some booze after, and the British Ambassador will be unveiling the plaque.'

McGinn thought of his old mate Derek Driscoll, outside the Mandrake Club in Meard Street, Soho, 'lending' poor dead Dylan a ten shilling note to get back to Wales where Caitlin, his wife ('When he met her she was *virago intacta*', Driscoll said) was waiting to give him hell.

'I'll try' McGinn lied. The British Ambassador? What would the Rimbaud of Cwymdonkin Drive have said to that? He would probably make a technicolor yawn all over the stuffed shirt's fancy trousers if he could be there.

Henry Thody, McGinn's old sparring partner from the Riviera and Rome had arranged to meet and show him the famous 21, Henry's paradise on earth, where he would grace the bar with his Dundreary moustache (it had become a well-known sight in Manhattan), drink Gordon's gin and tonic and meet the famous. The elegant bar was also the address of the most famous speakeasy in Manhattan during Prohibition, when it made its money selling Canadian whisky smuggled across the border by Legs Diamond who switched from hoofer (ten cents a dance) to chauffeur for the Mob.

It was closed on Sundays.

New York on a Sunday was like one half of election day, the pubs were shut in the morning, and the watering hole of Henry Thody was the bar in Rockerfeller Plaza, a little haven from the traffic in summer and a popular ice skating rink in winter. One particular client would stand at the bar, a paperback book in his fist to control the tremble, listening to the clock ticking towards the magic hour, all of this a throwback to Prohibition with the handsome young men from the F.B.I. shooting guys for importing that dangerous drug, whisky, into the United States. McGinn noticed with one swift, lynx-eyed glance that the bar's regular Sunday morning early-bird client was holding his paperback book upside down.

On the stroke of twelve, after the regular customer had been served, Henry Thody ordered a Gordon's gin and tonic and said: 'Well, here's to New York, old man, the greatest city in the world. Have you tried the apple pie here? It's the best apple pie in the world, old man, thick, juicy, a sugared crust and a flavour of cinnamon. What do those French know?

'And another thing which is great about New York, old man, is there are no dogs and no kids.'

'You mean there's nothing at all for an old fart to kick in this town?' said McGinn sarcastically.

'Only the bucket, old man — and do you know what the form is when that day arrives? They tart you up like a Tussauds waxwork, lipstick, powder, perm. — the lot —and you lie in state on the Fifth Avenue morgue slab, and, having left a few thousand dollars behind the bar of 21, your former pals come down to view the body —' I'm a friend of the corpse,' say the Irish, — and then proceed to get slaughtered back at 21. But you *must* view the body before you can have a drink, a New York custom, old man.'

'New York custom?' a voice snapped. 'What do you guys know about New York customs? You sound like a couple of Limeys to me. Can I get you a drink?

'My name's Berlitz. You heard of me?'

'The language schools?' said McGinn.

'Right in one,' said Mr. Berlitz taking off his beautiful 3,000 dollar vicuna overcoat and throwing it onto the floor.

McGinn went to pick it up, thinking he had dropped the coat by mistake.

'Leave that coat where it is,' Mr. Berlitz snapped. 'If I wanna throw my coat on the floor, I will. Now I asked you guys if you wanna drink - 'Hey, Charlie', he yelled at the bartender, 'Give my two Limey friends a drink will ya, before they die of thirst. What are your names, anyhow, and what are you doing in the Big Apple?'

'Henry Thody, of the London Times, old chap...'

'Pete McGinn, ex -newspaperman, now a novelist, here to promote my book, out this week, Three Cheers for Nothing, E.P. Dutton, price three dollars and ninety five cents, and cheap at the price, considering that a hamburger costs five bucks in 21.'

'You can't eat a book.'

'You can't read a hamburger, and a book lasts longer.'

'Well, sounds interestin', Pete, but I don't have time to read.'

'Yes it does tend to waste valuable drinking time...'

'Where are you staying?'

'The Chelsea.'

'It's a writers hang-out,' said Thody. 'And it caters for eccentrics.

And for people who are trying to be characters. I was in the lobby there one day recently when a girl from Greenwich Village walked through, and she had a lobster on a lead. Can you imagine that, going around New York with a lobster on a lead?'

'From Greenwich Village, huh? I knew some of them had crabs, but I never did see one with a lobster before.'

McGinn laughed, but Thody appeared annoyed. Henry was of the old school, an officer and a gentleman, and he didn't like what would have been called 'smut' at his old public school.

Mr. Berlitz called for more drinks and said: 'I only went to England once, and that was by mistake. I was seeing some friends off on a boat to Europe and I had a bit too much champagne. When they called 'all ashore who's going ashore' my wife tried to get me down the gangplank. I resisted, wanting more champagne, and she insisted. She insisted and I resisted, so I put my foot squarely between her shoulder blades and gave her a push, sending her in to the arms of the waiting crowd.

'When the ship sailed, the purser tried to have me for a stowaway, so I paid the fare to Europe. Two English guys came to the bar to see me and said: 'I say, old chap, are you the feller who pushed his good lady down the gangway as we were leaving?'

'What about it?' I said.

'Nothing, nothing, old chap, simply that we'd like to buy you a drink' So we drank our way across the Atlantic until a fog started to come down and they announced we were in Liverpool instead of Le Havre. The fog lifted and it was raining. I'd never seen rain like it. 'Where's the goddamn sun?' I asked the crew.'

'Not 'ere, mate,' they said.

'But you can't go ashore, because you haven't got a passport with you, sir,' the Customs officer said.

'Who the hell wants to go ashore?' I said. 'Haven't you seen that rain?'

'Would you mind moderating your language, sir, you're in England now.' he said

'Don't I fuckin' know it — look at that goddamn weather out there. Ducks would drown in it. Where's the sun for Chrissake?'

He went away and came back a little later and said: 'It's all right, Mister Berlitz, we've got permission for you to go ashore.'

'I told you, I don't wanna go ashore. I wanna go where the sun is shining. Can you tell me where the hell in Europe the sun is shining.'

He went away again and came back with a weather report.

'Nice, sir. The sun is shining in Nice.'

'So how do I get there?'

'Well, you will have to have a temporary passport, sir, before you can land and go to London airport.'

'So how do I get that?'

'Don't worry, sir, I think we can manage to arrange that.'

'And that's just what they did, and I took a plane from London to Nice and had a bit of what the Cockneys call the old currant bun, the jolly old sun, and had my wife air freight my passport to me. Now when we've finished our drinks here, I'd like you guys to come visit with me in my apartment.

Half an hour later they were in a taxi, heading towards the rich apartment blocks on the edge of Central Park, and Mr. Berelitz was directing Abe Smith, the taxi driver, all steamed up and yelling: 'Go, go, go, Abie. See that cop ahead? Go for him Abie. Go get him. Knock the son of a bitch sky high.'

The taxi driver looked back over his right shoulder with one frightened eye, as if to ask: Who is this madman in my cab and who are the guys with the London suits and why aren't they stopping him? and Mr. Berlitz, having digested all the details of Abe Smith's cab licence name and number, continued to yell: 'Go get him, Abie. I'll give you a thousand dollars to knock the son of a bitch six feet in the air. Go on, go for him — kill him, kill him, I'll give you a thousand dollars...'

'Calm down Mister, I ain't killin' anybody, an' I ain't runnin' anybody down. I gotta livin' to make, so calm down or get another cab.'

Mr. Berlitz calmed down a little, but continued jumping around in his seat and glaring at the figure of the cop on point duty.

'We're nearly there fellers. I need a goddamn drink.'

Berlitz threw the cabby a ten dollar bill for a two dollar ride, and the elevator took them to the Berlitz apartment, where they were met by a young, reasonably attractive and clearly long-suffering wife who was ordered to get the drinks, three gins and tonic, lots of ice, and was further ordered to 'gimme the tickler, baby,' after he had introduced 'my two Limey friends, Henry an' Pete.'

Two Siamese cats, looking with disdain at the two Britishers, strode with a haughty air over the room to Berlitz and curled themselves around his trousers turn-ups, mewing with delight. The long-suffering wife handed him a two-foot long electric back-scratcher, and Berlitz proceeded to rake the little juddering claw down the uplifted spines of the two spoilt cats.

A door opened onto the sitting room and a barrel-chested man entered, holding the lead of a beautiful Afghan hound, which looked with an even more supercilious stare at the 'Limeys' than the cats had done. The large man looked sideways, suspiciously, at McGinn and Thody, and said out of the side of his mouth: 'I'm goin' to take the dawg for a walk in the Park.' Thody looked at McGinn, and McGinn looked at Henry, and they both thought: Cop.

'You go ahead. See ya later.' Berlitz called.

The long-suffering wife looked at the back of the ex-cop's head as he went to the door. Thody and McGinn again exchanged glances, newspapermen on the *qui-vive* as they tried to fathom the situation in the millionaire's household, one aspect of it becoming immediately clear when Berlitz suddenly flung his empty crystal goblet at his wife so that she was forced to jump and catch it before it shattered against the wall. The man with the Afghan appeared not to notice, for he glanced away and made his exit with the supercilious Afghan.

'That's my heavy,' said Berlitz. 'And my dawg-walker. He used to be with Homicide. Say, Henry, your glass is empty. Nobody sits with an empty glass in my home. Hey, Baby, get a drink for Henry,' he called, taking the empty goblet from Thody's fingers and hurling it across the room in a direction that made his poor wife jump like a goalkeeper to 'field' it.

After she had delivered the sparkling drink to Thody, she turned and as she reached the door Berlitz grabbed McGinn's empty glass and shouted: 'Catch this one, baby, and threw it so that she had to make a spectacular dive for the expensive glass.

'Time we were going,' said Henry, unable to witness any more humiliation of the woman who had suffered all this in silence. He finished his drink and placed the empty glass out of reach of the frustrated baseball pitcher, and stood up. McGinn did likewise and Berlitz cried: 'You can't go now. Have another drink. Hey, come on, fellers...'

16

'Sorry, old chap, but duty calls. I have a story to write about your elections. About, in my colleague McGinn's excellent turn of phrase, about the two intellectual bantam-weights fighting it out up there.'

For a moment, McGinn thought Berlitz was going to argue, to defend the intellectual status of the future President of the United States of America, but he just lowered his head and coughed. He was clearly not in the mood for an argument, so Thody and McGinn made their way to the exit, and Henry called over his shoulder: 'Thanks for the drinks, old chap. Good luck to you.'

'And may all your sons be Bishops,' McGinn called

In the street they hailed a cab.

'What do you make of that?' Henry asked.

'Do you mean that poor wife?'

'Ah, yes, the 'poor' wife — but...'

'Sure, one day soon she'll be rich, when that monstrous old piss-pot croaks, and by the way he's hurling down the sauce, it won't be too long a wait, and she'll be flush with the Berlitz millions... but the things women have to put up with...'

'Of course, old chap. You've covered the Riviera, the film festivals, met the glitterati on the Cote d'Azure and in the London, Paris and Rome fleshpots, and seen it all before. As one hard-bitten newshound said to me at the Cannes festival once: 'Funny, isn't it, how many young women are here on holiday with their fathers?' And it's true — women will sleep with older men and put up with all kinds of things, just so long as there will be a pot of gold at the end of the rainbow. But have you noticed how rare it is for men to do the same thing. I mean, how many successful gigolos have you met in your life? Not many, I'll warrant.'

'Old Willie Maugham used to say that that was the hardest work of all. The ones I have met have always been quite specific about the rewards: the old ladies give them expensive clothes, pick up the tab for expensive meals, hotel bills, travel, etcetera, and they give as presents expensive gold and silver cigarette lighters, cigarette cases and Rolex watches, which are always, always, inscribed, so they can't pawn them or sell them, and they never, ever, get money. If they had ready cash they might be able or tempted to run away, or even to spend it on a younger woman...'

'You seem to know a lot about it, old man. Had any experience?'

'I've avoided it a couple of times.'

'Do tell...'

'Do you know about the special doggy school in Switzerland where they train poodles for rich old ladies and Frog Toms? You know that a French poodle has a specially long tongue? Well, the little doggies are specially trained...'

'Good lawd, how do you know these things, old man?'

'As a matter of fact, Noel Coward told me about the school. He sent his own poodle there...'

'How on earth did he find out about the school?'

'I asked him that. He said he was told by the American actor William Holden, who was living in Switzerland at that time.'

'Pray continue with your narrative Doctor Watson. You have my undivided attention.'

'Well, I was asked one day when I was in the Army in Fontainebleau if I was interested in earning some extra cash. I was an Acting Company Sergeant-Major but my rank was Sergeant, and my pay was about sufficient to tip a waiter at *le Tour d'Argent* in Paris. This French corporal knew of an organisation that put young men in touch with lonely old ladies who would pay for their services. When he told me exactly what the young men had to do to earn their pay, I said 'No'.'

'I suppose you had to stand to attention whenever required?'

'Er... rather more than that...'

'Oh, no...'

'Right. They didn't have poodles...'

'You said you'd avoided it a couple of times, old man. What was the other occasion?'

'Right there on the Coast — in Nice, to be exact. She threw me the keys of a powder blue Rolls Royce and the keys to a villa just above the old harbour. She was a very nice woman — from Oz. She'd planted three rich hubbies and brought her Rolls from Oz every summer and did the season in Nice. She liked me because I sang a few Irish songs at a lunch party at the end of one of the festivals.'

'So what did you do?'

'I said I couldn't drive, and I had my own pad in Vence. She was disappointed, and I never saw her again. I think she took off back to Oz with the car. I hope she found a fourth husband. She was a nice woman.'

'Well, there are plenty of nice women in this town, old man. They come to New York to make their way in the world of theatre and business, just as some go to Hollywood to try and break into the movies. As you appear to like arty Sheilas, you should try the Village, old man.'

'With crabs, or a lobster?'

Henry laughed: 'I did say they try to be characters, old man...'

'But if they're going to be pretentious, at least let them try to be original. What was the name of the Frenchman who went about Paris with a lobster on a lead? He's mentioned in the Journals of Andre Gide. People used to ask him why he had a lobster on a lead and he replied: 'Because they can't bark and they know the secrets of the Deep..'

'Yes, I suppose there's nothing new under the sun, old man.'

'Only an unpeeled egg or an unpeeled banana, old man.'

'Ha. Talking of eggs and fruit, old man, Bobby Kennedy is speaking on Broadway in the election campaign soon. Do you think they'll be throwing rotten eggs at him?'

'What the good-looking Bobby? It'll be roses all the way, just you watch. He's part of show-biz as they are.'

'Well I'll be covering it for the S.T., old man.'

'Henry? Why do you tell people you represent The Times when you are the stringer for the Sunday Times?'

'They've never heard of the S.T. here, old man, but The Times — that they have heard of, the one they see the butler ironing in the Limey movies.'

'Ring me at the Chelsea and we'll make a meet on Broadway.'

'Right. You're meeting Charlie Kelly tomorrow, aren't you?'

'He's picking me up at nine. We're going up to West Point, to see the passing out parade, then a tour of the New York pubs in the evening.'

'Charlie's got some tales to tell: ask him about Superintendent Bob Fabian of The Yard when he stopped briefly in New York after investigating the Sir Harry Oakes murder in the Bahamas.'

'How come Charlie's so well-known, Henry?'

'Why, don't you know, old man? Charlie's the cop who arrested Machine-gun Kelly and made all the headlines...'

* * *

'Limehouse Charlie' as some of the New York cops called him, packed a .38 Smith and Weston revolver down the belt holding his pants up, and it looked to McGinn as if it were well oiled, clean, and ready for immediate use. It had, in fact, been in use quite recently, when Charlie had to shoot it out with a crazed gunman in a hospital ward, where he had taken refuge. 'The son of a bitch ran into the children's ward. Forty sick kids lying there, screaming, while I fought it out with this fruit cake who was shooting over and under the beds. The kids were lucky — not one of them was injured, and I managed to plug the son of a bitch when he ducked for the last time.'

Charlie, or Detective Kelly, or Limehouse Charlie, or Limey Charlie, got his name from his liking for visiting Englishmen, starting off with Chief Superintendent Robert Fabian of Scotland Yard, who stopped in New York after failing to solve the Harry Oakes murder in the Bahamas. Charlie drove a battered motor-car which would not have passed an MoT check in Algiers, but he drove like fury and double-parked where he felt like it, often with a patrolman charging into the bar and yelling: 'Hey — who the hell double parked out there?... Oh sorry, Mister Kelly, I di'n see you there.'

Henry Thody had told McGinn: 'The perfect trio for drinking in New York, old man, is a cop, a millionaire and a newspaperman: the cop for double parking and to keep out of any trouble, the fat cat to pick up the tab, and the newshound to whom all doors are open in the Big Apple, because journalists are respected here in America — highly respected, not like in England where they are scorned.'

McGinn jumped into Charlie's jallopy outside the Chelsea and they took off at a rate of knots for West Point Military Academy. The day was magnificent, an Autumnal tinge in the trees on the banks of the Potomac river. Flags fluttered in a light breeze and drums played and bugles were blown as the new intake of cadets marched on their passing out parade.

On the sidelines, Charlie, an ex-Army man himself, watched with pride. 'Among those young men,' he said 'there could be the future President of the United States...' McGinn's heart sank. Not another military man, surely? Eisenhower had been a good President, a very human man — the filmed image of him looking with loathing at the outstretched hand of a concentration camp commandant was one that stayed forever in the mind —but another military President could turn out to be a hawk, and bring the world to the bring of disaster.

When the parade was over, and the cadets had marched back into the Academy, Charlie and McGinn walked slowly down Kinsley Avenue and visited the West Point museum where they saw, in a glass case, the Field Marshal's baton that had belonged to Hermann Goering, of ivory, and studded with precious stones, a ludicrous and pretentious accoutrement which spoke volumes of the fat fraud who had been i/c Luftwaffe during the war, who died, like Himmler, with a cyanide pill he had secreted in the folds of flab around his belly.

Back in Manhattan, Charlie drove up alongside a yellow cab and yelled out of his window: 'Hey, hackey — where's Katz?' Any other taxi driver in the world would have given him the prongs for rudeness, but the New Yorker just yelled back: 'Toin left after t'ree blocks, den toin right on toid an' six, den t'row a left.' At least McGinn thought that's what the cabby had said. Some native New Yorkers had a strange sense of direction and geography. The day before a 'soda jerk' had said: 'Hey — you're from England — right? I wuz dere in de Army, in de war an' we did some good sail an' marlin fishin' off dem shores, and the broads. Man! Tits like watermellons, especially in Athens. You want more cawfee?'

Charlie had located Katz delicatessen. They stood in line. 'Hey, Joe,' Charlie called, 'A hot pastrami for my Limey friend, Pete. An' gimme one, heavy on the mustard.' At the cash-desk the man on the till said: 'Hi, Mr. Kelly,' and they walked on without paying.

'This is the deli. that sent all the chawclate cake for birthdays to our boys in uniform during the war. You wanna try some chawclate cake after?' McGinn said no, but had an instant flash of a scene in a film where a German Panzer General is shown a cake, taken from a dead American soldier, and says: 'If they have the gasoline to fly cakes across the Atlantic...'

At the next port of call, McGinn was glad he had refused the chocolate cake, because Charlie walked into an establishment where he pulled out his .38 and pointed it at the staff, calling: 'O.K. you guys, get 'em up. Come on, get your hands up.'

The manager put up his hands and said: 'You got me, Charlie, you got me.'

'O.K., Louis, gimme a dozen ursters for my Limey friend, Pete here, and a half-dozen for me.' The staff were smiling now, accustomed to Charlie's habitual act.

He put the .38 back in his belt and they sat down to eat their plates of oysters.

'I took Bob Fabian to Chinatown,' Charlie said between mouthfuls of 'ursters', as the staff poured them glasses of cold white wine.

'What's the story on Fabian, Charlie?' McGinn asked.

'He stopped off in New York on his way back to London after investigating the Harry Oakes murder in the Bahamas, an' I wuz delegated to show him round the town as a visiting celebrity. He said he wanted to see Broadway, Chinatown and Harlem. I brung him in here for ursters, then I phoned the Harlem Precinct and talked to Captain Campbell — that's 'Soupy Campbell' — and asked him to lay something on for the famous detective from London, England, Fabian of the Yard.

'Seems like 'Soupy' called the Sahara Bar where the jazzmen hang out, and asked for the boss. A voice on the phone said: 'De bossman ain't here. There's only me, an' Jelly Bean.'

'Who's dat speakin' on de phone?' said Soupy.

'This is Sugar Lips speakin' on de phone.'

'Now listen good, Sugar Lips, this is Cap'n Campbell of de Harlem Precinct. In about a half hour I'll be comin' in there with Detective Kelly of the Bronx Homicide squad, and Detective Chief Superintendent Robert Fabian of Scotland Yard, and I want you to give Mr. Fabian a big Harlem Welcome, you hear me, Sugar Lips, a real Harlem Welcome and a big drink, an' I mean a big drink, whatever he ask for, you hear me?'

'Yes sir, Cap'n Campbell, I hear you. Me an' Jelly Bean gonna give ya'all a big Harlem welcome an' a big drink, yessir, Cap'n.'

'So 'Soupy' drives us over to the Sahara bar, and when we walk in we're the only customers in the place, being mid-afternoon. The two bartenders are standin' there, and one of them starts to polish a glass an' the other one says: 'I's Sugar Lips, an' I'll just adjust ma tie here an' give a big Harlem welcome. Why hello dere Sherlock Holmes, welcome to Harlem an' I gotta give you a big drink...'

'Before Bob had time to order a scotch, 'Soupy' went round the bar and tugged Sugar Lips by the sleeve of his shirt and I heard him say: 'Sugar Lips, you have gotta be the dumbest black man I ever saw. Don't you know nuttin'? Don't you know that durin' that there bombing of London Sherlock Holmes wuz kilt by a Doodlebug?'

'Bob started to laugh. He said: 'He's not that far wrong, Charlie. In the film where Basil Rathbone plays the lead role, Holmes was killed by a flying bomb.'

'That's right,' McGinn said. 'That film was the last one of the series.'

'Hey — Pete. You wanna take a look at the Bowery? Let's go down there, see the bums.'

'O.K., Charlie, but you know what Henry Thody says about it? He says those poor guys are just the same as us, only we've got better suits.'

'That's for sure. They're working guys who hit the sauce and are down on their luck.'

'America can be a hard place, Charlie. I wouldn't like to be broke here.'

'Right. They don't like failures here. They only like success.'

'I heard a story about the head of the American Communist Party when he was indicted years ago for sedition or whatever you call it here, and during the court hearing he went into 21 for a drink, and all the millionaires who drink there gathered around him and offered to buy him whatever he wanted and he said he couldn't understand them because he was a Communist and they were all Capitalists and why on earth did they want to buy him a drink or even talk to him, and they said: 'So what, you're a celebrity. You're in all the newspapers...'

'I believe it. I've seen it happen to murderers if the headlines were big enough. Americans love a celebrity. You know what the American dream is?'

'To de-odourise shit?'

Charlie laughed. 'Yeah, that sure is one of them, the other is to be a celebrity, even if it's just for a day.'

'You're one yourself, Charlie. You arrested your namesake with a machine-gun...'

'Did I ever tell you about the first time I arrested a guy?' Charlie said, changing the subject quickly.

'I'll tell you on the way to the Bowery.'

Charlie drove at great speed through Manhattan, talking all the time, screeching to a halt on red lights and roaring off on green.

'So there I was, a rookie cop in my nice new uniform, and I think

23

I'll just go into a bar and see my old friend the bartender and maybe have a swifty. The temperature is up there in the nineties and they are getting an egg to fry on the sidewalk for the photogs. I walk into this nice cool, dark interior, and when my eyes get accustomed to it, what do I see? A guy with a gun. He's holding up this other guy and he's saying: 'Hand it over or I'll let daylight into yer.' The whole scene freezes when they see the uniform. My heart starts poundin' like a steam-pump, and I think: maybe they can hear it. I walk up very, very slowly and put both hands, palms down, on the bar. My friend the bartender looks at me with fear in his eyes and his lower lip trembling and he says: 'There's a guy there with a gun.'

'The sweat's pouring down my collar. 'I know,' I said to the bartender. Just gimme a Scotch before I die.'

'He reaches for the Scotch, but his hand is shaking so much I can see he ain't goin' to make it, when the guy with the gun raises his voice, looking at me all the time, and says: 'And the next time you don't pay me what you owe me, I'm coming in here with a REAL gun, not this thoity-five cent toy I got for my little boy...'

'He puts the gun in his pocket and as soon as his hand is in there, I jump him. I bang him up against the bar. 'You're under arrest.' I get his hands behind his back and 'cuff him. I push his head down on the bar and with my right hand holding my .38 on his neck, I use my left to take the gun out of the guy's pocket. Goddamnit, if it ain't a .38 like my own police issue. I put it on the bar, near his eyes, and I say: 'That's a real gun.'

'He looks at it where I put it, about three inches from his nose, and he says: 'Well, waddya know? That doity li'l carkserker switched it for a real gun. I'll beat a worm outa him when I get home tonight.'

'You ain't going home tonight, wiseguy, or for a lotta nights. Let's go, down to the Precinct. I'm going to throw the book at you...'

'I start to pull him to the exit. The bartender rattles the bottle on the glass and says: 'Charlie — you forgot your Scotch', and pours me a slug that would choke a mule. I down it in one.'

'On the house,' he says.

'Gee, thanks, I said. Here's to living.'

They drove down the Bowery. Men were huddled in doorways, looking into garbage cans, slugging gut-rot vino from bottles in paper-bags, hustling passers-by.

'Henry Thody tells me he came down here just after Irving Berlin died. The great musician and song-writer had bequeathed his collection of a hundred or more fancy silk waistcoats to a down-and-outs Charity on the Bowery, and Henry came down hoping to find a bar full of men wearing these five hundred dollar silk fancy waistcoats that Irving Berlin wore on all occasions, being a snappy dresser as well as a millionaire.'

'And did he find them?'

'Not a sign of even one of them anywhere on the Bowery. Either the people who ran the Charity kept them for themselves or secretly sold them to a collector, so Henry never did get his story of the Irving Berlin bums of the Bowery.'

'That would have been some sight — a barful of bums in fancy vests. They don't drink much — they spill most of it. I've seen guys in those bars with a string around their necks, glass and one end of the string in left hand, and string around the neck so they can pull s-l-o-w-l-y on the right hand and raise the glass to their lips.

'You're a hard man, Charlie.'

'It's de tru't. But as our friend Henry says: 'We're the same as them, only we got better suits, an' we know how to control the booze. A guy loses his job, he goes on Welfare, next thing he's on Skid Row.'

'I wouldn't like to be broke in New York.'

'Right. This is no place for failures. See that bar over there? That's the bar where I had my first run-in with a corpse...'

'What happened?'

'I was still a rookie. Bin on the streets a couple weeks. I hear these shots comin' from that bar. Bam. Bam. Bam. Bam. Four shots rapid fire — an' it ain't no Derringer. It's a fort-five or a fuckin' Magnum. I get my gun out and go into the bar. Just inside the doorway, stretched across a table, is the body of a guy on his back with four bullet holes pumping blood like little artesian wells. except one which must have hit an artery for it was gushing out like he'd struck oil. There's nobody else in the bar except the bartender, who's standin' there lookin' at me as if I'm Father Christmas.

''What the hell's goin' on here?' I yell at the bartender.

Cool as an ice-pack, the son of a bitch starts to polish a glass.

'Don't ask me, buddy, he wuz like that when he came in.''

McGinn laughed. Thody had been right about Charlie Kelly — he could certainly tell the tale.

'We never did catch the guy that done it. It's a tough neighbourhood down here. Even the rummies clam up when the cops come round. They don't trust their own mothers down here. Come on, let's hit McSorley's, get us some cold beer. You drink down here on the Bowery you gotta break the glass after...'

They drove to one of New York's most famous bars. McSorley's, another Irish pub, boasted: WE WERE HERE BEFORE YOU WERE BORN, and over the door it said: NO WOMAN EVER CROSSED THESE PORTALS. Scrubbed plank floor, bit of sawdust around and an Irish bartender in the long white apron they all sported in Manhattan.

'Hey there, Mr. Kelly — what'll it be?'

'Two beers, Joe. Cold. Cold as a well-digger's ass in the Yukon.'

'Comin' up...'

McGinn pulled out some change and tried to pay. Charlie pushed his hand back into his pocket, and said: 'This is on me, Pete.'

The bartender placed the beers on absorbent paper drip mats, and Charlie paid him with a dollar and pocketed the change without looking at it.

'See that sign above the door, about no women ever coming in here? Not true,' Charlie said. I had a friend called Schlesinger, the guy who makes the tennis rackets, multi millionaire, and we arranged to meet here and he came through that door with his wife. She was dressed like a man, double breasted suit and Fedora. We sat in the corner over there and she drank a beer, then we left — just to prove that notice is bullshit.'

'I like women in bars. What are these old farts playing at?'

'It's a hangover from the days when this would have been like a workingmen's club, a place they could get away from their wives — from before Prohibition.'

'They still have all-male bars in the North of England. The working man's equivalent of the Gentleman's Club, as you say, and in many bars a little room called the 'snug' where the old ladies go with their white enamel cans for take-away beer because they're not allowed in the bar. Of course they can take a little nip of Mahatma while the barman is pulling their beer...'

'Mahatma? What's that?'

'Oh, sorry, Charlie — Cockney rhyming slang, originally to confuse the police, like backslang.'

'What's backslang?'

'Ouldway ouyouway ikelay an Otchskay ithway ouyre eerbay?'

'Jesus — what the hell's that?'

'Backslang, Charlie. You simply put 'ay' on the end of each word after you've taken the first letters off the front of the word and put it on the back, so beer becomes eerbay and Scotch becomes Otchskay and I'm buying the next round for Arliechay Ellykay.'

'Don't even try it. I'm buying here. Hey Joe — two more beers. Cold as a witch's tit.'

'Comin' up Mr. Kelly.'

Charlie turned to McGinn and said: 'Ohnoay, I ontday wanna Otchskay ithway my eerbay — how's that?'

'You're picking it up. But the Irish have one even better than that for confusing the Law, Charlie, it's a language spoken by Irish tinkers, called Shelta and no British cop would understand it. Sometimes I.R.A. men use it. It's a bit like during the war in the invasion of Italy and Normandy, wireless communicators were Red Indians, so the best codebreakers didn't stand a chance.'

Charlie paid again, with a dollar bill.

'Hey, Pete — you wanna see an execution Thursday?'

'An execution, Charlie? What do you mean?'

'We're fryin' a guy Thursday.'

'Where'

'Sing-sing. A cop killer. He gets the electric chair early Thursday morning — you wanna come in as a witness? The Press get invited here in New York.'

'No thanks. I don't think so, Charlie. It would ruin my day.'

'O.K. — take a rain-check.'

'I don't want to see an execution Charlie, thank you.'

'Yeah, Henry said the same. But he took a rain-check.'

'Really?'

'Well, he asked who we were fryin', and I told him it was a cop-killer, a black guy from Harlem, and Henry said: 'No thanks, Charlie. Let me know when it's a woman. That might be more interesting.' He is one cynical son-of a bitch, that Henry.'

'That's just his British sense of humour, Charlie. He wants you to think he's cynical. Now let me buy a drink here..'

'C'mon, let's go. My wife will be wondering what's keeping me so late.'

Outside McSorley's, Charlie took a handful of change out of his jacket pocket and showed it to McGinn. Din you see what wuz happenin' in there? Every time I paid with a dollar the bartender gave me ninety cents change one time and a dollar ten the next.'

'You don't pay anywhere in New York?'

'That's right, Pete. Say, what's Cockney rhyming slang for an American? I know where Limey comes from — British sailors drinking lime juice to avoid scurvey and what do they say for a German? And what about an Irishman?

'Are you sure you want to get into all this, Charlie? It can get pretty complicated.'

'Shoot.'

'An American is a Septic — septic tank — Yank; A German is a Brussels — Brussels sprout — Kraut. For reasons I don't know, Irishmen are Turks. In a pub you hear an order for two apples, a George and a Vera and fisherman's. That means two apple fritters, bitters, a George Robey, a Toby ale, a Vera Lynn, gin, and fisherman's daughter, water...'

'Holy Mike...'

'A motor-car, Charlie, is an 'addock. Haddock and bloater — motor, get it? A Richmond is a technicolor yawn. The railway line ran from Richmond to Kew, so a Richmond is a spew. Now if a true Cockney wants to admire a young lady's beautiful bum as she wiggles by in the rubbidy-dub-dub, the pub, he says to his mates: 'Cor, she's got a nice April..."

'April?'

'April in Paris — Aris. Aristotle - bottle. Bottle and glass — arse...'

'Stop, stop, my head's going round in circles. It's time I went home to the old Trouble and Strife — that right?'

'You're getting there Charlie.'

'Where do you want to be dropped off?'

'Jim Downey's.'

'O.K. I'll have one swifty with you there then home.'

* * *

The bar was crowded with theatregoers. Jim Downey's bar was a meeting place for the New York Giants, racing men and jockeys, newspapermen, British and Irish actors playing Broadway and off-Broadway, off duty cops and gamblers, and all kinds of men planning to fix the World Series. Archie Downey, Jim's good looking son, a United States Air Force fighter pilot during call-up, was showing off pictures of his new house, and the washer-up was busy with a gigantic pile of glasses. The glasses had held Irish coffee, the genuine article made in the Irish tradition. Downey's staff put out two hundred glasses on trays near the entrance to the bar and when the coffee in the big urn was hot they put a shot of Irish whiskey into each glass and added sugar. As the crowds poured out of the theatres all around the bar the coffee was poured into each glass, rich cream poured over the back of a spoon to lie on top of the hot coffee, and two hundred dollars went into Jim Downey's till as the bar filled up.

The Irish bartenders were distinguished looking and wore the traditional long white apron, occasionally saying: 'You from the old country, sir? On the house.'

McGinn drank in the whole scene — Irish America. It seemed as if every cop in New York was Irish. If you asked one of them: 'Can you direct me to Jim Downey's bar?' he'd say: 'You from the old country?' and give directions. If you said: 'Excuse, pleez, where is Japanese Embassy?', the cop would probably say: 'Buy a fuckin' map.'

'Do you think Henry is anti-women?' Charlie asked. 'That's what I thought when he said he wanted to see one fry at Sing-Sing.'

'As I said before, Charlie, that's his British humour. He's certainly not against women in general or any in particular. He has a beautiful Jugoslav ex-wife and a very beautiful daughter in Rome. He loved his Missus so much, Charlie, that he gave her as a wedding present a two-weeks' course in Paris on how to cook Indian curry. He was a cavalry officer in India before the war and he comes from a generation of Englishmen who were very shy with women, with a rather schoolboy 'slap-and-tickle' attitude towards them in general but with a great respect for the effofess...'

'The what?'

'Oh, sorry — the Female Of the Species, as P.G. Wodehouse called the ladies.

'I'll give you an example of what I mean by the men's attitude towards women then: there were about two hundred prisoners in a German P.O.W. camp, and the prison guards paraded them saying: 'Today vee haf somezing special for you — Frauleins! and from the wooden huts on the other side of the barbed wire they saw stark naked women and girls being herded by the German guards towards a row of open showers, and it was clear that when they did shower they would be ogled by the British prisoners lined up for the spectacle. The German guards were guffawing as the Polish women prisoners were pushed towards the showers, trying to hide their nakedness. The British major i/c parade heard the men mumbling angrily, and called out: 'Parade! Parade 'Shun.' The two hundred men came to attention. The Major called: Parade — About...TURN!' and the two hundred soldiers and the Major did a smart about turn so as not to embarrass the Polish women prisoners. They had respect for women. Probably every man there would have stood up for a woman on a bus or tram car or train. It may be hard to believe now, Charlie but women never had to pay for anything. The boyfriends paid fares, cinema tickets, meals, drinks. I distinctly remember when I was a young reporter, seeing a woman buy a round of drinks. She was a Daily Mirror reporter, one of the boys, and she paid her round of drinks. That was in 1958, Charlie, and after that it was downhill all the way, and now they have to pay their corner. Maybe women were the losers by wanting to be "liberated".'

'It's different in America,' Charlie said. 'The broads expect to be paid for, and when it comes to divorce, watch out, cos they'll take you to the cleaners. But, as Mickey Rooney said, and he should know, 'When it comes to the family home it's shared equally — the wife gets the inside and the husband gets the outside.'

McGinn laughed: 'Sometimes it's like that in England, too, Charlie.'

'I gotta go. There's a party in a rich guy's house tomorrow night, Could be interesting for you. You wanna go?'

'Sure.'

'O.K., I'll call you with the address and time, but we'll meet at P.J's. What are you doing tomorrow?'

'I go to 21, and usually meet Henry if he isn't filing. The British newspapermen have to file by mid-day to catch the lst edition in London for inside pages, seven hours difference. Their work takes place in the mornings so they have the afternoons free unless a big story breaks and they have to go out of town. New York is a great posting — every door is open, they respect the Press, and there's an information officer or public relations officer ready to help newsmen. In England and Scotland there's a lot of hostility towards the Press. Every little minion seems to think it's his or her duty to withhold information and be as obstructive as possible — except when they want to promote something or sell something, then the drinks come out.'

'If you have a newspaper column here, you're a star, a celebrity, and everyone wants to be your friend. A colyoomist gets invited everywhere.'

Charlie finished his drink and shook hands with McGinn, saying: 'See you tomorrow for that party. There's a guy over there at the bar you should meet — Paddy Cheyevsky. You've heard of him?'

'He wrote The Bachelor Party.'

Charlie took McGinn over to Cheyevsky and introduced him.

When Charlie had left McGinn said: 'How did they manage to persuade Mickey Spillane to appear in the movie of The Bachelor Party? He certainly didn't do it for the money.'

'Maybe he did it to get near those Hollywood babes. But I think he just likes acting. Besides, he was promoting his own work.'

'I remember his line: 'Gee, that Mickey Spillane — boy, can he write!'

'Self promotion — and he got paid for it, but, as you say, Pete, he didn't do it for money.'

'Dutton are paying him a straight million dollars for each new book...'

'Is that right?' The poor feller.'

'The publicity man for Dutton, Elliot Graham, goes down to Florida once a year, walks across Spillane's lawn to the pool where the Great Author is usually lying in a hammock, drinking a mint julep and fondling a platinum blonde. Spillane presents him with a manuscript, which is carried back to New York as if it is the Holy Grail, and there the Dutton executives pass the pages around. Elliot then goes back to Florida and walks across the lawn to a similar scene, except that the platinum blonde — has been replaced by a redhead, and he presents Mickey with a cheque for exactly one million dollars.'

'Now that's the kind of writer publishers like.'

'Yes, and A.A. Milne, too. They publish Winnie the Pooh and make millions out of it. And when they do a promotion in England, Elliot carries that bloody toy bear which Dutton's bought in an auction, across the Atlantic, sat on his knee while he tells the thrilled passengers that this is the original bear which Milne based Winnie the Pooh on...'

'You mustn't get bitter about the bullshit business, Pete.'

'Not bitter — angry. The bloody bear travels first class and I go tourist class.'

McGinn had a vague recollection later of having met Leo Gorcey's sidekick from the films about the Dead End Kids or the East Side Kids, who wore a baseball cap on the side of his head and had a big nose and spoke through it, and when McGinn was introduced as a novelist, the actor looked carefully at him and said: 'There's one question I always wanted to ask a writer: 'What is knowledge?' It was after this that McGinn decided to take a cab back to the Chelsea. It had been a long day...

CHAPTER TWO

A Clammy Mary

IT WAS one of the most famous bars in the world — 21. At the entrance a line-up of miniature jockeys in their racing colours rose up the wall, models denoting that 21 was a gambling man's bar and had been since it was the most famous Speakeasy in New York during Prohibition.

It was not an easy bar to enter. McGinn's Saville Row suit helped. As Henry Thody had said: Americans take note of such things, and the owners of the bar, Jack and Charley, the bartenders and the negro cloakroom attendant, not to mention the girl on the telephone switchboard, recognised wealth when they saw it, and they would associate McGinn's £90 Huntsman's three-piece suit with riches.

McGinn was learning things about America, apart from the deliciousness of their apple pie, from Mr. Thody, who had laid the law down to the Daily Mail's correspondent in New York, Jeffrey Blythe, who had complained he wasn't receiving telephone messages from his office. 'This is America, Jeff, not Tyneside (Blythe was a Geordie). You give the switchboard operator ten dollars, and I mean ten. She will remember you for ever.'

Henry was right, as usual. Hemingway had said the same about the French — give them a big tip and they will always remember you and give you good service. You had to know the form: if you crossed to Mexico, the officials asked for a tip. If you offered one to an official in Spain, they'd take it as an insult and throw it back in your face.

McGinn had always respected older men and listened to their advice, gained from years of experience. He had always prided himself on being a learner rather than a teacher. Now, aged 29, he was learning about America.

The specialities of 21, apart from their famous $5 hamburger (when a White Castle cost 10 cents in their chain of snack-bars,), were hash-brows, Little Neck clams, and soft-shell crabs, which were eaten whole. Bing Crosby sat in the restaurant, eating slowly. His head resembled a pink snooker ball, for Bing did not bother with his wig except on the film set. He looked healthy. A reformed lush who had given his sons hell when torched up, he looked now as if he had definitely kicked the sauce. He kept looking in the direction of Barry Goldwater who was being admired by John Birchers and military hawks (one of whom was a celebrity because he had persuaded the Queen Mother on a visit from England, to fly with him in a helicopter over Manhattan and see the sights).

The man standing next to McGinn at the bar turned to him and said: 'I have to make a decision and it's difficult.' He showed McGinn a brochure containing full-colour pictures of small aeroplanes. 'I've just flown from California in this one, but I want to get rid of it and buy a new one and I can't decided between these two.'

He pointed. McGinn suddenly recognised the man. He was William Randolph Hearst Jnr., son of Citizen Kane, heir to the newspaper fortune. Henry Thody had said he drank there when he was in town and the game was to try and persuade him that he should move out of journalism and into television. Mr. Hearst continued discussing the merits and de-merits of the various private planes in the brochure while McGinn tried to make intelligent comments, knowing nothing about the internal combustion engine, cars in general and planes in particular, but William R.H. seemed happy to have someone to talk to. Was it lonely at the top, McGinn wondered? Soon after the millionaire newspaper proprietor left to meet his daughter, Patty, McGinn recognised the voice of a newcomer to the bar and turned to see Robert Mitchum ordering an Irish whiskey.

'Have I see you somewhere before?' he asked

'The Star, Belgravia?' McGinn said.

'Right — Paddy Kennedy's. I love that bar. And Paddy Kennedy too, the mad Irish son of a bitch.'

'He has to buy a new television set,' McGinn said. 'When the Reverand Ian Paisley came on the box the other day, Paddy threw a bottle of Bushmills through the TV screen. An expensive gesture of disapproval if you ask me.'

'I sure felt at home in that bar.'

'There was one night when I was working a Saturday shift for the Sunday Pictorial to make ends meet when we had a call from Paddy Kennedy after midnight. He'd been woken up by a noise outside his bedroom window and looked out to see a heavy set man on a ladder scraping away at the gold star which hung outside advertising the bar. He shouted he'd call the police, but it was the police! Someone had tipped off the Sweeney — the Flying Squad — that the gold from the London Airport gold-bullion raid had been melted down and was currently replacing the star outside Paddy's boozer. Some villain had wound up the Sweeney, and they were very unhappy about it.'

'I put the word out I wanted some Bob Hope — preferably Red Leb. A sexy blonde job came in to make the delivery, and her name was Mandy Rice Davis.'

Mitchum bought the drinks and said: 'Talking of blonde jobs, you see the blonde behind me over my left shoulder... don't make it obvious...'

McGinn moved his head very slowly to glimpse a beautiful blonde who was looking in their direction.

'What about her?'

'She wants my body.' Mitchum said. 'Say, do you know Kenny Hutchison?'

'He drinks in The Flask in Hampstead. Scotsman. He was in that movie with you when you played a priest with a machine gun, and Ken ran naked out of a knocking shop...'

'When he stayed at my house, he screwed my daughters. He thought I didn't know. And I've got a worthless son. Gave the little asshole a million dollars for his birthday, and he disappeared. I eventually track him down, sitting in a fuckin' rockin' chair gazing out over a field of poppies — he's growing opium, for Chrissake, fields and fields of it. Did Kenny Hutch mention anything about that movie in Mexico?'

'He said the Chief of Police wasn't very happy about your visit.'

Mitchum laughed. 'You should have seen that son of a bitch's face! The filming was rained off so we were invited to do the tourist bit in Mexico city. This asshole was dressed up an a uniform with gold braid everywhere and he said: 'I am Chief of Police. All traffic stop for me. I have motor cyclists clear way through traffic. You stay right behind me, no *problemas.* Remember, Mister Mitchum, stay right behind me.' We set off, visiting art galleries, museums, the works, then on to a buffet lunch in another gallery, where the Chief said to me: 'Excuse, please. I go make pee-pee.' He went onto the gents toilet and I followed him in. He was standing there looking at the porcelain when he felt something warm on the back of his legs. He looked around. I was taking a piss all over his fuckin' uniform trousers.

"I'm right behind you," I said.

McGinn laughed and ordered two more drinks. If Bob Mitchum was in a story-telling mood, he was certainly ready to listen. Mitchum, the first Hollywood star to be arrested for smoking marijuana, certainly had some tales to tell, yet McGinn suspected he would never tell it in print. Mitchum, like Hemingway, had what they called 'a built-in shit detector', meaning that, with their artists' mile-high antennae, they could detect sycophants, frauds, phoneys and bullshit merchants a mile off. When Mitchum was riding the rods, jumping trains all over America, black and white travelled together as buddies. Black men would refer to themselves as 'us niggers' because it simply meant 'black', from '*negre*', and at that time Jew wasn't looked upon as a derogatory word, so when Mitchum referred to Kirk Douglas as 'Superjew', he was not being anti semitic, merely scornful of affectation. And when Mitchum told the story about his experience with a substance known as 'Congolese black' some were shocked by his language. While the Big White Hunter waited for his jeep to take him into the jungle to start filming with Deborah Kerr and Ava Gardner, a 'plane landed and a huge African in uniform, covered with medals and scrambled egg on his cap got out and entered a darkened limmo. The back window of the limmo slid down and a huge black hand, like a bunch of aged Fyffe's bananas, came out and a finger beckoned to Mitchum, who looked at the small plane, the large car and the big black hand and swaggered over and said: 'Yeah?'

'I know who you are', said the occupant of the car.

'Is that right?'

'Yes, you are Mister Mitchum, de film star.'

'Right on', said Bob.

'Do you know who I am?' asked the Idi Amin lookalike.

'Looks like you're the Head Nigger round here,' said Mitchum, and sauntered back to the jeep which then shot off into the jungle.

Next day, during a lull in filming, a small 'plane appeared overhead, circled twice, then a little parachute was thrown out and it slowly floated to earth. On it was a shoe-box, addressed to: MISTER MITCHUM - FILM STAR.

The package was taken to Mitchum's tent, where he opened it to find two kilos of superior Congolese 'black' hashish, with a note attached which read: FROM THE HEAD NIGGER

Mitchum finished his drink. 'I'm splitting. I'm on the town, but if anybody phones here — like my wife — you haven't seen me.' He sauntered out of the bar of 21.

McGinn looked around, hopefully, at the beautiful blonde, quietly eating her salad. He smiled, but, although she was still glancing at the bar, at the space which had been occupied by the film star, her look was blank. He smiled in vain, for single blondes like this in New York, especially ones who eat alone in 21, have an inbuilt detector, too, but it is a dollar detector, and it is a star detector a celebrity detector, and it can also detect paupers, even ones wearing Saville Row suits...

* * *

When Mitchum departed, McGinn looked around. The bar seemed to be full of millionaires. Henry's friend, the man with the golden pencil, was inviting McGinn to lunch on Little Neck clams and soft-shell crabs. Alternatively, if in a meat-mood, there was the famous $5 hamburger with hash browns, a speciality of the chef. The Irish bartender said to McGinn: 'Do you know who that is at the top of the bar?'

'Yes. Barry Goldwater.'

'Seems like he was electioneering up in Minneapolis and when his street parade reached the office section of town, one of the typists was looking out of the office window at the passing parade below when one of the four guys in the office slammed the window frame down on her waist and all four of them took her from behind. Later she complained to her boss about these guys taking advantage of her and her boss said: 'But you should have called out...'

"What?' she said, 'and let people think I was a Goldwater supporter?"

McGinn laughed but the man with the magic pencil did not seem to find it funny — perhaps he was a Goldwater supporter himself.

'Have a drink...'

'A bloody Mary,' said McGinn.

'Bartender — a bloody Mary for Pete, and a Virgin Mary for me — I'm on the wagon,' he explained.

'Well why not try a Clammy Mary, sir?' the barman asked.

'A Clammy Mary — what's that?'

'A Virgin Mary with just a touch of clam juice to give it a bit of flavour, invented right here in 21. And ya know what? Some guy in here in marketing canned goods picked up on the idea and he says he's going to produce cans of it — called Clamato. Just add vodka.'

McGinn thought of the party he had been invited to by Charlie Kelly, and was looking forward to meeting the celebrities who were sure to be present, but a man at his elbow now was inviting him to another party, his own birthday party and he gave McGinn the address: 'The Sixes Building - seventh floor.'

McGinn asked: 'What number?'

'The seventh floor.'

'But...'

Someone tugged at his elbow and whispered hoarsely:

'The guy owns the whole of the seventh floor, for Chrissake, stop asking him what number.'

McGinn felt his liver twitch at the thought of more booze. Americans were the hardest drinkers he had ever met. One of their dry martinis (Why call it that? Why not 'wet gin'? because that's what it was). Some had the squeeze of a zest of lemon in it, but the joke was: 'If I want lemonade, I'll ask for it.' One in Toots Shore's would choke a donkey. Three would just about kill a donkey. McGinn had always been an *afficionado* of beer, but New Yorkers thought that was a soft drink. It didn't give them a 'kick' so they stuck to the hard stuff, and the sight of the Madison Avenue men in their neat suits, coats, collars and ties and small brimmed hats slurping off a couple of quick ones before hitting the office made him wonder how the advertising agency business managed to function in America.

'Come about 6 p.m.,' the millionaire was saying.

'I'll be there,' McGinn said, without any intention of going. He needed an early night, meaning getting to bed before two o'clock in the morning.

* * *

The party he wanted to attend, however, lived up to his expectations. Schlesinger and Galbraith (who later became Ambassador to India — the joke being because he was skinny, and Washington didn't want to send a fat Ambassador to a country plagued by famine) made political speeches, but McGinn didn't take much of it in because he was busy eyeing up the beautiful women who were there, even though there was a sameness about them which was startling, for they really did look as if they had come off a conveyor belt: all wore 'little black dresses', all had the neatest, cleanest, immaculately groomed blonde hair at exactly shoulder length and each sported a broad diamond bracelet on the left wrist. McGinn did not know anything about diamonds, the only diamond he had ever had was a Double Diamond, which was a bottled beer in England, but if he had had to estimate the value of one of these bracelets he would have guessed at 40,000 dollars, but the interesting fact was that all the bracelets were the same width, an inch, none being half or three quarters of an inch or one and a half inches. Was it fashion? Would a one and a quarter inch be vulgar? Would a three quarters of an inch signal signs of hidden poverty?

But one woman at the party had neither a little black dress nor a diamond bracelet. Oona Chaplin, daughter of Charlie Chaplin and wife of Eugene O'Neill, the playwright, wore a maternity dress, and it drew more attention from the partygoers than the political speeches or the show of diamonds, and there were whispers of: 'Oh, no. Not again' at the sight of Oona about to parturiate for the umpteenth time.

After being shown the way to the bathroom, McGinn made a discovery which he often recalled to friends when discussing America: the toilet paper in this millionaire's loo was three times thicker than British toilet paper, and six times thicker than Spanish toilet paper. Only in America, he thought, but was it to save time tearing off two, three, four, or in Spain six sheets to make a thickness that the digit could not penetrate such as this American paper was specifically designed for,

39

and did only millionaires order their servants to buy it at special shops, and was it 'medicated with Izal germicide' without saying so? McGinn made a mental note to investigate the phenomenon of the ultra thick loo paper, U.S. style.

Upon returning to the crowded room, he overheard two guests discussing the paintings of one of the Rothschild girls there, who had recently had an exhibition in New York. 'I like it, but if only she would stop. She keeps on adding more and more paint. Somebody should tell her when to stop. I think she's been copying Peggy Gugenheim's Pollocks...'

'Peggy's collecting Polacks now?'

'No, no, darling, Jackson Pollocks.'

'Yeah, he's another one who didn't know when to stop.'

Charlie Kelly came over and introduced one of the guests to McGinn. 'I'd like you to meet Irwin Shaw. Pete's just had a novel published in New York.' Charlie moved off, talking to Oona Chaplin with her enormous belly. 'That's good news,' said Irwin Shaw, 'Who's your publisher?'

'E.P. Dutton.'

'They're a good company. Did I see an ad. in the New Yorker about your book, about a guy who lives inside a whale in the British Natural History museum because he doesn't like paying rent?'

'That's the one.'

'And his name is Jonathan, right?'

'That's it.'

'Good name. Jonah and the whale. Sticks in people's memories. Well, good luck with it, Pete. I have to go. Got an appointment half an hour ago. See you around.'

He was off, pushing through the crowded room. McGinn was elated. He had met the famous Irwin Shaw, and remembered his father handing him a thick novel entitled The Young Lions by Irwin Shaw when he was a teenager and recommending it as a good read, and he recalled that Shaw also had a main character whose name stuck in his memory — Christian, the German soldier who stayed a Nazi to the bitter end, and he recalled that the film people had changed the story to make it more acceptable to the Germans, and Shaw had protested to no avail, not wanting, as a good Jew, to whitewash the filthy Nazis just because the war was over the everyone was being friendly to Lufthansa. It was a jibe, of course, giving the schweinhundt a name like Christian, but Irwin Shaw, like Leon Uris, was touchy about anti-semitism. There had been some other hidden scandal surrounding the book by Shaw which had made him rich, as The Naked and the Dead had made Mailer rich, and the book which McGinn thought of as The Great American Novel, From Here to Eternity, had made James Jones rich. The scandal was something to do with the Jewish boxer who took on the whole red-neck platoon. He made a mental note to ask someone someday what it had all been about, someone who knew the New York literary scene.

Charlie Kelly was back, whispering in his ear: 'Oona just left. Did you see her go?'

'No.'

'She snuck out. And did you hear all the dames sneering because she's in the family way again? Asking if she knows what's causing it?'

'Sure.'

'It's bullshit. She was winding them up. That was a cushion up her dress.'

'Why?'

'Maybe it's the only way she's got to make 'em talk about her.'

'Well, it worked. They're talking about her.'

'Say, aren't you going up to Minneapolis soon?'

'Tuesday. Staying with an old friend from Rome, Burt Anderson, he's the police reporter on the Trib.'

'That's a fine newspaper, the Minneapolis Tribune, one of the most respected papers in America. Get him to take you to a couple of good restaurants there — trout from Lake Superior.'

'What are they called?'

'Charlie's and Harry's.'

Now McGinn knew he was in America. Charlie's and Harry's. Not 'La Truite qui Chante' or 'Le Poisson bleu,' just Charlie's and Harry's. No frills, no bullshit, no pretension, and probably damned good food, if a New York cop was recommending them. Good old America...Minneapolis on Wednesday. He'd be in what Americans called The Bible Belt. He would just catch the heel of summer on White Bear lake, the one F. Scott Fitzgerald had called Black Bear lake in his short stories. The land of many lakes.. and the romantic Minnehaha Falls...

CHAPTER 3

Minneapolis

THIS was Red Indian country; all the names came from the Indian language, and most of them had to do with water, in the land of blue water, and Minnesota was the land of many lakes, and the world famous Indian name which meant Laughing Water — Minnehaha. It was also the land of giants, for the area had been settled by immigrants from Sweden and Denmark, and those men, descended from the Vikings, were head and shoulders above the average tall American. The town planners had the motor car in mind when Hennepin and the surrounding streets were built, and it was possible to drive through Minneapolis with the speedometer set exactly on 40 miles per hour and catch every green light on the way through town. And everyone had a car. The bus service was terrible. To go to see a film in one of the outlying districts might take three bus journeys. Acceptable in late summer, but when that Minnesota winter came down, watch out, for the cops donned electric suits on point duty and the natives wore ear muffs to stop their ears dropping off with frostbite.

On Sundays the ghost of Prohibition reared its ugly head, and the natives who wanted to celebrate with a couple of beers had to drive towards Wisconsin and cross the State line in order to quench a thirst, for all they had on sale in Minnesota was 3.2 beer. This was half strength, watered down, beer which tasted like swamp water and that's all the real natives - Red Indians - were allowed by law to drink, the excuse being that if they were served full strength beer or spirits they would get blind drunk and fall asleep in a shop doorway and freeze to death in the regular 40 below zero temperature there in winter.

McGinn joined his old sparring partner from Rome, Burt Anderson, staying for a while in his parents' home on the beautiful White Bear lake, and then they found an apartment to share not too far from the offices of the Trib. Opposite the apartment there was a hole between two large 4 or 5 bedroom houses, where workmen had demolished a house the day before in order to build another on the spot. McGinn was amazed to see a brand new house built within a week and the new owners move in.

'The builders are on bonus to finish quickly, that's why they work so quickly.' Burt explained, and McGinn had an immediate flashback to the day he had asked Geoffrey Brierly the manager of Lloyds bank, Haymarket, London, what was wrong with Britain, and he had replied: ' P.A.Y.E., lad. Pay as you earn destroyed Britain. The men work, they are taxed on earnings, pay unions dues, a health stamp and they get taxed on overtime, and when they look at the depleted pay packet, it's not worth their while to do overtime. Then they're taxed on everything they buy, taxed on the money they've already paid tax on. It puts a premium on iniquity, lad, that it does.'

They had been in the apartment a week when the phone rang.

'A.T. and T, sir, to enter your name or names in the telephone directory.

'Would you care to give me your name and profession, sir and the name or names and profession of anyone else who shares your phone?'

'Sure,' said Burt, the cynical police reporter from the Trib. 'Burton Anderson, occupation mortician, and Peter McGinn, occupation embalmer.'

'Thank you, sir. That will appear in the next issue of our directory.'

Burt had an intense dislike of morticians, embalmers, the employees of funeral parlours, and ambulance chasers who profited from death. Visiting him in the Tribune office one day, McGinn overheard him interviewing one of the above mentioned after an accident in which three people had been injured and one killed, and listened in out of curiosity on an extension line. He heard Burt say: 'Where's the stiff now?'

A shocked undertaker said: 'Sir, the deceased is lying in our loved-ones' memorial chapel.'

'What time's the plantin'?' Burt asked.

'Sir, the Loved One will be interred at 15.00 hours in the Garden of Remembrance...'

'The cops said he was decapitated by the windshield, is that right?'

A strangled, choked sob followed, then the undertaker said: 'Sir, really, I cannot discuss this, but I assure you our embalmer has made the loved one presentable to his nearest and dearest...'

Burt winked at McGinn and said: 'What an asshole.' when he rang off.

They adjourned to Seven Corners. The whole gang were in the bar: Shevlin, Connoly the ex-cop, Larry Sullivan the Irish bartender, his girl, the beautiful Lorna, Bruce and Marvin, both Jewish, Doctor Chang, Elk, the Sioux Indian, Doctor Maximillian von Rabinov. Big Momma, also known as Roberta and Berryman. The Irish bartender who had admired McGinn's sports coat made of Irish tweed with a Dublin label in it, had given McGinn a tab after he had seen him signing the six free copies of his novel, his way of helping The Arts. Burt's girl, Nancy, a beautiful blonde of 19, joined them.

'Who is that guy with Larry?' McGinn asked Burt. Larry Sullivan was having an animated conversation with a handsome young man using deaf and dumb sign language.

'That's Joseph. The poor guy's deaf and dumb, from birth. A good-looking guy, huh? If he doesn't get laid three times a day he starts to worry.'

McGinn liked this particular bar, and he had made friends with the citizens of Minneapolis quickly. They were an easy-going crowd, and they were a generous bunch. They sensed that he was coming close to broke and would be stranded in America unless his book suddenly took off, which was unlikely, and both Larry and Bruce who was also a bartender, had been pushing him beers, Larry in his new bar around the corner on the way to Dinkytown, the thrown-up flats where the students from the University lived, and Bruce down in Caesar's bar, which was the hangout of a student called Zimmerman, who would take his guitar in and sit and play at one of the tables until one of the bartenders said: 'He's playing that goddamn guitar again. Throw him out will ya, before he drives me nuts. Zimmerman, who later changed his name to Bob Dylan was often thrown into a snowdrift at the back of Caesar's.

Burt's girl had just come back from Europe, staying a while in

Venice, and was recounting how she had met a fellow American in St. Mark's square. "She said: 'You an American?' I said: 'Yeah. You like Venice?' She said: 'Sure'. I said: 'How long you been here?' She said: 'You mean Europe?' 'No, Venice.'

'Oh — a half hour."

Burt laughed, and John Shevlin bought a round of drinks.

McGinn looked around the group who had befriended him in the bar called Mixters.

The last two members of this Seven Corners drinking team entered the bar: John Gorman, quiet as a mouse and out of work, and John Coughlin, a round-faced Irishman who loved to drink and was one of the mathematical geniuses at the University. Gerry the Irish bartender kept an eye on the tabs, contained in a little drawer near the till, and there were about 100 cards in there, tabulating the small fortune owed to the bar over the years by passing businessmen, itinerant visitors, students long gone, and the immediate fraternity who were on Welfare, and one visiting novelist called Pete McGinn who owed at that moment seven dollars and fifty cents, and rising rapidly. Shevlin was a heating engineer, temporarily 'resting'; Connoly had left the police force but was thinking of re-joining; Larry Sullivan had just found a job in a new bar which was getting new custom because Sullivan with his slow delivery and Irish charm, was one of the most popular men in Minneapolis; Lorna was all beautiful woman but one of the boys, holding her own with the drinks and the chat. Bruce was the black sheep of his Jewish family because he had a brother at Princeton who was always being held up as an example to him; Marvin was almost the black sheep of his Jewish family because he did not go to work, like his brother, who worked for City Hall as a road sweeper and lived at home with his mother while Marvin was out protesting in the Age of Protest in America, against iniquities everywhere, the latest one having been his march from Canada to the South in protest against segregation in Southern schools, getting himself gaoled in Alabama and getting skeletal thin on a hunger strike while incarcerated. When Marvin's long suffering mother in the Jewish tradition ('eat your cereal', 'eat your salad'), was interviewed by the local newspaper, she confessed she was not happy with the way her two sons had turned out in life. 'Two sons I've got — and look at them: one sweeps the streets, the other lies in them.' Doctor Chang was a Chinese nuclear physicist, a professor at the University. He wore tennis shoes, a T-shirt, baggy trousers and a white raincoat and drank with Elk, the Sioux Chief who had engaged McGinn in conversation the moment he had entered the bar at Seven Corners by asking him if he had attended school in England, and followed it up with: 'What did you learn about Columbus in England?'

'That he discovered America.'

'And do you know what he found when he 'discovered' America? He found a bunch of fuckin' Indians chargin' about. And today they tryin' the moonshot. And do you know what they gonna find when they get up there? A bunch of fuckin' Indians chargin' about, an' they gonna take it away from them.'

So Doctor Chang and Elk drank together nursing the paranoia of being a Chinaman and oriental in the West and a deprived Indian Chief on his own home ground, the land of blue water and many lakes. They had so fortified themselves against depression one night that they had been found by a patrolling cop asleep together in a shop doorway and arrested for being drunk and incapable.

The lady magistrate fined Elk but said to Doctor Chang that he had disgraced the good name of the University, but as it was his first offence she was being lenient with him in her sentence.

'Two months suspended,' she announced, and Doctor Chang passed out in a dead faint in the dock. They had ascertained from him that he had thought he was going to be hung up by his thumbs for two months.

Doctor Maximillian von Rabinov was not a doctor; nor was he a 'von' or his first name Maximillian, but the Rabinov, pronounced ray-bin-ov, was thought to be authentic. Max was an affable, friendly would-be confidence trickster, and when he heard that McGinn's comedy novel was about a con-man who lived inside a whale in a London museum to save paying rent, he was immediately friendly and gave McGinn a useful tip: to avoid paying fifty cents car-park fee in the centre of town, park in one of the bank parking lots, pretend to be a customer and thus save fifty cents. McGinn immediately compared this with the advice John Shevlin had given him: 'If you want to make a phone call tell the operator you've lost your ten cents in the coin box and she'll put you through to the number free of charge.' The great A.T. and T. and the great Bank car park scams...

Roberta, or 'Big Momma' as she was known was the mother figure to the group, except on Sunday afternoons when she donned a black plastic macintosh, buttoned it up over her ample breasts and invited Gorman, Coughlin, Shevlin, Connolly or McGinn to divest her of the coat with their teeth, this tedious ceremony appearing to give her a slight frisson and enliven the deadly Minnesota 3.2 beer Sunday rather than drive to Wisconsin for a real drink.

Roberta's customary drink took a while to order. In the bar she would call for : 'A double Fleischman's bourbon on the rocks with tall-charge and a twist — and what can I get you, Pete?'

'A beer,' was McGinn's customary reply.

After one of the Sunday sessions McGinn had crawled into bed with Momma at her apartment and passed out, to be awakened by her at 4 a.m., saying'Hey - Pete: look who's on the other side of me.'

McGinn looked over the mountain of flesh which was Roberta in bed and perceived in the gloom a fat man snoring.

'That's him — the Man himself..'

'Who?'

'Fast Eddie, the pool-player. Jackie Gleason played him in the movie, with Paul Newman.'

'How did he get here?'

'He got in from Miami at three o'clock this morning. He always sacks out here when he comes north to play a game. So does Henry Miller. He was here last week. He left me a couple of presents — go look in the bureau drawer over there.'

McGinn looked. In the drawer was a dildo and attached to it was a book: Tropic of Cancer by Henry Miller. He opened the book, and the inscription said: 'Sorry about last night Roberta. Try this instead. You are straight out of the pages of 'Capricorn'.

Fast Eddie was snoring. McGinn could not get back to sleep. The name Paul Newman had triggered off a chain of thought. He had met a show-business reporter on the local paper who had told him about interviewing Newman in the town of Hurley, Wisconsin, famous as the gangster hide-out in the '20s, where Dillinger and his gang had hidden out when he was Public Enemy No. 1 in the United States. Al Capone was also a regular visitor to Hurley which was a wild town in the '20s and '30s and was not doing too badly in the middle sixties. Newman had expressed a wish to the show business reporter that he would like to see what the inside of a 'cat-house' was really like, so they visited an establishment and were directed upstairs to talk to the Madam proprietor. She met them half-way, having heard appreciative noises from the girls downstairs and as Paul Newman mounted the stairs she paused on the top step and looked at the star and said: 'Hey — you're Paul Newman. What the hell are you doin' here? You couldn't get laid in Cat on a Hot Tin Roof!'

Berryman was morose. John Berryman was one of the best poets in America, but he was not a happy man. When Larry Sullivan introduced McGinn to John Berryman he was friendly but distant. He asked about McGinn's novel but McGinn explained that it was far too early to think of sales as it had just been published and had not had any publicity. He was supposed to fly back to New York to appear on a radio show and two television shows, which Dutton the publisher had organised. Berryman said; 'Well, good luck with the book, Pete. See you when you get back.'

That was the first and last time McGinn met Berryman: a week after their meeting, Berryman jumped from the bridge that crossed the Mississippi river in Minneapolis. His death was recorded in every newspaper in America. The death of a poet always makes good copy, especially when the poet verged on greatness.

CHAPTER 4

New York

ONE of the things McGinn liked immediately about America was the lack of fuss and functionaries when a passenger took an airplane flight within the States. It was just like getting aboard a bus. The passenger was not required to turn up an hour or two hours before the flight as he is in England or Spain. Just as a motor-car was to an American a means of getting from A to B and not a toy or a proud possession to be polished and coddled and shown off, an airport was the same as a bus station. You bought a ticket, the flight was called, you stood in line and went aboard. In Europe they were still behaving as if Airports had just been invented and were full of fussy officials with rules and regulations and obsequious behaviour to people they classed as V.I.P.s which included anyone with a title.

Connolly and Sullivan split soon after they arrived in the Big Apple, for they had friends to meet, but first they tried a bar in The Village. It was 5 a.m. The bar stank of bodies, heat, beer and smoke. The guy sweeping up told them they were just closing. They gagged and left. Larry Sullivan had fixed McGinn up with a spare bed.

It was in an apartment owned by a woman who let rooms to actors. She claimed to read fortunes, specialising in palms. McGinn was a little taken aback when he saw that the two actors shared a double bed in their room, and realised that, at the age of 29, he was still naive and shockable by such things, for he had rarely encountered homosexuality, certainly not in the north of England, rarely in Fleet Street and scarcely ever in the British Army, although he had suspected a barrack room closet queen who pressed her uniform too often and too neatly, and had escaped an attempted seduction by a soldier who later became one of London's top fashion designers, in a barrack room at the Guards depot when he was doing a shorthand report of a War Office meeting while detached from his barracks in Aldershot, and was rather sorry to see, next day, the young fairy arrested by the Provost Marshall for wearing suade shoes with his uniform.

The two actors were impressed when they heard McGinn was appearing on two television shows and was being interviewed on coast-to-coast radio by Arlene Francis, although McGinn had never heard of her. The only name he knew from American radio shows was Lawrence Welk, because all Americans laughed at his old-fashioned orchestra.

Arlene Francis was not too pleased when McGinn turned up late (one of the rare occasions in his life that he was late) because of a hangover after a night in Greenwich Village bars, and even less amused when they had to move to another studio three quarters of the way through the interview and McGinn, still suffering from the effects of the Village pub crawl, asked the producer: 'Shall I take this stick?' and she replied: 'If you do, Miss Francis won't be able to walk.'

In the next studio the famous (in America) actress asked, when McGinn talked of his days on the William Hickey column of the Daily Express in London: 'Did you ever have your face slapped?' She asked the question, or rather snapped out the question, with all the post-menopausal frustration and vindictiveness of the members of a new sorority which had just been formed, called S.C.U.M., the Society for Cutting Up Men. He did not reply and she became even more frustrated, trying to goad McGinn and his horrible hangover into anger as if he were the British equivalent of a muck- raking American Hollywood gossip columnist, when in fact, if she had been nicer, he would have confessed that all that he and Driscoll and Peter Baker were trying to do was bring down the British Royal Family with ridicule, destroy the Aristocracy and the Honours system, expose the crimes of politicians, smash the Tory party and that old hypocrite Harold Macmillan (who had been expelled from Eton for buggery) end the public school system and class distinction in Britain and nationalise the banks and the building societies.

The television appearance was a more pleasant experience except that American TV studios and their inhabitants have a horror of drink, and the slightest sniff of alcohol on a potential visitor's breath brings out gallons of hot black coffee, but they try and ensure no one has a drink by making everyone stay in the waiting room for an hour before the show goes on.

Zachary Scott and Eve of Rome (who had brought her mother along) were on the same show in which a group of celebrities had to guess the missing word in the sentence supplied by the participant. Zachary Scott had been famous in cowboy films but he had not had a good part in films for some years, and when one of the 'celebrities', a handsome young actor currently in one of the 'soaps' asked him what he was working in at that moment and he replied that he was touring in the part of Professor Higgins in My Fair Lady and the young actor sniggered, McGinn's heart when out to Zachary Scott, an international star reduced to afternoon games shows and touring in a musical, and he saw the pain on Scott's face at the sneer.

But Eve of Rome (who had married Guy Elmes, the film script writer, in Rome, and had just made a fortune selling her scent and face cream business ('products based on Eastern European recipes passed on by her ancient grandmother') was celebrating in New York and, with her Mum and another lady 'd'un certain age', was gushing over Scott, ogling him like a teenager and at least cheering him up a little.

McGinn told tales of an old friend Jocelyn Kelsey an ex-BBC man from Hampstead who, while in bed sitter-land, washed his socks in the British Museum Reading Room toilets (constant hot water) and dried them on a radiator and upon exiting saw one of the eccentric habitues of the museum notice she had a flat tyre on her bicycle, pumped it up, massaged the tyre with the thigh bone of a turkey, and rode off, satisfied. The 'celebrities' managed to guess the missing word 'socks' but could not guess that anyone would massage a bicycle tyre with the thigh bone of a turkey. English eccentricity appeared to be beyond their grasp.

Full of black coffee, McGinn managed to get down a couple of swift ones before reporting to be interviewed on a New York TV channel which was just starting up, appearing with another writer who had just published a book of interviews with famous American writers. The interviewer, another handsome young would-be actor at least showed the front cover of McGinn's book with its New Yorker type illustration of a man living in a model whale. His first question was: 'Have you ever lived inside a whale?' and McGinn replied: 'No, but I once took up residence inside a sabre-toothed walrus, ' (thinking of the one in a foyer of Sunderland museum).

To his amazement the interviewer said: ' Tell us about that' and McGinn had to explain that he wasn't being serious, it was a joke. 'A joke. You know — a joke?', and he realised again that American humour was much more naive than British humour, especially black humour which Americans found distasteful, and he also realised he had been lucky to get a comedy novel published on both sides of the Atlantic and that it must have international appeal.

He was taken aback when his agent Willis Kinsley Wing, said he was offering it to Hollywood for 50,000 dollars plus 5 percent of the producer's net profit. Wing told him he was handling two other books at that time: Svetlana Stalin's memoirs and The Death of a President by William Manchester. Mr Wing was a cripple, clearly having spent a life in pain, for, using his huge shoulders and arms for leverage, he managed to cross his office to some files with a scalene shuffle. This wonderful man who had overcome his adversity as Roosevelt had, was the top literary agent in America, and McGinn had a feeling that Willis Kingsley Wing might just crack it and change his life.

Fifty thousand dollars...it didn't bear thinking about.

Back in Minneapolis, winter had set in. The temperature was sinking to a regular 40 below zero. A woman on Hennepin said: 'Where's your ear-muffs? What are you? A Canadian or somepin'?' They made holes and ice-fished on White Bear lake. He was broke. He sold his Irish tweed coat to Gerry the bartender. He looked in the window of a pawnshop, only because it happened to be next to a barber's shop where one could get a free haircut if the apprentice barbers could practise on the poverty stricken client's head, for he had nothing to pawn. He looked closely at an array of fob watches in the front of the window, about twenty, some with the cases open, and he read the inscriptions: they were presentation watches to railway men, mainly train drivers, who had served their 45 or 50 years on the famous railways of America: The Rock Island Line, and The Soo line. The sadness he felt at the sight of the watches was only equalled by the sight of men eating plates of watery beans at 10 cents a plate in a down-trodden cafe.

Back in the bar at Seven Corners, it was Brucie, who had a brother at Princeton who called out: 'I'm for Mexico, anybody coming along?'

Half a dozen girls said: 'Yeah, I'll come, Bruce.' and several of the men said they were interested. McGinn was experiencing the American frontier spirit, the spirit which had driven their ancestors from Scandinavia, Germany, Ireland, Scotland and England across the Atlantic to the shores of New York and up into the middle west in covered wagons. He knew that if someone had suggested a similar trip in a bar in Rome, Paris or London, the suggestion would have met with incredulity and sneers, but Americans, like Australians, were always ready for adventure.

The trouble was: Brucie's car. He had bought it for five dollars. It was not in good running order. The back doors were closed and kept closed by the simple expedient of tying them with a rope, but this necessitated the back seat passengers having to untie the rope every time they stopped. When the pub adventurers heard about the transport, many discovered that they were committed to their jobs and families. The final group of volunteers was Bruce, Larry Sullivan, Marvin and McGinn. Marvin's brother, whom they interviewed in his bed at midnight, said he had a date with a snowplough next day and couldn't afford to lose his job.

The lovely Lorna packed some sandwiches and put two plastic bags in the trunk which later turned out to be the accumulated unwanted goods from her larder, tins of custard powder, bottles of sauce, shoe polish, meat paste, tinned cheese, old crackers and a can of chilli con carne with rust on its edge, and a tin of Irish Tea which could only have been packed in America. The Irish Tea, Lorna had insisted to Larry, was a farewell present to McGinn, the only one who knew how to brew the stuff anyway.

The temperature had dropped to 44 below zero.

The streets of Minneapolis were deserted. The hunters who drove around showing off the deer they had slaughtered by strapping it to the roof of their car, had long gone to bed. The bar which served the venison in the form of a hamburger, was closed for the night.

McGinn made sure the rope was secured properly, stretched between him and Marvin the Peace Marcher in the back, while Brucie drove and Larry tried to sleep as he would be taking over the wheel as co-driver. The moon shone on the snowy fields of Minnesota as they drove through the night, crossed the Mississippi and headed south, and Brucie shared one last joint with Larry before Larry dozed off. The great highway of America stretched ahead of them, and they were on the road at last and the next stop was Brownsville, Texas, then south to Mexico city and Acapulco.

CHAPTER 5

Mexico

NIGHT had fallen by the time they crossed the State line into Texas. McGinn had seen night skies in the Mediterranean, over Norway, Ireland, southern England, Italy and Spain, but he had never ever seen a sky that stretched from horizon to horizon in a vast star-filled expanse that was the Texas sky. Everything they said in the famous song was true, the stars at night were big and bright, deep in the heart of Texas, and McGinn would value that experience as they headed south towards Dallas.

He was shocked in Dallas. A big sign on an hotel said: NO COLOREDS.

In the middle sixties, they were still exercising a strict colour-bar in Dallas, where Jack Kennedy had been assassinated, and McGinn had not seen a sign like this since the Fifties in London where boarding houses put a sign in the window: NO IRISH, NO BLACKS. Larry had seen it too, and so had Marvin and Bruce, both Jews, and, without a word being said, they drove on, through Dallas and on, out into the desert highway to Brownsville.

At the frontier McGinn was shocked again by the attitude of the Mexican customs officials, who actually said to Marvin: 'No tips?' When McGinn reached into his pocket, the Customs man said: 'not you, sir,' because they had seen his typewriter and his Press card. Marve gave him a dollar.

Again McGinn thought of France and Spain, Spain where a customs officer, offered a bribe, would have thrown it back in the face of the person who offered it, but as Hemingway had said of France, give them a tip and they will remember it and treat you with respect. It worked in France and it worked in 21 in New York and it certainly worked here in Mexico.

They had eaten a hamburger and drank a coffee in Brownsville and McGinn immediately remembered what had been said about America, that you could eat a 'burger in New York, travel three thousand miles to San Francisco, and it would taste exactly the same; eat chicken in Paris, Lyon and Nice and they would all taste different.

Brownsville was a honky-tonk kind of American town of gas stations and eateries and pin table arcades and 'Wetbacks', the Mexicans who had crossed the frontier over the river and were desperately trying to get work, to earn a living, to stay in this fat, rich country rather than live in the poverty of their own. After the frontier, the loud music and neon lights behind them, they saw villages which looked as if they had been bombed. Here was the poverty the Mexican 'Wetbacks' were running away from, here the donkeys brayed raucously, chickens ran in and out of houses which appeared to be derelict but were occupied by families with thin, ragged children. They stopped at a cantina for bottles of cold Mexican beer.

There was a filthy toilet a few paces from the bar and he almost laughed when Marve asked the proprietor for a beer mat, for McGinn had seen that the toilet did not have plumbing, but a stall and a groove which ran along the bar near their feet and out into the street to water the dust there.

They drove on through the heat of the day, passing many blown-out tyres at the side of the road, and dead animals, an occasional donkey lying in a ditch being consumed by vultures. Larry suddenly decided that the ache at the base of his spine needed medical attention and insisted they pulled in to the next hospital for him to have a check-up. Night had closed in when they found a hospital, but one view of the wards, filled to capacity with Mexican indians who looked like Aztecs, grandmothers with their families and crying children, that Larry decided that he had had an instant cure for the ache in his lower back and they drove on.

One town had the air of the end of a carnival and they stopped for a drink in a bar near the centre of the town where it turned out the town had been celebrating a bullfight that had taken place that day and most of the men were drunk. Ordering bottles of beer, they were conspicuous in the bar as Americans, and McGinn noticed a few hostile stares and the muttering of the word 'gringo'. He was not sure of the origin of this word, but it was used by all Mexicans to describe Americans. One theory was that the word came from the Mexicans hearing American soldiers singing songs around a camp fire: 'down where the green grass grows,' or 'green grow the rushes - O', but whatever the origin, it was being hissed in his left ear right now by a fierce Mexican with greasy hair, ringlets, and a silver six-shooter in his hand and it was pointing directly at McGinn, whose Spanish was not very good, but good enough to ascertain that the man was angry because he had lost money on the bullfight and he intended assuaging his anger by shooting a 'gringo' and that 'gringo' was McGinn, the nearest of the foursome. He thought quickly. The man was drunk. He was armed. He had to be distracted from his purpose in some way:

'Mais, alors, Monsieur, quesque vous voulez avec mois? Je suis un Francais dans votre superb pays, et je voudrais bien boire une biere tranquillement dans votre jolie ville. Vous voulez boire quelquechose avec moi?'

The Mexican's mouth hung open. He was baffled for an instant and then he heard one of his drunken friends say that he was a Frenchman, and suddenly the atmosphere changed and the man with the pistol smiled and with a flick of his thumb opened the chamber of the revolver and out fell six silver bullets. Why were they silver-coated bullets? McGinn asked himself. Was this man the local vampire slayer or was he just the local Jack the Lad who wanted to show off with the silver six-shooter and bullets? The Mexican accepted a drink and so did his companions and all was friendly, but the foursome of 'gringos' decided to beat a hasty retreat into the night.

They slept fitfully in the car until daybreak and finally as they were nearing Mexico City the old banger failed to take a hill.

The hill was steep, the side of a mountain, in fact, and the clapped-out piece of five dollar junk was refusing to perform, so Bruce turned it round with a swift U-turn in the road and headed back down the mountain. He took a second run at it, and failed 200 metres from the summit, so it was another U-turn and back down the mountain.

On the third try, they made it.

The most prominent buildings in Mexico city were the banks: there seemed to be new banks on every corner. In contrast to the glass and marble and steel banks, old ladies slept in shop doorways and begged from passers by, one man spent all day making four paper napkins out of one by quartering it in a cafe, another spent his life picking up waste newspaper and discarded paper bags to sell as waste to a dealer. The three Americans, however, having suffered a partial Minnesota winter, wanted a beach and sunshine, so they drove on to Acapulco and checked into a cheap hostel which was a sort of courtyard.

On the beach they met two American girls, and when Larry asked them where they were from, and they said: 'Dallas' there were sounds of dismay from Bruce and Marvin and the girls said: 'Why does everybody hate Dallas now, just because of Jack Kennedy? It's a fine town and the assassination of the President had nothing to do with the people of Dallas.'

Larry, ever the diplomat, changed the subject and asked where they were staying, and how much they were paying a night. They mentioned an hotel and said: 'Fifteen a night' and McGinn thought that wasn't bad for an hotel for it was the same as they were paying in the doss-house in the smelly part of town, until it dawned on him that they meant American dollars and he was thinking of pesos, and fifteen American dollars was about what he had in his pocket, that, plus a Saville Row suit by Huntsman which he doubted if he could sell, or even find a Mexican it would fit. It would just have to stay in his suitcase.

That night, Montezuma had his revenge and McGinn lay on a bunk in the room he shared with Marvin and groaned as the stomach spasms came every twenty minutes and he dashed to the outdoor lavatory which would have disgraced the Moroccan army, every half hour throughout the night. Everything the Americans had said about Montezuma's revenge was true, as McGinn suspected he had contracted it through ice made from dirty water. He vowed never to scoff again at advice to avoid certain food and drinks in Latin and Arab countries.

That night trouble hit the foursome when Larry and Bruce were arrested and had the car impounded after a motorist complained to the police that they were drunk. The normal procedure in Mexico is to have a couple of hundred peso notes in the driving licence for the traffic cop and you drive on, but Larry and Bruce had not yet learnt this, so they appeared in court next day pretending to be shame-faced, and Larry, the experienced bartender, told the judge that they were not accustomed to the strength of that great Mexican drink, tequila, and that was the cause of their dizzy spell.

The whole courtroom reacted as if Sullivan had paid them the highest compliment, all muttered together: 'tequila... tequila... tequila...' and a lecture followed from the judge that Americans could not handle this special nectar made from cactus, so they had best avoid it in the future. He gave them a fine sufficient to ruin their trip and they got the car out of the pound.

As they were about to shake the dust of Acapulco — the only place in the world McGinn had seen vultures on a beach — they were approached by a man who said: 'Hello, boys. You looking for gold?' and McGinn thought of The Treasure of the Sierra Madre, and realised this was Mexico where such things happened, and trains had armed guards or soldiers aboard to fight off bandits.

'No, but do you know the direction we take for Zihuatanejo?' Larry asked

'You're not looking for gold?'

'No, we want to go north of here to a beach place...'

The man moved on, having lost interest; he would have to con someone else that day.

'Donde es Zihuatanejo,' Larry asked a Mexican next, pronouncing it the way he had been told: Zee who watta ne-hhrro.

'Donde?' the Mexican asked, puzzled.

'ZEE WHO WATTA NE-HHRRO.'

'Donde?'

Bruce tried: 'Zee who watta ne-hhrro.'

'Ah - you wan Zee-who-watta ne-HHRRO!'

They sighed with relief, for a moment having thought they would have to spend the rest of the week in Acapulco repeating Zihuatanejo to numerous Mexicans in order to find their way out of town and into the countryside.

The road was bad, the old car rocked from side to side as they hit potholes and drove into gullies. They paused to look down from one bridge and women and girls were washing clothes in the river, every item of clothing was white and the scene reminded McGinn of his favourite film O Canganciero and the beautiful Rossana Podesta before

Hollywood ruined her with make-up, and the wonderful guitar playing as the banditos crossed the horizon which some cretin turned into: 'Ole, I am a bandit, a bandit of the hills.'

Zihuatanejo was a Paradise. A few tiny hotels on the beach and one big one away from the town. Pelicans dived into the lagoon which lapped the fine white sand of the beach and turtles waded ashore to lay their eggs. A mad diver with the 'bends' sold the oysters he had recovered for about 50 cents a dozen. McGinn regretted being broke now, but he would survive. Soup was 10 cents and a tortilla 20.

But first things first, for Bruce had not come here for a sun-tan and a plate of soup and oysters. He wanted marijuana, and seeing a man on the harbour pier who looked American, Bruce asked him where he could score, and the man asked him how much he had to spend. When Bruce said five the man looked disappointed but said he could fix it and asked for the five pesos. Again the misunderstanding, for Bruce had meant five American dollars.

'You mean FIVE AMERICAN DOLLARS?' the man asked.

Bruce nodded.

'Man — no problem. Gimme the sawbuck and meet me here tomorrow at the same time.'

They checked into a cheap flop-house off the main street.

That night the town came alive and groups of young men attended a billiards hall where a woman was cooking something on a hot-plate at the entrance and whatever it was that she occasionally sliced was kept under a white cloth. She made 'boccadillos' and handed them out to the youths. Whatever it was, McGinn promised himself he would try it before he left Zihuatanejo because it smelt so good in the open air. He noticed that most houses were open, the front door left ajar, and assumed it was because the inhabitants had nothing to steal, whereas an occasional house had a high wall with barbed wire on the top, and they clearly did have something to steal.

One thing the three Americans made McGinn understand — it was impossible to work in Mexico. If a broke American tried for a dishwasher's job they would laugh in his face. The other thing McGinn had come to understand was that these Mexicans had no admiration for adventurous students, explorers or back-packers who ran out of money. Why had they left that rich, fat land to come here and bum around?

They could go home and earn good money in a job, just as all those 'Wetbacks' were trying to do. What they really admired was some flash Yank in an open Cadillac driving with one hand and fondling a gorgeous blonde with the other as music blared from the car radio. That's the one they wanted to emulate — not beach bums counting every peso.

There were very few Americans in Zihuatanejo in 1964. Three men who looked like ex-servicemen drank beer and kept to themselves in one of the seafront hotels. In another Miss Mable and her daughter lived, arriving at the lunch table stoned out of their minds and started on the munchies. They called her Miss Mable but did not know her real name. She was in Mexico to smoke dope, and she immediately palled up with Bruce when he told her he had ordered some charge for the next day and they made a date to turn on together and have lunch on the hotel terrace, the whole group. McGinn looked in his pocket. This would probably be the last proper meal he would have for some time as he was down to fifteen dollars. The place they were to meet for a smoke was just on the edge of town, a rather tatty part of the beach but hidden from public view by a sea wall. This was Shit Beach, where joints were rolled and smoked away from the prying eyes of the police. Not that the police would have stopped them, but they would have wanted a bribe.

They had seen bribery at work at close range the night they had arrived, visiting the local dance hall and whore-house, where the girls danced with the cops and with potential clients, and every hour, on the hour, the Chief of Police took out his whistle, blew it, and the music stopped. The cops went to the bar, the hookers sat around the dance floor, and the manager of the dance hall crossed the floor and gave some peso notes to the Chief who looked at his watch, blew his whistle, and the music struck up and the dancing continued.

The only other Americans in the little town were a grandmother, her beautiful 26 year old daughter and 7 year old grand-daughter, staying in rooms on the seashore.

The daughter had a man friend who occasionally flew into Mexico city where she would go to meet him, spend 2 or 3 nights and come back flushed with happiness while 'Grandma', who flinched every time her grand-daughter called her that in front of the men, stayed on as childminder. She flinched because she was an American grandmother, which meant she had been married at eighteen, was 19 when her daughter

61

was born and was a very attractive 45 now, and interested in men, especially Englishmen. Harriet Murphy, the 'Grandma' had her eye on McGinn the scribbler from The Old Country.

Bruce met his contact on the pier. This American was on the run, wanted by the police in Los Angeles for some unknown crime, and was hiding out. He had acquired a Mexican girl friend and they had a baby daughter. All lived in a tent made from an Army blanket held up by bamboo poles on the edge of town.

'Something really great happened to me this morning,' he told Bruce.

'What was that?' Bruce asked, thinking that perhaps he had won the national lottery or found a 1,000 dollar bill or heard he was no longer wanted by the cops in LA

'This guy gave me a fish.'

'A fish?'

'Yeah — I was on the front here early this morning and this guy gave me a fish he'd caught.'

'Did you get the charge?'

'It's leaf. Sinsemilla. You won't be disappointed, Bruce.'

Bruce was pleased, although he had been expecting a piece of Acapulco gold hashish, this was even better, locally grown, and sinsemilla in Spanish meant without seeds, he knew it would be good stuff, but he would ask the guy later to get him some seeds to send to Amsterdam where he had a buddy who was trying to grow his own and wasn't too happy with Tangier Green or Red Leb. His instruction was to put the seeds behind the postage stamps on the envelopes addressed to Amsterdam.

'Come into the town and I'll give you the goods you ordered,' The man said, and Bruce disappeared into the back streets of the little town and emerged five minutes later carrying an American army kit-bag under his arm.

'Jeez,' he said, 'You guys ain't going to believe this, but this duffel bag is full of leaf, grown on the mountains round here somewhere. Come on, we've got to try it. I'll stash this and take some out. Five bucks. For a fuckin' Army duffel bag full. Gentlemen — welcome to Paradise.'

On Shit Beach, Miss Mable and her teenage daughter were already skinning up by the sea-wall, and Bruce and Marvin produced joint-size papers which had the American flag on the pack, and made two joints about the size of a White Owl cigar. Bruce shared his with Larry and Marvin shared his with McGinn.

'Of course this place will be ruined when the goddam tourists find out about it,' said Miss Mable, sucking in a lungful of Acapulco Gold and holding it in with all the expertise of a whore in Venice hiding from the police under water. She passed the joint to Betsy the lumpy teenager who had a brace on her teeth, who drew in a lungful, held it, let it go and said: 'Wow!' And she said it in the way that only American girls can say it, with feeling: 'Waaaowww.'

'Are you guys coming to eat with us today? I'm inviting you, but only this once, mind, because you're new in town...'

McGinn was already feeling the effect of the joint, and the lagoon before him seemed to be suddenly more blue than it had been and the pelicans seemed to be diving more slowly, more gracefully and the voices of those around him faded and went and he tried to remember what Bruce had said to Larry and wondered why Larry was laughing. He let Marvin finish the joint. He had smoked Red Leb in Istanbul and Tangier Green in Spain, and Afghani in Happy Hampstead and Congolese Black in a Soho afternoon drinking club, but he had never smoked anything like this Acapulco leaf. He vaguely heard Miss Mable say she would like to borrow a copy of his book to read and would give it back to him, and then he distinctly heard Bruce describe a cow drowning in a vat of mayonnaise. It seemed hours since Miss Mable was talking about the possibility of tourists finding the town in the future. Everything after that was vague. He was eating fish on the terrace of Miss Mable's hotel. Betsy was eating chicken and he was horrified to look at her plate and see the carcase of the chicken come to life and move around on the plate. Larry was chuckling over some private joke and Marvin had fallen asleep with his head in the unfinished soup plate.

Miss Mable seemed to be having difficulty placing morsels of food in her mouth. She kept missing and putting it on her cheek instead. Betsy the teenage daughter had disappeared in the direction of her bedroom.

Next, McGinn was in a bar on the waterfront and the man with the bends was screaming and shouting, and no-one took any notice because this is how divers with the bends act. Then he was wandering up the street, the main drag, in the direction of the billiards hall and the woman who served those interesting-looking boccadillos from something she hid under the white linen cloth on a tray which lay on a charcoal brazier.

He had the 'munchies' and tried to order a boccadillo from the woman, but she told him in Spanish that she would not serve him. One or two youths nearby were laughing and one said, in English: 'Heez not for you, Gringo. Heez for Mexican peoples honly.'

McGinn said, or thought he said: 'Da me uno boccadillo por favor. Soy Ingles. No Americano.'

'You mus' be very hongry.'

'I am hungry. Da me uno. Quanto es?'

Suddenly the woman took pity on him and threw back the cloth and picked up her carving knife.

There, on the hotplate, steaming gently, was the carcase of a dog. It was about the size of a small, thin Jack Russsel or a very thin Corgi, and the flesh was black. The woman briskly cut a slice from its thigh, placed it neatly in a cut breadbun, and handed it to McGinn The Mexican youths regarded him, smiling.

He had to admit he was shocked, but at the same time, he had seen these youths eating the boccadillos from the stall and if they could eat them, he could. Never say no to an experience, had been his lifelong motto (except suicide), and he knew that the Mexicans had specially-bred dogs for eating and were probably fed on a vegetarian diet with rice so the flesh would not taste like that of a carnivore.

He took a bite. The Mexicans watched him. It tasted like rather high roast beef, which was the closest he could come to describing the taste. He swallowed and took another bite. The Mexican youths laughed and one of them slapped McGinnn on the back and said: 'You no Gringo, Ingles. You amigo.'

One of them passed him a joint. It was different from the stuff he had had earlier. This was hashish. This was the Acapulco Gold they raved about in New York.

The next thing he did was lift his head from the table in the bar and night club where he had been taken by his new found friends. They were about to run a beauty contest. A few couples were dancing on the tiny circular glass dance floor which was lit from below and glowed green in the dark. One man who sat near the edge of the dance floor

64

would occasionally spit, not on the floor beneath his feet but right onto the dance floor. The Mexicans were great spitters. He heard a call: 'Hey, Gringo,' then another: 'Hey, Gringo.' A quartet of Mexicans in their late twenties or early thirties were looking over at him at his single table and were clearly spoiling for trouble.

McGinn knew the best way to handle it was to ignore them, pretend not to have heard, pretend to be deaf and concentrate on the beauty contest which had just started. Four of the young girls were quickly eliminated by votes, and the contest was now between two 18 year old beauties, both local girls, but the contest was to be decided now, not on beauty, but another commodity — money.

A group of raucous American visitors, probably businessmen on holiday, were vying with each other to choose the winner by putting dollar bills up so that the girl who drew the most dollars would eventually win.

When she did, the other contestant burst into tears.

Naturally she believed that she was prettier than the other contestant, and in McGinn's opinion, she was, but in the end the almighty dollar had won.

McGinn was suspicious of Bruce next day when he asked him if he really wanted that tin of Irish tea, the present from the beautiful Lorna, and he knew as he handed it over to him and watched him tip the tealeaves out, that he was going to wire it under his car packed with leaf. It also signified that the Americans were getting ready to split after a few days. Marvin and McGinn spotted Larry and Bruce eating oysters in the little palm-covered beach bar and they looked guilty when they saw they had been caught. Two had a little money and two had none, and the two with were not sharing. Larry was waiting for money from Lorna but it had not arrived after ten days. Bruce had the car and wanted to go to Mexico City and then head north if they didn't get Lorna's dollars within a week. Marvin said he had to go along for the lift back and he was not too worried about being broke.

'You can go without food for several weeks,' said Marve the Peace marcher, who had the experience of being on hunger strike in jail in the Southern states of America.

'Sure, Marve. Gandhi did,' said McGinn.

'How long did he last out?'

'A hundred and sixty three days.'

'Jeez, that's amazing.'

'Yeah, but he faked it. He had women visit him supposedly to pray, but in fact they were nursing mothers, and the cunning old fox was living off mother's milk.'

'Yeah, right. That's over five months. I could go a month. The first two weeks are the worst. If you can stand the pain for two weeks then you go through the pain barrier and your stomach starts to shrink and as it shrinks the hunger abates.'

Marvin was right. Two weeks later, McGinn's stomach had shrunk to the size of a cricket ball. Larry, Bruce and Marvin had gone to Mexico City and he had their address, a hostel in the back streets. McGinn had to forward any mail with a Minneapolis date-stamp on it. It would be Lorna's dollars.

The most interesting thing about hunger is that it makes the hungry one resent and even hate the eaters in restaurants. He lowered his sights when he saw Grandma's little grand-daughter peeling a banana

'You wouldn't mind if I had a little bite, now would you?'

She minded.

She let out a howl then went in search of her Grandma.

McGinn felt guilty. What was he doing, nicking the kid's banana? Not long ago he had been on TV in New York and coast-to-coast radio and his book was reviewed in the New York Times review of books, he was an item in the Daily News gossip column, an habitue of the famous Chelsea Hotel (although, on his second visit the management, suspecting the first stages of penury, had put him in a 14 dollars a night dump of a room near the basement boilers) and now here he was, in a town built on a swamp, with scorpions in a toilet and in his suitcase a Saville Row suit by Huntsman that would now only fit him where it touched.

Grandma appeared. She smiled.

'Would you like to have dinner with me tonight? I'm cooking steak.' she said

Is the Pope a Catholic? Can a duck swim? Do bears shit in the woods?

Two hours later he was eating steak, the granddaughter was tucked up in her little bed and Grandma was touching his knee under the table. Half an hour after that he was in bed with her, thinking: there's a lot of truth in the old sayings, like There's No Such Thing As a Free Meal.

Next day the daughter was back, glowing, a far-away look in her eye: amore...

She was a happy woman after three nights in the city with her airline pilot.

Next day McGinn got a letter from Willis Kingsley Wing in New York. It said he had been offered 35,000 dollars for the film rights of McGinn's novel with three years options of 3,500 dollars a year until the deal went through.

He was saved.

Not only that — he was out of journalism.

That had been his real reason for writing a book in the first place, but only by writing something which would earn a crust could he hope to quit the Street of Shame.

He had never, ever expected to sell the book to Hollywood. He bought a stamp and wrote a note to Elliot Graham at the publisher's office, asking for money to fly back to New York to sign a contract with the producer, Paul Benson. Elliot was a good guy, but he knew how to keep his job, which, apart from meeting Mickey Spillane twice a year and sitting A.A. Milne's toy bear, Winnie the Pooh on his knee to be admired by the 1st class passengers en route to London, he had squired Francoise Sagan around New York on her visits until her Paris agent had the temerity to ask for more money whence she was immediately dropped by Dutton. McGinn knew Elliot from his visits to Hampstead where he had an old friend, Jon Rose, an Australian writer who had been Sandy Wilson's boyfriend about the time Wilson wrote The Boyfriend, both Jon and Sandy claiming to have given Elaine Dundee the title for her book The Dud Avocado.

Elliot came through with enough dollars to get McGinn off the beach.

A small plane took him to Mexico City, where he met up with the three Americans and gave Larry a letter from Lorna, then they went to a side street and smoked four big joints inside the car and sailed into a restaurant full of middle class Americans. Before the first course of soup arrived, they were out of their minds, and when McGinn asked Bruce what had happened to that cow he had seen drowning in a vat of mayonnaise when they had been blowing up strong with Miss America of 1936, Miss Mabel, Marvin fell off his chair laughing and Larry fell on top of him while trying to help him up. Having disgraced themselves in front of the bourgoisie they managed to get the soup down and then left and had some tortillas as 'munchies' in the cafe where the little man was still dividing one paper napkin into four pieces.

McGinn felt that Larry and Bruce were feeling guilty about abandoning him, broke, on the beach and were a little bit jealous when he showed them the agent's letter with the film offer, but they said nothing, except that they had just enough to stay another week with Lorna's dollars and then they would head back to Minneapolis.

At Mexico City airport, McGinn waited with his suitcase containing the Huntsman suit (unworn for a month) and his typewriter. An official gave him a form. One of the questions for the Tourist Board was: Please estimate how much money in American dollars you have spent during your stay.

McGinn wrote: 15,850 dollars.

As he set off to walk to the plane, another official in uniform ran up to him, stopped him and carried his suitcase and typewriter to the plane for the New York flight, shook his hand and wished him a happy journey. He often wondered what they would have done if he had put the true sum: 25 dollars.

It was a magnificent flight over the mountains of Mexico.

In New York he took the advice of a longshoreman he had met on the beach in Acapulco and checked into the Cornish Arms Hotel, which was owned by the Longshoremen's Union, opposite the Chelsea, and then he headed uptown to Jim Downey's and Toots Shore's.

CHAPTER 6

New York

THIS time he was being feted in New York. But the situation was not exactly as he had thought: it was a private producer, Paul Benson, who was financing the original options until they got a script and then United Artists would take over. Benson was a Press Agent straight out of the movies, cashmere overcoat, big cigar, smooth patter, a big hooter and a tall, blonde, beautiful ex-showgirl wife. 'When those sons-of-bitches on the noospapers went on strike I said ferkit and went freelance. I'm not going to have my business held up to ransom by a bunch of half-assed noospapermen, so I represent a coupla restaurants now: HEY - - BUSBOY, take this ashtray away an' bring me a noo one an' gimme some firm butter. This butter isn't firm. I want some firm butter. I represent this restaurant we're in now, and tomorrow we go to Four Seasons. I'm going to write a name on this piece of paper and you tell me what you think, right?'

He wrote a name, folded the paper and gave it to McGinn.

It said: Cary Grant.

'Well, wadda ya say?'

'About what?'

'To play the part of Jonathan in your book.'

'But my character is 25 years old.'

'So what? If we can get Cary Grant he's box office. He's already expressed an interest, and so has Bette Davis, who wants to play the part of the Countess.

'So when are you goin' to write your next book?'

'Soon.'

'I'll tell you what you gotta do in your next book. You know this guy Eye-on Fleming? You gotta do what he did in his book — he painted a broad GOLD. Are you hearing me? HE PAINTED A BROAD G-O-L-D. that's what you gotta do...'

McGinn let his mind drift, took a swig of brandy hoping to drive out the sound of the voice in his ear...

'No, you haven't started writing your next book because you got dough now. If you were starving in an attic you'd be writing it...'

'I can assure you,' said McGinn, taking another swig of brandy, 'that if one is starving in an attic, one thinks of food, not literature...'

'Yeah, yeah, I know, excuses, excuses...'

McGinn wanted to be somewhere else: at Minnehaha Falls with the 23 year old divorcee who was looking for a new husband, making love to her in the back of her father's car, by the rocks with all the lovers' initials scratched over the years. Or smoking a joint the size of a small Christmas cracker on Shit Beach, Zihuatanejo with Miss Mabel or in bed with Grandma full of steak-inducing energy.

'My darling wife and I do not have children but we do have our adorable poodles, and we love and cherish them as much as we would any child. They are our babies...' Benson was onto family matters. He would be telling his life story soon.

'I ate a dog in Mexico,' McGinn said

Benson's face became a whiter shade of pale. His eyes stared and his mouth hung open.

'You what?'

'It was outside a billiards hall in Zihuatanejo, and I was starving. The woman though I was a gringo and didn't want to sell me a slice — in a boccadillo, of course...'

'Hold it. Stop. Jeez, you shouldn't tell me things like that, Pete...'

The manager of the restaurant interrupted them to ask if everything was all right and Benson recovered enough to complain that the butter hadn't been firm. The manager asked him if he would like some ice in the butter dish but Benson waved him away with his cigar.

But somehow he seemed to have lost his appetite and after bullying the busboy — who was stooped, thin, and about 65 years of age — decided to call it a night.

McGinn was to call at his swell apartment and Benson and his wife would take him to Four Seasons...

McGinn knew he should not have done it, but he was tipsy when he arrived at the Bensons beautiful pad. There was a single, beautiful rose in a vase in the hall.

'Good Lord — it's real,' said McGinn.

'Sure it's real.' Benson snapped, looking sideways at the tipsy scribbler and suspecting that the Britisher was taking a rise out of him.

Then he introduced him to his gorgeous long-legged wife and his two 'darling boys', their white poodles.

Benson watched McGinn the dog lover fondling the two spoilt yapping animals, all white fluff and diamante collars, as if he expected him to order a jar of mint sauce, but the dogs licked his hand as if he were an old friend.

At Four Seasons, rated the most expensive restaurant in New York at that time, the manager again gushed at their table, but kept a beady eye on McGinn whom he suspected had been hitting the sauce before he hit the restaurant. He offered them champagne on the house and brought three slender fluted glasses. McGinn had always drunk champagne out of round champagne glasses (and ladies' slippers, depending on the lady and the state of her feet) so he said: 'Out of these?'

'Yes - out of t-h-e-s-e,' said the manager, with a homosexual sneer.

But when the drinks were poured he tried to make friends:

'Have you seen Dah-ly?' he asked McGinn.

'Is Salvador in town?' McGinn said, and Benson chuckled and kicked his wife under the table.

'He means the show — Hello Dah-ly.

'No. I scarcely ever go to the theatre although Mr. Benson here has kindly given me a ticket for Sammy Davis Junior's show.'

'You don't go to the theatre? Why is that?' the manager asked, trying to be friendly.

McGinn thought about the two actors he had met on his last visit who had told him he could get a part in a Broadway play if he went along for an audition for 'Alfie' where they needed an actor who must be British to fulfill the Equity rules. Juliet Mills, daughter of the famous John Mills was in it, and he suspected that the part was that of the abortionist, played by Denholm Elliot in the film, and how annoyed he was when Elliot Graham had said: 'You should have gone. There's more money in acting than there is in writing.' as if he didn't know, and now he made the same reply to the manager of Four Seasons that he had given to the actors:

'I never go to the theatre because it encourages actors and it stops me smoking.'

The manager had clearly had enough of McGinn's sarcasm.

He said goodbye to Benson and his wife and moved swiftly to glad-hand some new clients.

'When we go, can we drop you off anywhere?' Benson asked.

'I doubt if you'd want to,' said McGinn, 'I'm going to Harlem.'

'Are you crazy?' Benson snapped. 'You'll get killed down there. There's cops on every corner. Malcolm X was killed..'

'Yes, I know. His body is in the morgue on 125th street, and that's where I'm going. I wanted to meet up with an old colleague from England, John Wilcock, on the Village Voice, but he's in Japan. He's writing 'Japan on $5 a day', so I'm meeting two friends of his, one black, and one white.'

'That won't save you.'

'Fergus Cashin tried to take Liz Taylor and Richard Burton down there last night. They wanted to go but they were talked out of it, the way you're trying to talk me out of it.'

'Who the hell's Fergus Cashin?'

'A Scottish Irishman. He was walking down Fleet street in 1945 in the uniform of a Captain in the Black Watch when someone said there was a sub-editor's job going on the Daily Express. They gave him a trial. There was a story about an old schoolmaster who refused to be transferred to another school because there was no trout stream near the other school, something like that, and Fergus put the headline on it that secured his future in the Street: NO FISH FOR MR. CHIPS'

'OK, OK, well, if you're still alive tomorrow you can go to the bank and pick up your dough. Then you can go and get your castle in Spain and a whole new wardrobe. And you better start eating again, one lamb chop and a lettuce leaf is not sufficient...'

Benson's voice droned on, lecturing him...

The next thing he knew he was in a taxi going to Harlem, with the driver trying to talk him out of it, but McGinn had an appointment with Bobby and Sue on 125th Street and he intended to keep it.

They were there in the bar, and the bar was all black. A bouncer who looked like Joe Louis stood by the door. Music started up and the women in the bar started to sway their hips from side to side with the music. A flash from a camera went off.

Someone was photographing him. He fought his way to the bar to get drinks for Sue and Bobby, but they wanted to split for another, less crowded place, a jazz bar. As they tried to force their way out, the bouncer said to McGinn, who was wearing his Saville Row suit: 'Don't crowd the door.'

McGinn was annoyed. He had been threatened. He went back into the bar and said to the bouncer: 'I'm not an American racist. I'm British.'

'Just don't crowd the door,' the bouncer said.

'Look, I've got nothing against you guys. I'm from the other side of the Atlantic — a Britisher — and I'm not, repeat not, a racist.'

'Just don't crowd the door.'

McGinn looked at the negro. He was built like a large barrel, and could probably have torn a telephone directory in half with hands that looked like bunches of bananas that had been too long in the shop. He realised he was drunk, and by arguing with this very patient, cool, calm man mountain, he was risking a fractured jaw. He left and joined Bobby and Sue on the street corner, where six cops were standing and talking and looking over at the other six cops on another corner.

Bobby, rolled a big joint and lit up, passing it to Sue. He looked at the cops and the cops looked at him, knowing he was defying them by smoking Bob Hope in the street, and he knew they wouldn't start anything because he was black and one incident there on 125th street would have probably set Harlem ablaze in revenge for the death of Malcolm X.

In the tiny jazz bar where a first rate group played, Bobby said: 'Sorry you missed John Wilcock. He does love a smoke.'

'Years ago when he was on the Gateshead Post and the Daily Mail his passion wasn't for pot, it was for potato crisps — or potato chips as you call them, but they were rationed in England in the 1950's just as sweets and chocolate were, so he would watch for the Smith's Crisp van and then chase it, from shop to shop and buy a packet of crisps in each shop. Ah, the innocence of youth...'

'Yeah. Europe On Five Dollars A Day...'

'Aye yer reet lad, them were t' days. You could tek a tramcar to Essoldo, meet yer lassie, have some cow-heel pie and pigs trotters after show, and still have enough left out of a shillin' for five Woodbines and t' tram 'ome.'

'He's stoned,' said Sue.

'What's the Essoldo?' Bobby asked.

'A chain of cinemas in the North of England owned by Mr. Solly Sheckman, who had a wife called Esther and a daughter called Dorothy. Es-Sol-Do.'

'Would you two heads mind if I listened to the fucking music instead of you talking scribble?' Sue said.

And that was the last thing McGinn remembered before he woke up in the Chelsea Hotel to the sound of the central heating boilers groaning and hissing, an ancient system which made McGinn remember Italian 'central heating' about which Henry McLemore had written:

'Visiting the basement in my apartment block in Rome, I discovered the secret of Italian 'central heating'. Seven moths fly around a candle flame. They generate heat from their wings but as they hit the flame and die, one by one, the janitor boils a kettle, catches the steam in a paper bag and runs with it, forcing it into the radiators...'

McGinn jumped out of bed. Today was the day he got paid the first option money of 3,500 dollars.

In the bank on 5th Avenue he was shown to a chair. A large, sad man approached and offered his hand and said he was his personal banker, and seated him at a small table. He produced the documents, McGinn's request for three hundred dollar bills and two hundred in tens and twenties, and a bundle of American Express travellers' cheques worth 3,000 dollars. The sad man seemed reluctant to part with the money, as if he were the rightful owner, and warned McGinn to be careful with such a large amount. McGinn imagined this man, commuting for twenty five years to his little suburban house. Every day the bank, every day the same train, probably the same restaurant or snack bar for lunch, envious of his fellow New Yorkers who had made their working week four and a half days by quitting the office at mid-day on Friday and scuttling off home for the weekend. He would be loyal and faithful to the bank. Now he was making sure McGinn signed every travellers' cheque. Now he was lecturing him again, playing the father figure, about being careful with all this money. McGinn felt sorry for this bank clerk who had sold his soul for security.

He met Henry Thody next day, Saturday, in the Press Club. He had paid Elliot Graham for the ticket loan from Mexico and now he paid Henry for the loan when he arrived. The Saturday feast in the Press Club lay spread out before them: pate, ham, gherkins, salads, roast pork, beef, smoked fish, chicken, fruit and cake and all kinds of delicacies, like a Norwegian smorgasbord. And it was free. It was a gesture from those who were not forced to work over the weekend in the city for those who were working. It also attracted a few hangers-on, one of whom McGinn had met before and who was now stuffing his face with beef and horseradish sauce.

This man was a gangster. He had been Frank Costello's right-hand man in the days of Prohibition and his pal was Al Capone's chief accountant, Jake 'Greasy Thumb' Gusick who died in 1956. This guy Lou had wielded the machine gun in the good old days and here he was free-loading with the Press boys like some fading star hoping to get his name in the papers again. McGinn said: 'You want a beer, Lou?'

The retired gangster said: 'Yeah — I'll join you in a minute, but first I gotta go to the little boys' room.'

It sounded so American genteel. Little Boys Room. Bathroom. Powder Room. Comfort Station. Were lavatory and toilet dirty words? Puritanism and Prohibition still lurked throughout America, with laws against kids under 21 drinking or 18 buying cirarettes, or the open bottle law whereby you could be arrested for an empty beer can in your car, and his friends in Minnesota having to drive to Wisconsin for a beer on a Sunday. It was about time the Land of the Free changed some of its laws and brought about real freedom.

Suddenly McGinn realised he was tired of America. He had booked passage on the Paqueboat 'France' the following day, and five days later he would be in Europe again.

He left before loud-mouthed Lou could come back from the loo.

He phoned to say goodbye to his friends in Minneapolis, a town he would never forget for the kindness and hospitality of the people he had met there. Lorna answered. Larry and Marve were fine, but Brucie-boy was in deep shit, having been caught on the Brownsville frontier by drug enforcement agents with a certain Irish Tea tin wired beneath his car packed solid with sinsemilla. A sympathetic visitor to the bar where Bruce was working listened to the tale of woe and then asked if he could score. Bruce sold him enough to make four joints and he was arrested. The sympathetic client was an undercover cop, so what with the smuggling and the dealing he was due for a lot of hot dinners in the State Pen.

Broadway was booming, and Jack Kennedy's brother Bobby was running for office and was about to speak. McGinn was trapped in the crowd — and what a crowd. They looked up at the balcony where Bobby had appeared and a roar of welcome went up. By his side was Sammy Davis Junior, rooting for Bobby. McGinn had met him in London when he got engaged to Mai Britt when he told the assembled reporters: 'I'm a one-eyed negro Jew and she doesn't care if I'm green, pink or polka dot.' and had seen his Broadway show and wondered how one little man could have so much energy. Bobby was asking the crowd to vote for Freedom and Justice and against Racism and Prejudice, and the crowd roared approval, but then show business took over, and Sammy Davis started to sing: 'GIVE MY REGARDS TO BROADWAY...'

The crowd joined in, and they all knew the words, and they swayed to the rythm of the song, and when it ended they roared and clapped and cheered and when Bobby stepped forward and started singing: 'THERE'S NO BUSINESS LIKE S-H-O-W BUSINESS...' and the crowd joined in again and swayed along with the song, and McGinn looked around at the smiling, singing faces. This was America, and Broadway, and showbiz, and Bobby Kennedy must have known, then, that he could not lose...

When the crowd started to dispel, McGinn walked up to Toots Shore's bar. Although Toots Shore had an international reputation for rudeness, he had been more than friendly and affable with McGinn when he drank there with Henry Thody, but he was not in the bar, and the barman who served him said:

'Hey — you're British, right, sir?'

He must have seen him drinking with his boss and remembered the Saville Row suit by Huntsman which had become almost as well known in certain New York bars as Henry Thody's Dundreary moustache.

'I just saw a great movie — Zulu. All them Limey soldiers shootin' all them niggers...'

76

'Do you know the famous British drink, called a Black and Tan?' McGinn asked.

'Never heard of it.'

'It's half Guinness and half beer in a large glass.'

'We got Guinness an' we got beer.'

'OK, then, half and half.'

McGinn watched as the red-neck bartender poured a bottle of Guinness into a large glass and then put it under the beer pump. He smiled an evil smile and waited.

Suddenly the drip-tray was full of froth; it spilled over onto the floor and onto the barman's shoes, and he started cursing as the Guinness became depleted and the beer failed to fill the glass. It was an old trick, used by drinkers of 'light and bitter' when a publican, out of meanness, poured the bottle of light ale in the pint glass first, then topped it up exactly to the amount with beer, whereas a generous Irish bartender would pull well over half a pint of beer and give the bottle of light ale for the customer to pour. The other customers were laughing and the barman still cursing when McGinn called to him: 'Next time put the Tan first and the Black second.'

He left the bar and hailed a yellow cab.

'Jim Downey's bar, please.'

At Downey's, McGinn put his hand in his trousers pocket and gave the cabby a bill for the fare, then, as the taxi shot off, he realised with horror that he had given the man a 100 dollar bill instead of a five. He started to run. The cab was going a fair lick but the lights changed to red. As McGinn got near, they changed to green and off sped the cab. It stopped again at red on the next block, and McGinn, out of breath and panting, caught up with the cabby on the next red light.

'Can I see that bill I gave you at Downey's?' he gasped.

The cabby looked and saw the hundred.

'Jeez — you gave me a hun'erd dollar bill...'

'Yes — sorry about that,' McGinn said, taking the hundred and giving the cabby a five — and another ten for luck.

He walked away from the bemused cabby, and calmed down and had a few beers with Archie Downey and some of the New York Giants. He recognised one of them from the New York Athletic Club where Henry Thody had insisted he join for the steam, the pool, and the exercise, and McGinn was more conscious than ever of the divisions in New York, for the Club did not admit Jews or Negroes, a place of total discrimination, like golf clubs in England, and the bar he was in was an Irish-American bar, like P.J. Clarke's on 3rd Avenue, and it also appeared that the Irish in the city were more discriminatory than any other group.

He took another cab to Clarke's, but made sure this time the bill was a five.

Within ten minutes he was drinking with an Irish cop who was inviting him home for dinner with his family, and Paddy Cheyevsky the playwright and Leo Gorcey's side-kick in the Dead End Kids films, the one with the big hooter and the baseball cap who, when told McGinn was a writer, again said: 'Can you answer me one question?'

'I'll try.'

'What is knowledge?'

By now McGinn was too drunk to answer, and he did not like asking actors their names because they were usually insulted, believing their fame was more widespread than it actually was. They were joined at the bar by the singer Alan Jones, who rambled on for a while about what a great honour it was to have met the British Royal Family after appearing in a Royal Command performance in London, and been applauded for his rendering of Donkey's Seranade.

Far away, a voice, the Irish cop, was asking him about 'Limehouse Charlie'. McGinn realised that he was drunk and he asked the cop to show some ID and he flashed his badge. Just then a man came through the bar and everyone greeted him with: 'Hi, there, Pick-up-the-tab.' and 'Hey, there where've you been hidin' Pick-up-the-tab'? The cop told McGinn that this was the guy who had worked for Howard Hughes and his job was the follow the boss around and 'pick up the tab' because Hughes, a hygiene freak, would not soil his hands with money.

McGinn heard a voice far away, saying: 'His eyes are closing,' and he knew it was time to leave. He weaved his way out of P.J.'s and took a direction that he hoped would lead to the Cornish Arms hotel. Carefully placing one foot in front of the other he attempted to maintain an equilibrium. Then, out of a doorway stepped a slim brunette, who said: 'Hi, honey.'

The next thing he remembered was lying, fully clothed, on his bed in the hotel room and realising with horror and dismay, that the brunette was a man.

The next thing, he awoke in daylight. The creature from the black lagoon had gone. He felt in his pocket. The hotel key. Another pocket. nothing. Another...nothing again. His wallet — empty. BUT — The 3,000 dollars in American Express travellers' cheques was there, intact. A pro. thief, cash only, no incriminatory evidence if stopped in the foyer. He phoned Charlie Kelly. 'He's out. You'd best ring the local Precinct.' Mrs Kelly said. She gave him the number and ten minutes later a detective knocked on his door. 'So what happened, Pete?' he asked. 'I was picked up by a slim brunette but she turned out to be a man — a transvestite. Took the dough but left the travellers' cheques. I'd been drinking at Downey's and P.J's...'

'You wuz bombed.'

'Right.

'It happens. How much missing?

'Two one hundred dollar bills and... some change, I don't know exactly.'

'It's deductible.'

'What? What's that mean?'

'Oh, you being British, it doesn't apply. Robbery is deductible for internal revenue purposes in the U.S. Guys fake it...'

Cops, thought McGinn. Always suspicious.

'When you leavin', Pete?'

'Today. On the 'France'

'Well, gimme your address in Europe an' I'll contact you... but...'

'Yes, I know. No hope...'

'Shit happens. A guy gets bombed. There's whole teams of these freaks pretending to be hookers on Third. I'll tell Mr. Kelly I'm dealing with it but...'

'Yeah, OK, I understand. Good job I had the travellers' cheques.'

'Right. Well, Pete, sorry this had to happen to you in America. Have a good trip back. Next time I have a suit made, I'm goin' to have a vest with it.'

McGinn packed and took a cab to the Pier where the Paqueboat France was berthed. The French complained about the cost of running it, with 2,000 crew, and it would not be in service much longer. This voyage was to Gibraltar, Cannes, Naples, and back to New York In Cannes, his ex-partner Lucas Lime would be waiting...

CHAPTER 7

Aboard the S.S. France

THE menu on board this, the last of the great French liners on the New York run, was about the size of The Times newspaper. McGinn did not count, but there must have been 200 dishes on it. The tragedy was, he could not order them, for his stomach, after the hungry sojourn in Mexico, had shrunk from what he had believed to be the size of a football to the size of a cricket ball: hence his daily and nightly order for a cup of soup.

All the dishes a glutton, a gourmet, a gourmand, a bon viveur, a trencherman or a 'foodie' could possibly desire were on that enormous menu, and all around him the other passengers tucked into smoked salmon, caviar, pate de foie gras, quail's eggs, trout, sole, beef and lamb, with various wines and champagne and brandies and desserts that would wring the heart of a Billy or a Bessie Bunter.

McGinn, pencil thin after Mexico, and burnt dark brown by the sun on Zihuatanejo beach, believing a trip to the kitchens might bring back an appetite, walked through teams of white-clad French chefs slaving over hot cauldrons and ovens, and noticed three wire baskets which would be plunged into boiling water each morning. The baskets had about 100 eggs in each one, and a notice above said: 3 mins, 3 1/2 mins., 4 mins. So that's how they get the eggs timed correctly for the breakfasts, he thought, and left the kitchens feeling that his stomach had shrunk to the size of a ping-pong ball at the sight of those 300 eggs in baskets.

There were women aboard the 'France' — hungry women, voracious women, predatory women, single women, married women, divorced woman, and one McGinn believed to be a virgin, a 19 year old American blonde on her first trip to Europe. He invited her to lunch at his table (having asked for a table on his own for just this purpose) but the table was immediately surrounded by flashing eyed, dark, moustachioed jealous French waiters who were protesting at her changing her seat. Was it because they had worked out a tipping system whereby if a passenger changed tables that waiter would lose the Big Tip at the end of the voyage? Did the empty space on her usual table (a round one with 11 other passengers) cause chaos with the orders? Or were the little twerps just jealous in case McGinn got his leg across before they could? The latter, he thought.

He did not get the chance, anyway, because a 19 year old American girl straight out of college, did not stand a chance against experienced Canadian, French, and French-Canadian married and divorced ladies who made up the main female passenger list.

McGinn realised that everything they said about women at sea, aboard luxury liners especially, was true. They changed from being dutiful wives into huntresses.

On the second night out he also realised that their husbands didn't care, for they were either on the lookout for fresh crumpet or into a big poker game with the boys. McGinn had taken the advice given to him by a woman who said: 'When you board an ocean-going liner or cruise ship, always keep away from the bar on the first night until you can spot the ship's bores. Having spotted them, avoid them, because if you weaken and talk to them, you will be lumbered for the rest of the voyage.'

It was good advice except that by staying away from the bar he missed the chance of getting one of the three beautiful French models aboard who had been working in New York, and the ship's officers had zeroed in on them and commandeered them so cleverly they were not seen again in the bar. McGinn was left with the wives, and what annoyed him was that, having been seduced by a brown-eyed beauty whose young husband was in the poker game, he was greeted next day by a middle-aged man who said: 'Hi, Pete. How was my wife last night? She says you gave her a good time.' She had lied to him to make him jealous, but in the battle between the poker school and his wife's charms, the game won. McGinn, at the age of 30, was learning about the wiles of women...

Up on deck, lying on a deck-chair and watching the long rollers in the grey wastes of the Atlantic sea, he thought about women and tried to recall all the things that had happened during that momentous time between quitting the Rome job and getting his first novel published and falling in love for the first time in his life, and he wondered where Stephanovitch (his pet name for her) was now: in a play in the West End, in television, teaching drama? She had sat next to Julie Christie in drama school in Swiss Cottage, but their careers were so different. Joseph Janni had spotted Julie Christie's photograph in Spotlight and had signed her up. She was famous overnight with her part in Billy Liar, but Steph haunted the offices of agents and the Kismet Club and the only part she got was a walk-on as an au-pair, saying 'Dinner is served'. The lovely brunette who sat on the other side of the aisle at drama school had also walked miles between agents' offices until, after six months, she climbed five flights of stairs in Soho to be told by a down-at-heel theatrical agent: 'All right, darling — I'll represent you.' The lovely 21 year old would-be actress put her C.V. on the agent's desk and asked: 'Do you think I have any chance of a part?'

'I don't see why not,' the agent replied, 'After all — Margaret Rutherford can't last for ever.'

McGinn wondered if this cynical agent would have accepted Joseph Janni's contract with Julie Christie, which gave him 60% of her earnings over seven years...

It was a hard and cruel world, the world of show business. It was no business for nice girls to be in. He hoped that Steph had become a drama teacher, but he also knew that this, to the young hopefuls at drama school, meant failure, and he remembered the words of Carl Sullivan as they had passed the Royal Academy of Dramatic Art in a taxi: 'That's where they go for four years to make themselves miserable for the rest of their lives.'

A ship's steward came to him and interrupted his reverie.

'Something to drink, sir?'

'Gordon's gin and Schweppes tonic with ice and lemon, please.'

The drink came in an enormous goblet, choc full of crackling ice, the size of drink Andre used to serve in Nice when he dined with Steph on pepper steak and Camembert just before Andre took off for the summer holidays. He was the only restaurateur in Nice who closed in August, the busiest month, preferring the cool mountain air high in the

Alpes Maritime to sweltering away with his wife just for money. The day after Andre closed there was an invitation from Harry Mellors to race his new Riva speedboat from just below his apartment in Villefranche to Cap d'Antibes, a foursome made up by Betty, one of the women Harry invited down to the Riviera from Manchester to show them his new lifestyle. Harry Mellors had started Radio Rentals in the North of England and made a fortune. But he insisted on making money even on Sundays by advertising: 'Electric blanket — unwanted wedding present — for sale' and would spend all day Sunday selling electric blankets to Mancunians.

'When I were a lad, Peter,' he once said, 'I wanted a swank apartment, a big red American car and a speedboat, and now I've achieved my ambition.'

Harry's long red Cadillac turned every eye on the Coast and he was a happy man. 'I've found a little restaurant where you can eat for next to nothing,' he would boast, always economising, except when he filled the tanks of the Cadillac and the Riva with fuel, which would have paid for fifty meals in good restaurants.

'We've brought sandwiches,' McGinn and Steph told Harry.

'Eee bah gum, that's a good idea. Why didn't we think of that, Betty?' said Harry, upstaged by McGinn on the economy stakes. There was one thing that McGinn knew for certain: if Harry Mellors suspected for one moment that he was being taken advantage of because of his money, he would have backed out of the friendship, but McGinn always paid his corner, and Harry knew it.

It was much later that McGinn read that Oscar Wilde had a friend called Harry Mellors from the North of England during his last days in France, and revelled in the coincidence.

They had been happy days on the Riviera, in love with Steph, but she had to go back to England to work in a touring theatre company, then a season at Butlin's holiday camp in Filey, Yorkshire, and he had promised to stay in Christian Dior's house, up in Montauroux and work on a book, at the request of Monsieur and Madame Poulain who were the guardians of the house, she maintaining the furnishings and he with a 12-bore shot-gun to ward off burglars, for the house was now owned by a Paris millionaire and his wife who came twice a year on holiday and, apart from the solid silver dolphin taps in the bathrooms, installed by Dior, there were valuable paintings and antiques on the premises.

There was a strange atmosphere in the great house, and McGinn began to realise that one of the reasons he had been asked to keep them company was because Madame Poulain was afraid. Not of burglars, but of ghosts. There was a distinct atmosphere in the sitting room and the library, of dread, as if there were a presence that would not leave the house, and McGinn felt it as he chose books. Madame Poulain would not enter these rooms unless she had to. Had Christian Dior been unhappy here with his group of young men? Was he haunting the premises?

The month-long stay in Dior's chateau was memorable for two other reasons: he received a telegram from Peter Watt, his agent, the man whose father founded the world's first literary agency, telegraphic address LONGEVITY, LONDON, with authors such as Kipling, Somerset Maugham and Conan Doyle on his books, to say that an American publisher had accepted McGinn's first novel; and a postcard from Evelyn Waugh wishing him success with it, but declining an invitation by his editor Lord Hardinge of Penshurst, to do a blurb for the jacket. Waugh had a fearsome reputation for rudeness and snobbery, but having experienced the agony of the creative act and suffered the derisory financial returns of authorship (once threatening to emigrate to Ireland to escape punitive taxation), he was always kind to young authors.

He had proudly showed the card to Steph when he finally caught up with her on a weekend in Filey, but she shattered him with the news that she had been seduced by one of the actors in the company, and McGinn returned to London experiencing for the first time in his life, the hurt of a broken love affair, and the only aspect of her unfaithfulness which amused him was when the theatre director promised the actor not to make him redundant if he slept with him, causing her,when he did, to doubt her choice of profession. Her doubt was raised once again when, in a small TV part, she briefly shared a dressing room with Joan Collins and, when she asked her: 'How do you get parts?', the famous actress lifted up her skirt, pointed and replied: 'That's how you get parts, darling.'

McGinn's train of thought was again interrupted by a steward who asked: 'Something more to drink, sir?'

He felt drunk already, the alcohol reacting on his empty, shrunken stomach, but he ordered another, promising himself to go for a swim later to work it off, and let his thoughts drift back to America, and his new-found mates in Minneapolis. Were they all in the bar at Seven Corners now? Before they had left for Mexico, someone had asked if anyone had seen Doctor Maximillian von Rabinov, the man who had never been known to disagree, saying constantly: 'Right. Right. Absolutely. Yes. Sure. You're right. No doubt about it. Right, I agree. Right...' and Larry Sullivan had given his half grin and drawled: 'He's upstairs now. Agreeing himself off...'

Larry, the most popular bartender in Minneapolis, had recounted his experiences to McGinn after they had split in New York. A panhandler had hustled him on 3rd Avenue, and Larry, feeling sorry for the poor down-and-out, said: 'Hey, feller, you know I'm really sorry I can't help you. I'm broke myself (pulling out his pockets) but if I had some dough I'd lay it on you because I know what it's like to be hungry.'

The panhandler said: 'Are you hungry? There's a good restaurant right here. Come on in...'

'No, I can't. I'm broke.'

'Don't worry about it,' said the panhandler, and took Larry into the resto. and paid for a lavish meal for both of them with a wad of notes, confessing that he made about a hundred dollars a day and changed the dimes into notes at the bank on the corner where he was a regular customer and had an account.

That night Larry had slept on a bench in Central Park.

He was awoken by the sound of voices. They came from an adjacent bench, where four men sat, and one of them, who appeared to be the leader, was saying: 'But you had twenny cents last night, Charlie. What in hell happened to it? Look, we got eighty cents here. Joe has put in thirty cents, and I've put in my twenty-five and Jack has put in his twenty-five, now where, goddman it, is that twenny cents you had last night to make up enough for a bottle. Come on, now, Charlie, what happened to that twenny cents?'

'Yeah, Charlie, come on now,' said the one called Jack, 'I saw that twenny cents you had. You lorst it or somepin?'

'I bought two White Castles with it.'

'You what? '

'I was hungry, goddamnit. I got two burgers with it.'

'You were hungry? Hungry? You sonofabitch, do you realise you've ruined our chances of gettin' a bottle, and here I am, with a mouth like seven rows of ratshit, an' my goddamn tongue on the ground for a drink and you had to go and buy two stinkin' burgers with it...'

'I'm sorry...'

'You're sorry? You think we ain't sorry... twenny lousy cents short of a bottle because you had to go and eat...'

The rummy who was doing all the talking, realising that Larry on the next bench was listening to everything, must have thought that he had a possible solution to their dilemma. He looked long and hard at Larry, then slowly smiled at him, while Larry, embarrassed, tried to look away, pretending he had not heard.

'Of course... anybody can get in on this...'

Larry hung his head pretending to ignore the pleading.

'For a mere twenny cents, anybody can get in on this...'

Larry had got up off the bench and sidled away, starting to wonder if it had been a mistake to leave comfortable Minneapolis and the gorgeous Lorna to try and seek his fortune in New York. Not long after that Lorna wired him the 'plane fare back to the security of Seven Corners and the land of sky blue water and many lakes. The steward arrived with another large gin and tonic. He sipped it and remembered an invitation to a party with Burt and suggesting they take the almost full bottle of gin with them as a contribution, when Burt made him wise to America's 'open bottle' law. They could not transport a bottle of any kind of alcoholic drink if the bottle had been opened. Police at a ball-game had been known to arrest spectators if they found an empty beer can in the back of a car.

McGinn came to the conclusion that America was still suffering the effects of Prohibition. The 3.2 beer law necessitating driving from Minnesota to Wisconsin on a Sunday for a drink, the ridiculous open bottle law, the checking of identity cards to stop 21 year old students at the university entering the bar for a Saturday night out, and the same kind of cop who gunned down drivers of lorry-loads of Canadian whisky across the border in the Twenties now persecuting and jailing kids for smoking a little marijuana. A little tin marked Irish Tea and a cop who was an agent provocateur had ruined Brucie's chances of getting any kind of good job in the future, for he now had a criminal record. It was time Americans started protesting. It was the Age of Protest.

Marvin and the protesters against segregation who had walked from Canada to the Deep South, beaten, jailed and on hunger strikes in those jails, should now start insisting on the revising of America's out of date laws and regulations that infringed on their freedom and human rights, and teach those redneck cops in the snake-eyed South the meaning of Civil Liberties, but would they? And the British: would the Aldermaston march stop the proliferation of nuclear weapons? The British could not even change their own ridiculous licensing laws, closing pubs between two and seven on a Sunday, causing more drunkenness with the quick swill as the clock approached ten, ten-thirty or eleven p.m. depending on the area.

McGinn sighed and finished his drink. In three days he would be back in France, where drink was not sinful, where children had play-rooms in bars, where lovers could take an hotel room without being asked for a marriage licence, where intimate sexual activity between husband and wife was not punishable by the death penalty, as was happening in certain states in America, where it was possible to smoke and drink alcohol at eighteen without being arrested.

McGinn realised that he was rather drunk, after only two drinks, and there he was, lying in a deckchair trying to change the world again. He forced himself to go to his cabin, change and go to the swimming pool below decks. A quick dive under water, almost a full length of the pool and out, feeling better. Not many people in the pool but, by its side, a hairy homunculus with a raucous Brooklyn accent, talking to two other men and pausing every few minutes to gob into the pool. McGinn stood the sight for three minutes then called out: 'Hey — stop spitting in the pool.'

'It's the salt' It's the salt,' the ape called back, looking guilty.

McGinn turned his back on the cretin and walked away. He realised he was beginning to hate people. He had started to hate people in Mexico when he was hungry and those bloated Americans were lashing into lobster on the waterfront and laying ten dollar bills on the beauty contestants. It was not a good thing to hate people, especially for a would-be writer, but he had experienced at first hand that hunger led to hate in a world full of selfish people. To be a good writer, you had to love people. He remembered Benson the would-be producer with the fat cigar, telling him he'd be writing if he was starving in an attic. What a joke. He wondered how Benson and his ilk would have fared on British wartime rationing.

On the fourth day out, he was bored. Winning a solid silver medallion for dancing did not alleviate it. He haunted the ship's library. After five days they were in Gibraltar. The sight of a British Bobby on the harbour was strangely reassuring and McGinn celebrated in every pub. His head swimming, he then had the traumatic experience of having to return to the ship along a half mile long mole and he had chosen the same moment as most of the crew, all with white shirts and black suits and ties were going ashore to buy their contraband in duty-free Gib. Hundreds of shifty brown eyes watched him as he staggered through the throng...

Next day there was a ship to shore phone line and he was able to call Lucas Lime and his wife in Vence. They had met him in Cannes, remarked how thin he was and congratulated him on selling the book. He took his old blue and white striped shirt out of his case and said to Mrs Lime: 'I don't suppose you could wash this?'

'Oh, no, not that bloody shirt again? I've lost count of the number of times I've washed that shirt. Didn't you buy a new shirt in America?'

'I didn't buy anything in America. I only got paid the day before I left, and that's only a yearly option, not a lump sum, but enough to live on and do a bit of travelling, just so long as I don't have to pay rent.'

'I always said you were the cuckoo, old man, always living in other people's nests...'

'And other people's cars,' said McGinn, starting to walk towards 'Noddy', the little Morris Minor that had done such good service on the Riviera in the last five years.

'You're out of journalism, anyway. That was your reason for writing that book, wasn't it?'

'Oh yes, but I didn't expect to sell it to Hollywood.'

In the tiny flat in Vence, there was roast beef and Yorkshire pudding for dinner, and McGinn hummed one of his little tunes as he looked for a clean shirt:

'My girl's a Yorkshire girl
 She wears no fancy clothes
But I've a little Yorkshire relish
For my little Yorkshire rose...'

'My God, just look at the state of him...' came a voice from the doorway.

Lucas Lime looked, at his wife's bidding, at McGinn in the annexe, changing, and whistled.

'Blimey, I can count your ribs, old man.'

'Yes, I'm afraid I won't be able to eat much of that Yorkshire pud.'

'What caused that, old man?'

'I was on the beach in Mexico. Not a good place to be broke. Nor is New York, come to think of it. If you fell down dying in the street, they'd walk over you.

The Middle-West wasn't bad, though, some good people up there in Minneapolis.'

Later that evening he asked permission to phone London.

'Jenny?'

'Speaking.'

'I've been thinking about you in America, ever since you kindly drove me to the airport last August — seven months ago.'

'Peter... where are you?'

'In France — but I'll be back in April. What are you up to?'

'Same old thing — still at Brighton, living in student digs. How was America?'

'Great. I'll tell you all about it. I'll phone you when I hit Happy Hampstead.'

'Will you be back before April the 12th?'

'Yes, five days before. Why?'

'It's my 22nd birthday. We're having a party here in Blomfield Road.'

'What would you like for a present?'

'Just a nice big kiss,'

He heard her lovely laugh, and hummed a tune: 'Spring is in the air...'

CHAPTER 8

Travelling

BACK in London, McGinn met Norman Miller, and told him he had an idea for a film: The Battle Of Waterloo. Miller had been the producer of 'In Which We Serve' and 'They Were Not Divided' two excellent war films about the Guards regiments and about the disastrous raid on Arnhem where 4,000 paratroopers were butchered because a British General, 'Boy' Browning, refused to believe intelligence reports that the Germans had moved Panzers and heavy armour into the area. McGinn roped in his old school friend Angus Hall and they met the Colonel of the Grenadiers who agreed to provide the men for the film. At Sandhurst they interviewed a Major who was the world's expert on the Battle of Waterloo. He lived in an old, decrepit Nissen hut, with shelves full of books about Waterloo, an Army cot with a khaki blanket on it and a rickety table where he worked. The Major was 40-ish, with thinning red hair and a military moustache, the type that prefects at public school try to cultivate in preparation for their lives in the armed forces, the police or prison service or as administrators, believing it gave them an air of authority. McGinn saw before him a sad, lonely bachelor, the type of Englishman afraid of the opposite sex, shy and kindly, a scholar in the wrong profession, too timid and polite even to ask about money, until Miller put him at ease by saying he would be well paid as military adviser on the film. Then they visited an exhibition of uniforms from the battle and McGinn was surprised to see that he could almost have spanned the chests of the infantrymen in Wellington's army, they were so puny.

For some weeks afterwards, whenever McGinn rang Hall to ask

about progress, he was told that Miller was still trying to raise the finance. After introducing them to Jenny's mother, Lady Helen Cohen, in Blomfield Road, he did not hear from them again, and assumed that the project had run into the sand through lack of financial support from Miller's bank.

McGinn spent his weekends at Buscot, with Jenny, in Basque Cottage, loaned to her step-father, Sir Andrew Cohen, by Lord Farringdon, a fellow Socialist who lived in the big house on the estate. The little cottage contained many souvenirs the family had been given in Africa, when Helen, who had been secretary to Professor Joad of the Brains Trust, ran Government House in Kampala, Uganda, while Andrew ran the country and worked towards its independence. Helen was a very attractive woman who had been a beauty in her day at Cambridge, and who would sometimes advise senior Labour politicians — including the Prime Minister, Harold Wilson — over tea in Blomfield road — on affairs of State from the women's angle.

She had been married to a Professor Donnington, a musicologist, who had fled England when the war broke out and lived in America and produced twin daughters and a son. She had one son by Andrew, a clever boy who had inherited his father's and his mother's brains and was doing well at Rugby, despite being constantly taunted by his fellows because he was a Jew.

Helen, who was also a magistrate, was a noted hostess, and recounted to the hilarity of friends how her husband would turn up late to a tribal dinner, claiming pressure of work, wave to the 40 Chiefs at the dinner table, gobble up whatever was set before him, snatch a pork chop off Helen's plate, eat it with great haste, get up, and, with a loud fart, which always amused the African chiefs, hurry back to his office.

Apart from the assagais, shields, masks, fly whisks and spears, there was an Army cap with the red band of a Brigadier. Andrew Cohen, one of the famous 'Apostles' at Cambridge when it was a nest of recruited communist spies including Sir Anthony Blunt, homosexual friend of Guy Burgess and linked with Maclean and Philby, had been knighted twice: once for the administration of supplies to Malta during the siege of the George Cross island, and then as Governor General of Uganda.

Helen recounted with glee the tale of Andrew in Malta when the local people got up a petition about the disgusting state of the weevil-infested greenish bread they had to eat. The petition organiser went to present it to Andrew, whose secretary told him to leave the petition and the sample of the disgusting bread on his desk and she would buzz him when he returned to his office. Ten minutes later the secretary said: 'He's back now. You can go in.' The petition with hundreds of signatures lay on the desk. The petition organiser said: 'I left a piece of bread on your desk there, sir, ten minutes ago...' Andrew looked guilty, brushed the crumbs from his lips, continued chewing: 'What do you want to see me about?' he asked.

'Oh, nothing important, sir. It will wait,' said the official, red-faced and backing out of the office.

There were daffodils on the lawn at Basque House, and two black swans on the lake. McGinn fished for carp and tench, and gave them to the housekeeper, a local woman who always baked what was called a 'lardy cake' for Helen and the weekend visitors from London

Strolling along the pathway which ran around the lake, there was a sudden movement in the long grass.

'Look, sweetheart — a little Jenny wren,' McGinn said, stopping on the path to watch. He heard her quick intake of breath at the sight of the tiny bird hanging on the stem of a tuft of grass, caught in the act of nest building. Jenny looked at him, sensing something in his words. He knew that he and she would remember this moment always, the way sights or sounds in nature stayed with one for ever: his first sight of a kingfisher, his first view of a red squirrel, the sight of a sparrow-hawk's 'larder', in the corner of a field near Beamish Hall, where a hawk had impaled linnets and blue-tits and sparrows on the barbed wire, and the little feathers on their bones blew softly in the wind. Suddenly, the tiny wren was off, flashing through the grass, and the captured moment in time had passed for ever. He felt her looking sideways at him, and knew that he was in love for the second time.

'I don't want to leave tonight,' she said. 'I want to stay here with you. I'll be glad when I get my degree, then we can be together more.'

'Oh, it's not long to Friday, and we have the holidays in July and August. *Tempus fugit.* Concentrate on your work and the days will fly by.'

The two black swans came gliding to the edge of the lake, seeking crumbs of bread. It was a great expression in English: 'swanning around', for the birds had a wonderful graceful movement, scarcely disturbing the surface of the lake's clear water.

'Don't you get lonely here during the week?'

'No. I have a routine, a *regime* which keeps me busy most of the day, and I walk in the countryside and there are books and the wireless in the evenings. To tell the truth, I have been lonely only once in my life. It was in Madrid. I was eighteen. I'd visited the Prado and sat in the public gardens nearby, on a bench. A feeling of aloneness came over me, but it lasted only ten minutes while I thought about home and the decision I had made to explore Europe, visit every major art gallery before my 20th birthday, and do the working man's Grand Tour. Apart from embarcation leave, before I went to France, I had decided not to return to England. Some of the men took their leave passes to Hull and Liverpool and Glasgow. I put up my thumb and hitched to Amsterdam, Munich, Geneva, Naples, Rome and Barcelona, or took a cheap train or bus ride. It was the chance of a lifetime to see Europe. Now Helen has let me use the cottage for work, and there are no distractions here during the week.'

Later, when everyone had gone back to London, McGinn looked through the rows of books in the little library on the landing. He pulled out a slim volume and opened it. It was a 1st edition of 'Frankenstein', and inside there was an inscription: 'To Lord Byron, from the author', and it was signed: Mary Shelley.

It was with a feeling of awe that he read the little volume that night, imagining the three famous writers, Byron, Percy Bysshe Shelley and his wife Mary, gathered there, sitting scribbling their ghost stories by the Italian lake as the rain poured down and a storm battered the shutters. She and Byron had held this little book in their hands. It was like visiting the British Museum and seeing for the first time the original manuscripts of world renowned authors in their glass cases, the opening words of 'Jane Eyre', the copperplate handwriting, penned by candlelight or storm lantern. It also brought back memories of Rome, the visit to the English cemetery where Keats lay, and the beach where Shelley had drowned, and where he, McGinn had swum out of the treacherous undertow off Viareggio when he was 18, hitch-hiking from Naples to Rome via Pisa with his Army buddy, Sawyer, the genius who had passed the Cambridge entrance when he was fifteen, scorned University, spoke five languages, *forced* McGinn to speak French and Italian. It was difficult to read, with his thoughts going off at tangents, and next day, when he replaced it, it had not crossed his mind either to mention it or to take it or to think about it as some object worth a small fortune to the people who buy and sell and sell and buy...

His thoughts had turned to what the woman soothsayer had said in New York when he told her he was a Sagittarian: 'Oh, you're a Saggy. A Saggy can never settle down. You'll be on the move all your life.'

A Sagittarian with 3,000 dollars a year for three years could travel, but not to Australia or India or South America because of the cost of getting there and back. McGinn was in the travelling mood again, with the old 'itchy feet' playing up, and he knew that as soon as his work was finished at Buscot he would have to get in one or two trips before the summer holidays started. He had no ideas where to go, for he always travelled on a whim, and as his old buddy-pal Driscoll had said: he had a 'whim of iron'.

In the middle of June he went fishing on Ullswater with his old school chum Arthur Varley. They had not met since taking tea with the Begum Aga Khan.

McGinn laughed at the memory: he had remarked on the wonderful display of flowers in her garden and she said: 'Yes, they are pretty. The gardeners put them in this morning.'

Back in London, Helen Cohen said Andrew would fly to Rome with his son, Richard, in August, and asked McGinn to drive with her through France and Italy for the meeting. Jenny would fly with a friend, Deborah Carswell, to Corfu, where they would all meet up. Deborah was from a literary family; her grandmother had typed the manuscript of 'Lady Chatterley's Lover' for D.H. Lawrence.

In Rome, Andrew, who was the Minister for Overseas Development (he had worked with Barbara Castle, and as he was the same shape as Robert Morley or Peter Ustinov, they were known in Whitehall as the Elephant and Castle) appeared to be close to a nervous breakdown through overwork. He scoffed when McGinn spoke Italian to the waiter, bickered constantly with Helen, and it did not help his temper when, after they had visited Paestum, found all hotels booked and had to share a room so that he was constantly awakened by McGinn's snoring.

He yelled at the crew of the Brindisi ferry to Corfu, and as he carried a Minister's black attache case with the crown on it in gold and had a voice of authority, a resounding cheer from the other passengers sweltering in the gangway and on the stairway greeted his complaints to the little martinet taking names and examining passports.

In Benitses there was a problem: Andrew had forgotten to pack his bathing trunks, so he sat in gloom and watched McGinn, Jenny and Deborah and two students, Adrian and Bill, run naked over the dunes of a far-off beach.

McGinn streaked ahead of the others, along a flat, hard sandy beach against the hilly backdrop, and later Helen said: 'When I saw you running along that beach I thought of Sparta and the Greek athletes — a wonderful sight.'

The sight she saw next was one none of them would ever forget: Andrew was dying for a dip and had decided to borrow his wife's corsets as swimwear. The corsets were black, of satin, with a strong bone frame, and the effort Andrew put into getting into them, or getting them around him, brought tears to their eyes, and helpless laughter as he waded in to the wine-dark sea, as dark as the corsets. The only one not laughing was Mrs. Bracegirdle, who sat, frozen-faced, worrying about the three legged cats of Benitses (she was devoted to the R.S.P.C.A.) whose greed at racing for and snatching the discarded fish thrown into the busy roadway under the wheels of buses and cars turned them into amputees, and the local fishermen did not care.

Apart from Jenny and Deborah there was a very beautiful and statuesque blonde from England, a friend of the family, who was sharing a bedroom with the girls, all of them topless or in a state of undress when McGinn had to go through their room to get to the terrace. He told Helen: 'I feel as if I'm working for the *Folies Bergere*.'

The owner of the olive mill on the hill, who had a visitor's book with the Kaiser as first guest, was madly pursuing the blonde and being rejected. Andrew asked McGinn (who knew the blonde was jealous of Jenny sneaking into his bedroom every night) to write a poem about it, incorporating the name of the Greek town of Urashitsa. So he wrote:

A black-bearded man from Benitsa
Fell in love with a tall, blonde turista
He said: 'Would you care
to come up to my lair?'
But she said: 'No thanks — You're a shit, sir.'

'Almost there, but not quite,' said Andrew, who then ran off before Mrs. Bracegirdle could engage him in earnest conversation on Greek poetry.

Next day they drove up the coast and looked over at Albania, a communist country which had diplomatic relations only with Red China. Another day McGinn climbed a mountain to try and discover how the town of Corfu got its water supply, and found a stone monument to the Royal Engineers who had organised and built it for the local people. Corfu, birthplace of Prince Philip, was the holiday home of the Kaiser in his day and he had had a little bridge built over the Benitses road so that he could walk in for a swim. Corfu had a cricket team that played the Royal Navy when in port, and a local industry was the manufacture of ginger beer, the recipe handed to them by the British, and called by them gin-jum-beer.

When the family left McGinn stayed on for another week with Jenny then took a lift back with an English girl via Rome and Paris. Their route was Brindisi, Naples, Rome, Bologna and through France, but they stopped the first night in Matera, a mistake. McGinn realised when they saw the hideous statue to Rudolph Valentino on the main street that it was the birthplace of the actor. In his colourful Arab robes, as the Sheik of Araby, he looked like a hideous Toby jug, done by Gaudi.

The main square of the town was filled with men, standing in groups of three or four or five, talking. McGinn was with two attractive blondes, and they had to cross the square to get to the hotel. They walked a gauntlet of hungry, lustful, angry, seductive, envious, jealous Italian eyes, and the remarkable thing was that every man there was trying to look like Rudolph Valentino, with long sideburns and arrogant air. One or two of the younger men, ogling, sidled in front of the girls, like matadors teasing a bull. For McGinn it was the same kind of Kafkaesque walk that he had had along the mole in Gibraltar with all those brown French eyes staring, as the crew came off the 'France' — an unnerving experience.

At the hotel McGinn asked for two rooms, one for himself and Jenny and the other for the girl who was driving them. The hotelier and his wife almost had a choking fit. They could see three passports with three different names and not a wedding ring in sight. In Matera, birthplace of the Great Lover, McGinn slept alone.

That night they had seen *machismo* Italy at close quarters, a restaurant with 60 men and no women, the wives and daughters locked up for the night while the men ate, drank and played cards. But it was also hard to believe that in the middle 60's in London, at the Dorchester hotel, Richard Burton and Elizabeth Taylor had to have separate suites with an adjoining door because they were not married.

McGinn sighed with relief when they crossed the French frontier next day. He always liked coming back to France, the only other country where he felt at home, knowing that at least they would get a good meal and a good hotel at a modest price. As dusk fell, the Parisians smiled at an English couple in love strolling the banks of the Seine, hand in hand, waiting for the stars and the moon to come out...

CHAPTER 9

London

B ACK in London, Jenny returned to Brighton University and McGinn was asked by Bill Graf and Irving Allen to write a film for them. Meeting Patrick Skene Catling in the Wig and Pen club ('We serve lunch until 6 p.m.') he roped him in as co-writer on a film about the Fountain of Youth, set in Ireland.

McGinn's haunt was a little Victorian bar in a back street in Hampstead, The Flask, in Flask Walk. He had first been there in 1953 on weekend leave pass from the Army in Aldershot. There was a billiards and snooker table in the back salon, and it was a favourite stop for travelling salesmen from the North, for a pint and a game before hitting the old A1 for home.

Now young people were buying and restoring old property, a flat for £4,000 and a whole house for £8,000, with four floors and a garden. On her return from Uganda, Helen Cohen sold the only Queen Anne house extant in London for £1,000. It stood in its own grounds opposite Hampstead town hall, and on the next corner up on the same side was the home of William Empson, author of 'Seven Types of Ambiguity' who let rooms to supplement a tiny income, or, to be accurate, one of the most eminent literary figures in England was broke, the only fruits of his work being an occasional trip abroad with his wife Hetta.Before he died, he was paid with a Knighthood.

One of Empson's tenants was Dr. David Jones, scientist, of Bristol University and Heidelberg. He, like other Flask customers, was an inveterate Times crossword puzzle fan. Returning to London without having seen the previous day's paper, he asked an Indian newsagent for a copy of yesterday's Times. He produced one from a tied bundle of returns in the back of the shop, and when Jones paid for it, asked: 'Would you like me to reserve a copy of today's Times for you for tomorrow, sir?'

Another crossword puzzle fan was Edward, who played the organ in St. Paul's cathedral, who had been arrested by a constable for counting the number of jam tarts in a shop window in Holborn after the pubs had shut in the afternoon. Warning him that he would be arrested for loitering, Edward moved on, but sneaked back to continue the jam-tart count, and when he got to over forty the P.C. returned and arrested Edward for being drunk. In court next day the magistrate asked Edward if he had been drunk. 'If I were, your Worship, I doubt very much if I could have completed the Times crossword puzzle in my cell last night.'

'Oh? And what did you have for four down?'

'Pythagora,' said Edward, consulting the paper he had taken from his pocket.

'And fifteen across?'

'Niagra.'

'Twelve down?'

'Transubstantiation.'

'Case dismissed,' said the magistrate. 'This gentleman was not drunk, and he has proved it.'

Some of the habitues of The Flask were quite well known, having made their marks in their own fields of endeavour: acting, painting, writing, fashion design, poetry, dance, choreography, film and TV making, and some became world famous.

Ted Hughes would come in to see his sister Olwen, a literary agent whose flat was said to have wall-to-wall manuscripts; J.B. Priestley visiting friends in Flask walk; Kingsley Amis, who lived in Flask Walk; Al Alvarez and John Hurt, who also lived there; David Warner, Marty Feldman, Patrick Wymark, Tony Booth and Frank Norman, who felt he did not fit in in 'posh' Hampstead, and moved to Battersea, telling McGinn: 'I get free drinks dahn there. They all know me. I get respect.'

'How long have you been there now?' McGinn asked.

'Six months.'

'With remission?' asked McGinn, causing a spluttering of beer.

Frank Norman looked like a villain, with a scar on his face, but his crime had been stealing books, and his first book was published as a 'gimmick' with all its spelling mistakes and grammatical errors and prison slang to give superior people a laugh, but he was really a softy, and Joan Littlewood made him famous by staging 'Fings Ain't Wot They Used To Be'. In Camden Town he had encountered three Irishmen, two persuading the third, Mick, to drink a pint of Guinness, saying repeatedly: 'Get it down, Mick, it'll do you the world of good,' as Mick manfully forced the pint down to cure his hangover. Later Frank saw the same trio in a cafe, eating what is known in London slang as 'Turk's connor', or Irish food. 'I counted the new potatoes on Mick's plate,' said Frank. 'There was nine, wiv meat and cabbage and gravy. When I saw them next, twenty minutes later, they were in an alley, saying: 'Get it all up, Mick, it'll do you the world of good. Mick lost his dinner, and they moved on. I looked down and there were them nine potatoes — and not a tooth-mark on one of them.'

A Flask customer known as Organ Morgan (he did not play, like Edward, but had acquired his sobriquet when he stole the organ from the church in Hampstead and was arrested pushing it down East Heath Street, under the influence of strong drink. He was let off with a warning, but later was caught in South End Green with a side of beef on his shoulder. He had burgled an Indian restaurant, cooked himself lamb korma, tandoori chicken, pilau rice, keema peas, bindi bhaji and a chapati, and then stolen the side of beef.

The magistrate asked him: 'Why did you do this?'

'I was hungry,' said Organ Morgan.

'In that case I shall send you to a place where you will be guaranteed at least two square meals a day for three months,' said the magistrate.

Tony Booth was a regular who started buying McGinn pint after pint one day until McGinn said: 'Stop. It's my round.' 'Remember your describing Jersey as 'three thousand alcoholics clinging to a storm-bound rock'? Well, I sold it to Les Dawson for fifteen quid, and we're drinking it now.' McGinn and Booth had served in the same posting in the Army in the '50s, Fontainebleau, where Booth, outside Napoleon's palace saw a big black limousine draw up. 'Out stepped this dwarf, accompanied by Lauren Bacall,' he recalled. 'Then I was amazed to see it was Humphrey Bogart, with big noddy head and tiny legs, his height about the same as the car.'

His own acting career was at the height of success with weekly appearances as the 'Scouse git' in 'Till Death Us Do Part, which was so popular with the Royal Family that the Queen Mother and Princess Margaret asked to meet the cast. In the line-up, the Queen Mother stood in front of Tony and said:

'You look very happy today, Mr. Booth.'

'Yes, Ma'am. I backed your horse.'

The Queen Mother laughed, always happy, like the Queen, to talk horses.

'And what odds did you get?'

When Booth told her she was surprised and said she had got less odds than he had, to which he replied: 'Ah, but I backed it ante-post.'

'How very clever of you Mr. Booth,' she laughed and moved on up the line.

'What were you saying to the Queen Mother to make her laugh so much?' Princess Margaret asked him when she shook his hand.

'I was telling her about the big picture I have of you on my wall at home, the one of you in Girl Guide's uniform, showing your navy blue knickers. The sexy one.'

'Oh, you didn't! You mustn't! You must *never* talk about *sex* with the Queen Mother. She *hates* that sort of thing...'

'I'm just kidding you.. We were talking about her horse,' said the incorrigible Tony, laughing as she moved up the line.

The poetry fraternity was represented in the bar by Kiedrych Rhys and Bryn Griffiths. Bryn, who was the Merchant Navy union leader who led the big strike in the fifties, had had a terrible, poverty stricken childhood in Swansea, whereas Kiedrych claimed his father was a railway owner who paid his workmen in gold from leather bags in the kitchen, but Bryn discovered his real name was Ernie Jones, born in Bethlehem, Wales, and that he had aggrandised himself when he started 'Wales' magazine, published Dylan Thomas and was rewarded by Dylan stealing all the petty cash from his office.

The two barmen were 'Blind Tom' and 'Deaf Tom', Irish and Scottish.

Two couples constantly changing their minds about what they wanted to drink ('I'll have a gin, no I won't I'll have a scotch.' and 'I'll have a sherry, no, on second thoughts a lager.') finally gave their order to Tom, who hid his Irish wit behind a stern and efficient exterior: 'And for me, barman, a glass of red wine, not the French, just the ordinary plonk — the ordinary, rough Spanish red, y'know.'

'With a fly in it, sor?' asked Tom, his glass eye flashing.

Deaf Tom so exasperated Driscoll, who had to repeat his order three times, he said: 'The only way to get served in this bar is to attach a fish hook to his ear, reel him in, and shout the order through a paper trumpet.'

Sandy Fawkes, divorced from jazzman Wally who did the 'Trog' cartoon in the Daily Mail, was a Saturday visitor with her two beautiful daughters. 'Water, Sandy?' Irish Tom asked her, pouring a double whisky. 'No thanks. Neat. These days I find I have to burn a hole through before I can get the second drink down.' On a visit to America she was stuck in an airport because of a cancelled flight. A man struck up a conversation with her and invited her to drive with him across the States, staying in hotels and motels. Her conversation and English accent must have fascinated him, for some time after the goodbye kiss the newspapers revealed he had been arrested as a serial killer. Her book, 'Killing Time' was a best-seller. Sandy was much admired because she had fought her way out of an orphanage and risen to the top in Fleet Street on talent and sheer grit, and could hold her own as 'one of the boys' in any bar.

Jon Rose, an Australian novelist, ex-boyfriend of Sandy Wilson who wrote the show, 'The Boy Friend', drank most days in The Flask , and ate there.

The reason was that the food was cheap and good, and it was there as a concession to the clients who drank there, not for profit, and it was what pub food should be: beautifully cured York ham from a farm in Kent, good quality sausages and sausage rolls in puff pastry, fresh salad and Russian salad, and chips made the way they should be, par-boiled, dried-off and cooked until golden brown, described by Driscoll as 'a nimble chip.'

The other reason was that Jon Rose, writer, published novelist, was broke, and so were many of the other clients. The bailiffs were due at Rose's front door. He had some valuable pieces of furniture and a big Persian cat, named 'Cat', given to him as a kitten by Sandy Wilson the night they gave Elaine Dundy the title of her first book, 'The Dud Avocado.' The bowler hatted bailiffs asked about certain items: 'Is that Victorian?' 'Is that Chippendale?', but when one of them looked at 'Cat' and asked: 'Is that a genuine Persian cat?' they heard a screech and a cry: 'Oh no! You're not going to take Cat!', and as they left with the furniture, another cry: 'Sandy gave me those...'

John Philby, son of the notorious spy Kim Philby was always accompanied by two well-trained Welsh Border collies, who lay quietly on his coat in a corner until offered a sausage each by an admiring customer, while John looked on with envy as he was also completely broke. John had been a photographer in Viet Nam and in the battle of Ke San heard an American soldier say: 'Goddamnit, the bastards have scored a direct hit on the ice-cream machine.' Like John Hurt, he was offered an apprenticeship as a carpenter, and became a good cabinet maker. He showed McGinn a letter from his father in Moscow which said: 'I have just read in my air-mail edition of The Times that the Beatles have been awarded the O.B.E. I am thinking of sending mine back in disgust.' McGinn asked him what Kim thought about him working for the Sunday Times. 'He said: 'Take the Capitalist Press for every penny you can squeeze out of them" was the reply.

John Lennon had his medal made into a belt buckle to go with a coat he had had made from nuns' hair (nuns' locks are sold to wig-makers, but a tailor had acquired enough to make Lennon's attire) McGinn, reading the item, wrote for the first time in his life to a newspaper, The Times: 'I suppose that, in Liverpool, this is known as his hirsute' They did not print it. No sense of humour at all.

Gerry Isoman, the editor of the local paper, the Ham and High, ate his egg and chips in The Flask, but appeared to resent the artists in the saloon bar, so that whenever an article in his paper mentioned the pub, he dragged up an old cutting from a paper in the 19th century which said: 'The Flask, at the bottom of Back Lane, is frequented by second-rate characters, occasionally in a swinish condition.' Isoman, with his regular salary could not understand the artists' desire for freedom to do their work despite impecuniosity.

John Hurt was saved from his apprenticeship as a carpenter, offered to him in the Salisbury Bar, after his play 'Little Malcolm and his struggle against the Eunuchs' had ended its run. His financial situation was not helped by the lovely lady he lived with, Marie-Lise, who had been one of Europe's top models in the '50s with more than a dozen Vogue covers. She had not lost her expensive tastes, and would hire a mini-cab to go to Hertfordshire to ride her horse for an hour, return in the cab and order lunch for two from Mr. Eddie's little restaurant opposite their tiny house in Back Lane.

Reduced to take-away fish and chips finally, M-L, as John called her, developed agoraphobia, a morbid dread of mixing with the public, so he had to collect the suppers. However Marie-Lise proved her worth later, and, as a friend of John Lennon she arranged his part in '10 Rillington Place' as Timothy Evans, which left him trembling in the pub because they used the real hangman as adviser and he actually put the rope around John's neck on the set to show them the correct way of hanging a man. She was also an intelligent adviser who stopped him playing Quentin Crisp in 'The Naked Civil Servant' on Broadway for a vast sum of money because he would be constantly cast in homosexual parts. McGinn cured her agoraphobia one day by telling them that a new glossy book had been published called 'The World's Most Beautiful Women', featuring M-L about postcard size, but in there nevertheless, and she dragged John out of The Flask and hurried off to buy the book on Haverstock Hill.

John sold his little house in Ibiza, not only because of the need for a cash-flow but while swimming off the beach in Santa Eulalia the flow of something else right in front of his nose made him hasten out of the jolly old Med. and vow never to swim there again. When the Sunday Times carried an item about the sale of the house, which he shared in partnership with Michael Ashlin (known as 'Ashcan') his agent told him: 'That's the worst publicity I ever had'. Soon after the Quentin Crisp part on TV, however, John's career was meteoric. He came into the Flask and told McGinn: 'Today I had to put the monkey suit on.' It was for his part in 'Alien', and Hollywood loved him, and all his financial problems were solved by the profligate Michael Cimino pouring millions into 'Heaven's Gate' while John and Marie-Lise, hotel-bound, waited and waited, banned from leaving the site by Cimino, on thousands of dollars per day, until the film was made and Cimino had ruined the studio for ever.

Some of the actors who drank in The Flask, however, were wealthy in spasms, up or down, in or out, rich or resting. One actor's wife said: 'When I met him he told me he was earning a hundred pounds a week — but he didn't say which week!' One such was Ronald Fraser (known as 'The Open Razor'), a brilliant character actor and mimic, who fought the demon drink and suffered from gout, wearing the club tie which had a salmon and a trout on it ('Salmon and trout — gout') who had an ambition to have his coffin carried by Sean Connery, Peter O'Toole, James Villiers and other cronies, at his funeral in Happy Hampstead. (He succeeded, and made all the newspapers). His agent telephoned him during one of his monumental hangovers to ask if he would go to Milan to be photographed for Oggi, or so he thought. He explained to McGinn: 'It wasn't anything to do with the magazine Oggi. I was taken to an hotel room full of naked doxies and told to strip off. It transpired they wanted me to take part in an *orgy*. The nerve! I fled, of course.' He then ordered his regular drink, which he called a 'Fraser water' which was a large vodka, what he called an avalanche of ice, and a splash of soda, but when McGinn asked for a 'McGinn water' he said: 'What on earth's that?' and got the reply: 'Half a pint of tepid mild ale with a red hair in it, in a cracked glass, on tick.' In an afternoon drinking club McGinn introduced him to a young Irish doctor who specialised in hair restoration and injecting the penis to produce a sustained erection, giving frequent consultations to couples whose marriages were fading through lack of activity in the marital bed.

Clearly fascinated by the idea of hair restoration and penile injections, Fraser immediately began giving the doctor a list of his ailments and asked for a consultation in the near future. McGinn wrote to him: 'Dear Ronaldo, You must not try to get free medical advice from my friend Dr. Skelly of Dublin and Harley Street, as he really cannot help you. You will recall, I am sure, the words of Louis Ferdinand Celine, who practised as a doctor in Pigalle before taking up the pen: 'Madam,' he would advise his ageing female patients, 'a fading rose is not a medical problem. It is a horticultural problem.' I suggest therefore, dear Ronaldo, that you seek advice in the garden centre and nursery opposite your flat in Belsize Park Gardens.' 'Oh ho, very funny' said Fraser when next they met. On that occasion another Irish doctor, Dr. Slattery (known as 'Slattery will get you nowhere') who had seen more suicides than a lazy lemming, entered the Sir Richard Steele pub and was told by the Publican, Fred: 'Blimey, Slattery, them tablets you gave me for my backache are no good at all. I couldn't even bend dahn to tie my bleedin' shoe-laces this mornin'' to which the noble doctor said: 'Soon fix that, Fred,' and scribbled on his prescription pad, folded it and handed it to his patient. It said: 'One pair, slip-on shoes.'

Frank Norman was visited by Christine Keeler in Hampstead before he fled to Battersea. She was filling the kettle to make some tea, when he yelled at her: 'Watch out, darling. Go easy on that bleedin' water. This is Hampstead, not Plumstead. I pay a fortune in water rates on this manor...' upon which she said: 'Sorry, Frank,' and proceeded to empty half the kettle down the sink, then put it on the gas.

There was another Frank who haunted Hampstead: Frank Smyth, who was famous for having fallen on a small African bishop at an Embassy cocktail party and crushed him to death. Smyth, who wrote about ghosts and poltergeists, gleaning his information from the hundreds of books on the subject ('One book is plagiarism — two is research' was a favourite saying of his) weighed about 17 stone. His weight crushed the tiny bishop of Basutoland so badly that he died in hospital ten days later. On the day that Independent Television held their annual ball in the Adelphi hotel in the Aldwych, Smyth met Dan Farson in the Swiss Cottage pub, and when Farson mentioned the ball, Smyth said: 'I'd like to go to that.'

'You have no chance,' said Farson. 'Invitation only. High security on the door.'

'I'll gatecrash it,' said the intrepid Smyth.

'You'll be wasting your time. Besides, you don't have a dinner jacket.'

'I'll see you there.' said Frank.

At the entrance Frank said: 'Mini-cab for Mr. Dan Farson?'

The doorman said: 'Do you know him?'

'Yes, I often drive him home when he's tired and overworked.'

The doorman laughed, having heard Fleet Street's excuse for being drunk before, and said: 'OK, you can go up and find him then.'

At the bar Smyth saw Fyffe Robertson, the tweedy stage Scotsman from the BBC, scotch whisky in hand. 'Still getting your end away, Fyffe?' Smyth asked him, and during the laughter and spluttering that followed, Robertson's false teeth shot out and skidded under the feet of the dancers.

Still chortling, the old Scotsman got down on his hands and knees with Smyth and together they retrieved the teeth from under the feet of the dancing couples.

A few minutes later the speech-making began, and Lew Grade sat waiting for silence. Sir Lew was surrounded by sycophants, waiting to clap and cheer the man who caused the expression 'dumbing down' to gain currency, who knew that to cater for the L.C.D. (Lowest Common Denominator) brought in the L.S.D. and knew instinctively what to dish up to viewers who thought Culture was something to do with market gardening. Smyth suddenly took it upon himself to represent the scores of actors and actresses who feared and hated 'Low-Grade Lew', and, fortified by a couple of large ones, strode across the deserted dancefloor, reached over, took the enormous Havana-Havana cigar from between Grade's lips, dropped it on the floorboards, ground it to dust with his heel, and walked back to join Fyffe Robertson at the bar. The band struck up to cover the confusion at head table and a few minutes later, while Robertson was doubled up with hilarity at one of Smyth's anecdotes, he felt a tap on his shoulder, and, upon looking around, beheld a policewoman, who said: 'Would you like to come with me, sir?'

'Why? Do you fancy me, luv?' asked Smyth, whereupon the policewoman put a swift half-Nelson on the cigar-crusher and frog-marched him out of the hall, down the staircase and into the street, with a dire warning on what would happen to him if he tried to re-enter.

Back in Happy Hampstead, where he was sharing chambers with Dr. David Jones in the attic of William Empson's house, the pangs of hunger caused him to pause at the open doorway of a young couple who had popped out to the pub for an *aperitif,* leaving a large pot of Irish stew on their stove, causing an ensuing row next day when the couple complained to Jones that their stew had been eaten by Smyth.

'Not all of it?' he asked.

'No, he only ate the meat out of it,' they explained.

Not long after this Smyth appeared in Bow Street magistrates court charged with being drunk. Fined five pounds and told by the magistrate: 'No speeches Mr. Smyth, we've heard it all before. Just pay your fine.' the prisoner at the bar was approached by the police Superintendent and asked: 'Are you a literary gentleman, Mr. Smyth?' 'A bit of a scribbler, yes,' said Smyth modestly.

'I thought so,' said the Super. 'because last night when my officers found you asleep in the gutter and it took four of them to lift you and get you back to be charged by the Station Sergeant you said to him:

'We are all in the gutter, but some of us are looking at the stars' — that's Oscar Wilde, isn't it?'

'Yes, that's right.'

'There you are! I *knew* you were a literary gentleman,' said the Super.

Smyth had been bemused earlier, in his cell, when the inmate of the adjoining cell started complaining loudly that he had been robbed and calling for the Station Sergeant, who approached the prisoner with a long-suffering look and asked what had been stolen from him. 'Some bastard's pinched the elastic out of my underpants,' was the reply, and, looking down at his feet, the Sergeant said: 'You've put your feet through the arm-holes of your undervest, sir.'

Sometimes at weekends, or when Hetta felt like it during the week, there would be a drinking session in the Empson's garden at the back of the house where old William, forced by poverty and publishers to eke out his living by renting rooms, had a makeshift table which was in fact an upturned door.

Unfortunately the old door had four panels and on the day Smyth and John Clark managed to spill seven glasses of burgundy on the panels and the uneven surface, the author of 'Seven Types of Ambiguity' grabbed two bottles of Macon and disappeared into his tiny 'den', almost in tears at the wastage of vintage wine. Later, when he was knighted, they said it was for suffering the reprobates Hetta invited to the afternoon sessions and William became known as the Knight of the Oblong table. They could have bought half a dozen garden tables for the cost of the spilt wine. The voice which was raised loudest at the spillage was that of Sasthi (pronounced Shasti) Brata, a very small, very angry Indian writer (who had been successfully sued by Nabokov for stealing a line from Nabokov's poem to use on his book about childhood in India, 'My God Died Young', probably because his wife, Pamela Duval Smith had bought at least two of the bottles. Sasthi was known to the literary fraternity of Happy Hampstead as 'Rat Vindaloo.'

Then there was Dewi Jones, another science graduate like David Jones, who occupied the public bench outside Barclays Bank on the High Street. Dewi, a drop-out schoolmaster, drank cider from a litre bottle inside a plastic bag, and would frequently call to friends: 'The bar is open' as they shuddered and hurried by. Arrested for vagrancy by a young constable, fresh on the Hampstead beat, he was brought to a halt by the Sergeant in the police station with the words: 'You can't arrest him. Take him back to where you found him.'

'But, he's a tramp, Sarge.' said the fresh-faced Bobby.

'Ah, yes, but he's a FIRST CLASS tramp,' said the Sergeant.

Dewi slept beneath a tree with a view of Hampstead ponds below during the summer months and moved into a squat in winter. One morning, curious to know how it could be raining where he was lying, yet the surface of the ponds remained undappled by drops, he looked up into his tree to observe a small grey squirrel in the act of urinating onto Dewi's head which was sticking out of a greasy sleeping bag nestling on a bed of bracken.

The drinking fraternity of The Flask continued to be mainly Celts and Northerners.

One Irishman, homesick and wanting to chat to former friends in the Emerald Isle, had been shown how to tap out phone numbers, dial the zeros and get free calls. Telling McGinn he was about to phone an old mate in Dublin who ran a Shebeen, an illicit drinking house in the back streets, he tapped and dialled until the number answered.

'Is that you, Pat?' he asked.

'Who's that?'

'It's Tony. Your ould pal Tony Waters, Pat.'

'You can't come in,' snapped Pat, 'the police are outside.' and slammed down the telephone.

Kiedrych Rhys had a figure like Robert Morley or Peter Ustinov, and caused Barry Driscoll to comment: 'One can sympathise with a *thin* poet, but never with a fat one.' Whereas Kiedrych, either because he was weight-watching or because of constant impecuniosity (until he got a job in the dole office) drank only half pints of bitter which brought the comment from his wife: 'Like feeding an elephant on strawberries', the other Welsh bard, Bryn Griffiths hurled down pints faster than most.

Bryn, who wrote an excellent poem on Aberfan, was spotted by McGinn on the steps of Hampstead Town Hall one Saturday morning, with a beautiful Australian blonde in a wedding dress. At three o'clock that afternoon McGinn went into The Flask for a last drink and saw Bryn hurling down a pint. 'Didn't I see you getting married at Hampstead Town Hall this morning, Bryn?' he asked. 'That's right, boyho.' 'So what are you doing in the pub?' McGinn asked. 'Oh, you've got to get away from the wife sometime, you know,' said the bard.

Then there were the painters. Two of them, Toby Tovey and Keith Burgess, had been called into the unemployment office and told that they had to take a job — any job — as their benefit was being stopped, and they were asked what occupations they had had before they became 'painters'.

'Shepherd', said Burgess with a wink at Tovey.

'Deep-sea diver', said Tovey, with a wink at Burgess.

Called in the following Monday, Burgess was told his new job was mucking-out the animal cages in the little zoo at the top of Hampstead Heath, and Tovey was told he was the new swimming pool attendant at Camden public baths.

Apart from Ashcan there was another dancer, or choreographer (of 'Oh What a Lovely War), Johnny Hewood, who claimed to be writing an autobiography entitled 'Take Two — They're Small'. Whether this meant spam sandwiches or choir boys, McGinn never managed to find out, as he did not wish to do verbal battle with Hewood and his waspish, homosexual wit. He had once brought a voice trainer to tears when told, again and again: 'Higher, dear, *sing higher...*' he replied: 'If I sing any *higher,* only dawgs will hear it!' Johnny Hewood had been a sergeant in the Canadian army in the Mountbatten-inspired disaster at Dieppe when they tried to scale cliffs with German machine-gun posts on the top which led to a massacre. He was a survivor in show-business, too. When their show folded in Manchester, Ashcan and Hewood walked disconsolately through the rain-sodden city, looking forlornly into shop windows. They came to a surgical goods shop, displaying trusses beneath neon lights. 'My God, darling,' he said, turning to the crestfallen Ashcan, 'I'm so *hungry* I could eat a *linear belt,'*

It had been on this inauspicious occasion that Ashcan formed his oft-quoted description of an actor. 'An actor,' said Ashcan, 'is a man sitting alone in a room in a lodging house in Wigan or Manchester or Liverpool, on a wet, windy, Sunday night, in front of a dead gas-fire, holding a half-done piece of toast between cummy fingers.'

As a drinker and a climber, having been at Marlborough school where the boys specialise in these two hobbies, Ashcan celebrated their return to London by inching his way along the outside of the London train, entering a colleague's compartment, stealing the bottle of gin he knew was secreted there, and returning to Hewood with it between his teeth as the train roared through the night to King's Cross.

Of this gang of characters who made up the Flask's clientele, only one other than Jocelyn Kelsey had actually been born in Hampstead — Patrick Skene Catling, a fellow pupil of Kelsey at King Alfred's school.

Catling was a tall, fair-haired, former navigator in the Canadian air force who had delivered planes to England during the war. The officers awoke in billets, girls in the WAAF came in, lit the fires, and then jumped into bed with the officers. to welcome them to England. After the war he joined the Baltimore Sun papers (old home of H.L. Mencken) and covered the Korean war for them. His oppo in Korea was that other brilliant journalist Patrick O'Donovan, on the Observer. Askance at O'Donovan's showing off by wearing his Irish Guards officer's cap, Catling upstaged him by donning the outfit of a coolie, flowing white robes, straw sunhat and flip-flops, and shuffling along behind O'Donovan as they went into Press conferences and cocktail parties, leading, in a moment of madness, to them setting fire to the American officers mess tent soon after one of O'Donovan's mind-bending Saint Patrick's day parties, the annual party being the biggest event in any year of the Korean war.

Catling, at the invitation of Howard Hughes, had gone to Hollywood to write Jane Russell's 'autobiography', Jane having taken a shine to Catling when he interviewed her on a night out together in Baltimore, and he ended up there living with Peggy Lee, who would add nausea to his morning hangover by eating pistachio ice-cream while sitting up in bed. She also annoyed him by employing a Polish butler who would ice the chateau-bottled French wine in the refrigerator and then serve a Nuits St. George wearing white gloves, possibly to avoid frost-bite or just to annoy Catling, who told her he objected to the white gloves more than the iced-wine.

Patrick Skene Catling was a master prankster. In 10 Downing Street he managed to purloin some sheets of the P.M's notepaper and on one sheet he wrote a gushing letter to his own mother back in Canada telling her how lucky the British were to have such a brilliant journalist as her son Patrick reporting the news with such accuracy and intelligence etc etc. He signed it 'Clement Attlee' and got a letter back from his Mum saying how proud she was of him.

While attending a political gathering in Bournemouth, Catling became bored to distraction at the boorishness of a Northern mill owner who held court in the hotel bar each night where he was attending a men-only textile manufacturers meeting. Catling 'borrowed' some hotel notepaper, got the mill owner's home address from reception, and wrote to the mill owner's wife a short letter: 'Dear Mrs. Harrison, We must apologise for the delay in forwarding your nightdress which was badly torn during your stay with us. The reason is that one of our seamstresses has been ill with flu and her apprentice was not able to do the repair to our usual high standard, but I can assure you it will be repaired soon and forwarded do you in Manchester. The Manager.

He ruined a few days for an overbearing landowner in his local pub by 'finding' some British Railways notepaper and informing the pompous squire that they would be seizing his land soon to build a railway line across it.

So it was with a watchful and wary eye that McGinn set off with the practical joker Catling to write a film in Ireland. At the Customs desk in Dun Loaghaire, the stout, very red-faced Irish customs officer regarded Catling, his portable typewriter with labels from the world's best hotels stuck on its case, and then his suitcase, which he pointed to and asked|: 'Have you got any guns in there, sor?'

'No.' said Catling, rather startled at the question.

'Are you sure?' said the red-face.

'Yes.'

'That's all right then, through you go.'

Half an hour later, out in the fields, driving his clapped out Ford Anglia, Catling was flagged down by a man who asked: 'Have you seen three black horses, sor?'

'Do you mean today?'

'They ran off half an hour ago. Thank you, sor, we'll keep on lookin' for them.'

Just then a lorry passed them. On its tail was a sign ANOTHER LOAD OF GRAVEL. Not Murphy's Gravel or Refined Gravel or High Quality County Cork Gravel. Just — Another load of gravel.

'Do you think we're in Ireland, Patrick?' McGinn asked.

'Where else?'

They wrote most of the film in the Zetland Hotel (after visiting the Lake Isle of Innisfree), a luxurious place owned by the Guinness family who used it for holidays. It was January and it was cold, but, although the Guinness was good and the work going well, Catling was missing his wife and wanted to get back to London. He knew what long separations could do to couples. His first wife had run off with Anthony Crosland, the first Minister of the Environment, and Catling had written about this episode in his autobiography, 'Better Than Working.' the title coming from his father, a former journalist, who asked Catling what he intended to do in life, and when his son replied 'Go into journalism,' his father said: 'Well, it's better than working.'

Back in London, taking a short break from the daily script-writing McGinn and Catling met Stephen Constant, the Russian expert on the Telegraph whose real name was Danev, pronounced Dan-yev.

Francis Bacon was in the French Pub and, recognising McGinn as an habitue of Maltese Mary's club, The Kismet, and Muriel Belcher's club The Colony Room, he invited the trio to supper in Wheeler's. Bacon was working in a semi-detached house under a single light bulb and the Marlborough Gallery were making a fortune out of him.* He drank in the afternoons, in clubs, explaining that he did not like to mix with 'people who work'. By this he did not mean the working class, but people who *talked* about their work in pubs and clubs: publicity and advertising people, glossy magazine and advertising photographers, agents, commercial representatives banging on about how great and successful they were in 'business'. and commercial artists in general. He preferred the company of off duty waiters, out of work actors, fellow painters like Lucien Freud; in general, the scribblers, mummers, daubers and smudgers** who hung out in the Soho Clubs between 3 p.m. and supper time. With other painters Bacon could be thoroughly nasty, hating the idea of anyone being in competition with him, and had been known to destroy a painter's canvases in The Colony Room when he dared to display them for sale. He was also very kind, especially to underdogs, was known to take tramps off the ramp to supper in the best restaurants, pay for holidays for people who spent the year sleeping in cardboard

* He managed to accumulate some, and left £11,000,000 to the last bodyguard.
** scribblers (writers) mummers (actors) daubers (painters) smudgers (cameramen)

boxes, and buying champagne for anyone who was with him, with the old Edwardian cry: 'Champagne for my real friends. Real pain for my sham friends.' When his antennae told him someone was free-loading, he would call to Muriel or Mary: 'Give him some more pain...' Although a homosexual with a pocketful of money, he was rarely hit or subjected to villainy because he always had a bodyguard with him. He had drunk three bodyguards to death. The endless supply of 'large Mahatmas' (on Francis Bacon's bill) drunk by these East End heavies was like giving them loaded revolvers. His final bodyguard when he died aged 80 in Madrid was the lucky one.

At supper, where they ordered Dover sole with lobster sauce and Pouilly Fuisse, Bacon was affable until McGinn said the French claimed there was a pecking order in the Arts: first of all came the great philosophers, then the great composers, followed by the poets and the great prose writers, followed by the painters...

'I'm not going to listen to this,' said Bacon, standing up.

He was clearly annoyed at painters being placed so low on the list, and, after all, he was paying for supper. Not exactly paying, for the manager had greeted him with: 'Mr. Bacon, you owe us £660. Can you settle it soon?' To which Bacon had replied: 'Oh — do you want a cheque or a painting?'

'Oh, a painting, of course, Mr Bacon,' gushed the manager, who had read in the papers that some of Bacon's work was fetching a quarter of a million pounds, with the Marlborough gallery ripping him off for a fat percentage of it.

McGinn was a little drunk and thought of saying the French were classifying pebbles on a beach, like sociologists, and how could they dream of not putting Rembrant, Michaelangelo and Leonardo at the very top, but he realised that Francis had taken umbrage and was about to storm out.

Two American businessmen at the next table were drinking in the scene and taking in every word of it.

'I'm leaving. I refuse to hear any more of this.' said Bacon, and walked out of the restaurant.

'He's annoyed because he's illiterate,' said Catling.

When he had gone the manager came over and asked: 'Who's going to pay the bill here?'

'Francis Bacon,' McGinn said. 'He invited us and he has an account with you.'

'An unpaid account.'

'You were quick enough to accept a painting, which will be worth ten times what's on his account now...'

'I'll pay it,' said Danev.

'Oh no you wont' said McGinn

'I'll do this one,' said Catling, taking out his cheque-book.

'Put that away, Pat,' McGinn said. 'Bacon is going to pay the bill. He invited us and it's going on his account.'

'I'll call the police,' said the manager.

'Go ahead and call them,' McGinn said.

Two enormous Bobbies came into the restaurant a few minutes later. McGinn explained the situation to them. They took names and addresses, and one said to McGinn: 'It's all right, sir. We know Mr. Bacon on this manor...' The policemen went into a huddle with the avaricious little manager near his accounts desk. Then they left the restaurant. When they had gone the two American businessmen, representing motor-car companies, asked McGinn if he could recommend an after-hours drinking club, and he explained they had to be members; he could get them into the Stork off Piccadilly, but the drinks were expensive there.

In the club the Americans who had clearly been impressed at seeing the famous Francis Bacon at close quarters, insisted on paying for all the drinks.

Next morning Catling, who had stayed overnight in McGinn's spare bedroom in Hampstead came into McGinn's bedroom to use the telephone. His first call was to Anthony Crosland, the so-called Environment Minister, during whose term of office Britain became even more of a rubbish tip than it had been before with filthy beaches, sewage and chemical waste pouring into rivers and streams, and the towns full of litter, and Catling, using some choice words of abuse, told Crosland that if he didn't deliver his children to him as arranged he would not only stop his ex-wife's allowance but would come down to the Ministry and punch holes in him. Then he telephoned Wheeler's restaurant in Soho and asked for the manager. 'You insulted me and my friends last night, calling the police. We don't need Bacon to pay for our supper, but he invited us as his guests. I've been a customer there for twenty years... what's that? Who? At the next table... all right then. Yes, I accept your apology, just don't ever let it happen again.'

He slammed the phone down.

'The two American gentlemen on the table next to us, the ones we took to the Stork, paid our bill as well as theirs. They must have been impressed at your driving Bacon out.'

'Yes, I'd forgotten just how touchy and egotistical Francis is. He can't stand competition, and his cry is: 'When that old bitch Picasso dies, I'll be number one.'

Catling laughed. 'Picasso wouldn't have stormed out. He'd have done a sketch on the tablecloth to pay the bill.'

'Wheelers would send Bacon a laundry bill.'

Soon afterwards, Catling moved to Little Camden in Gloucestershire with his wife and baby daughter, but before he left, McGinn ate with him in a Thameside restaurant when Catling revealed his plan for a best seller called *The Experiment*, based on the Kinsey report on human sexual behaviour.* As they drove off afterwards, in Catling's battered Ford Anglia, McGinn said to him: 'That's strange. I can smell death in this car.' Catling did not respond.

Early next morning, McGinn's sister called him to say she had been trying to reach him all the previous evening for their father had died and she was catching the next train North for the funeral. After the funeral they waited on the platform for the train to London. McGinn noticed Alan Brien, a rather pompous journalist, boarding the same train and avoided him.** There had been two five-pound notes in his father's wallet, and McGinn had given one to the priest in the cemetery, and told his sister they were going to have a bottle of Nuits St. George

---

* *The Experiment* did very well, and Anthony Blond, the publisher, told Catling he could expect to make more than £20,000 out of it. Breaking the good news to McGinn, he said: 'What on earth can I do with all that money?' McGinn replied: 'Why don't you buy a flat in Paris with it?' To which Catling replied: 'What? Like grown-ups?'

** McGinn, introduced by Catling to Brien in El Vino, reminded him that his uncle Pat had taught him at Bede College in Sunderland, a wartime arrangement because Brien was a Jew and the school was Roman Catholic, and Brien said: 'The P.T. master. I remember him all right. He was the twat who tried to stop us masturbating.' Silence followed. Patrick, an officer and a gentleman and a bit of a prude, was embarrassed. Then McGinn said, quietly: 'He clearly didn't succeed.'

in the dining car. Apart from his army pay book dating from Gallipoli, his medals and oak leaf on the ribbons, his wartime Durham Light Infantry arm patch and three Captain's pips from Home Guard duty in World War Two, there had been six Senior Service cigarettes and a packet of mint sweets which the Geordies called 'black bullets'.*

Back in London, Catling phoned. 'Where were you?' he asked. McGinn told him.

'Now I believe in second sight,' he said quietly.

An invitation to supper came from Jeremy Banks and Caroline Clogg who lived in a tiny flat in Knightsbridge with a nurse/nanny for their new baby daughter. A knock on the door and McGinn was introduced by Jeremy to the notorious Eddie Chapman, an affable character who, like Tristan Jones, should have lived in another era, the era of pirates on the high seas and plunder shared with the Crown. Eddie told how he had met a rich woman on the boat train, and, having watched her house in Kensington, rang the bell when she went shopping and told the German *au pair* he was the telephone engineer. He asked her to listen on the hall telephone while he repaired the fault on the one in the bedroom. He was to signal with three taps when it was working. He then rifled the bedroom wall safe, gave three taps on the phone, heard the girl say 'Ja Ja', and walked out of the house with the gems. Eddie told McGinn that his most successful operation had been to take the slats off the backs of the greyhound kennels at White City and dope the dogs with meatballs – except for one dog – just before the race. Then his brother in Naval officer's uniform to give confidence to the bookies, bet heavily on the undoped dog, and next day Eddie went to Barclay's Bank with a suitcase full of fivers, chucking one five pound note to the bank clerk for counting the money, but the clerk had to refuse as tips were not allowed by the bank.

His most unsuccessful operation was lowering a box of 'tools' into a pub cellar prior to a building job in the pub. At nightfall a little man emerged from the 'toolbox', cut a hole through to the furs warehouse next door, but Eddie found the furs expert was too fat to get through the hole, so the manikin had to bring the furs to the hole for the expert to identify sable, mink, chinchilla until he shouted that there was only

* His total estate came to £300.

some white rabbit fur left. 'Come out, let's scarper,' called Eddie, who was happy until he read a headline in next day's *Evening Standard*: THIEVES MISS FURS FORTUNE. The 'white rabbit fur' was ermine for all the Coronation robes.

When the Germans occupied Jersey, Eddie Chapman was in jail there, and claimed during interrogation that he was an Irish Nationalist who hated the British for occupying his country. Agreeing to work for the Third Reich, he was sent to spy school in Germany then parachuted into England with a radio and £50,000 in Sterling to finance a network. Giving himself up to the police as a loyal British subject, Eddie asked if he could keep the money, but M.I.5. took it and suggested Chapman work for Special Operations Executive (S.O.E.) as a double agent.

It was a mistake. He came up with one good idea (to disguise dynamite as a fake lump of coal to be shovelled into the stokehold of German ships leaving Lisbon) which worked a couple of times until the Germans got wise to how their ships were being blown up at sea. Eddie's friends, listening with the rest of the pub to his exploits, said they were surprised he did not wear a 'I AM A SPY' T-shirt.

He asked what had happened to the Podenca Ibicenca puppy Jeremy and Caroline had brought back from their holiday with McGinn in Cala d'Or, Majorca, intending to show it at Crufts as the only one of its breed extant in England. Their attempt to import the first Ibiza hound – taken to the White Island by the Phoenicians, the dog depicted in frescoes in the sarcophagus – into England ended in disaster. After six months' expensive quarantine and weekly visits to the kennels, the by then huge animal ran into their house, snatched a chocolate biscuit from the baby, licked chocolate off the baby's face, knocked over all the expensive wedding present china from Caroline's daddy, Derek Clogg, who was Profumo's solicitor, knocked over another table and chair, then ran out into the street and was run over by a passing lorry.

Soon after that entertaining evening with Chapman, McGinn met Frank Smyth and together they walked over Hampstead Heath for remedial hangover therapy. Their footsteps took them to Highgate cemetery and the grave of Karl Marx (who had lived in squalor in Grafton Terrace, on the fringes of Hampstead while writing Das Kapital in the British Museum reading room). It was awash with floral tributes from the Russian and Chinese embassies and their staffs. McGinn recounted to Smyth that Driscoll had been present when the coffin had been moved from its old site to its present site and had glimpsed the leonine head of the corpse through the side of the broken coffin, and had asked a gravedigger if he could take a snipping of hairs from the great man's beard, which he was allowed to do.

'What did he do with them?' Smyth asked.

'He never said. Probably lost them in a pub.'

'Or kept them in a tobacco tin with his collection of pubic hairs.'*

'Or sold them to an American tourist in the West End,' McGinn laughed.

Later, walking through Kenwood, by the lake and through the woods past the old duelling ground signpost,** McGinn looked at a hedgerow.

McGinn said: 'The blackberries are out again. It's time I left England.'

Smyth laughed. 'Where to this time?' he asked.

'Ibiza,' said McGinn, 'and tootle around the jolly old Med. Ibiza is calling me back. The old magnetism is working again.'

---

* Smyth was jokingly recalling that the mass murderer, Reginald Halliday Christie of 10 Rillington Place, had an old tobacco tin in which he kept samples of pubic hairs taken from the women he had murdered.

** The Heath groundsmen had to remove the 'Ye Olde Duelling Ground' signboard because, up until 1960, irate men continued to meet at dawn and fight duels there with pistols – which was against the law in England.

CHAPTER 10

Sailing

JENNY was back at her University, and McGinn had heard the call of the sea and the White Island again, and he also remembered the words of William Somerset Maugham that afternoon and evening in the Villa Mauresque when Maugham had advised him to go to Spain in order to find the unusual stories, and he wanted material for a book recalling the Spanish Civil War and what had happened in Ibiza. He had been told that more happened on that island than in any other part of Spain as they were trapped. The anarchists had machine gunned all the nationalist prisoners in the cells, and Franco's army put the same amount of republican prisoners in the same cells and murdered them. Prisoners had been thrown from the old town onto the rocks below, the *pistoleros* shot the eldest son of every republican family, trades unionists and intellectuals, and finally a bishop had to be sent from the mainland to stop the slaughter.

McGinn had found an unusual story in Majorca that summer with Jeremy and Caroline, but he had a feeling that it would not be published because the little men who sat in offices in London and New York tended to decry some sensational stories because they themselves had no experience of life outside their own little world of office and suburbia. A literary agent had actually told him: 'Just because it's true doesn't make it believable.' Critics had scorned the cannibalism in the Tennessee Williams film, *Suddenly Last Summer*, claiming that it could not happen in a country like Spain, the scene where beach boys attack and bite to death a homosexual visitor to Spain who used his girl friend (Elizabeth Taylor) as bait. Yet there was cannibalism in Spain. In Majorca a boy who worked in Palma mortuary took a 100 peseta bet that he would not eat the raw liver from a corpse – and won the bet. Fernand Legros, partner with Elmyr de Hory in selling fake paintings, wanted revenge on a boyfriend, Real Lessard, and paid two Algerians to bite and tear lumps out of him by the side of the swimming pool in the Ibiza villa and throw his car into the sea.*

McGinn always celebrated a return to Ibiza with a pub crawl to discover who was still on the island and who had left. Tristan Jones was ensconsed in the George and Dragon in fine form, drinking San Miguel beer and singing sea chanties and Welsh ditties (Jones insisted they were sea 'chanties' and not 'shanties'). After joining him in a loud version of *Bread of Heaven*, McGinn recited Tristan's favourite poem for him, *Drake's Drum*. Jones was a fervent British nationalist who believed that the idea of 'fair play' had been spread by the British throughout the world, although not many understood what it meant, especially the French, whom he disliked intensely.**

He repeated the words 'Nombre Dios Bay' from the poem and said to McGinn: 'I'll drop my hook there one day, matey.***

A messenger appeared in the bar and told Tristan that there was a job for him and one deckhand/cook on a yacht leaving San Antonio for Gibraltar to beat the Spanish tax on British yachts that had been there for more than six months. 'Fancy a look at Gib. mate?' Jones asked McGinn. Next day they signed on as skipper and crew of the yacht Primarosa, owned by one Sam Morse Browne, an ex-army adjutant.

Making enquiries that night as to the character of the owner ('owner aboard' often spelt misery to the crew and skipper), they discovered that Sam had been having an affair with the blonde wife of a retired air force officer who was out for revenge. So, Sam, a pompous little man with a pencil-thin moustache and rimless spectacles with the vestiges

* Both stories of this cannabalism were edited out of McGinn's fourth novel.

** Years later, on Desert Island Discs, Tristan asked Roy Plomley to play the 1812 Overture celebrating Russia's defeat of Napoleon's army, in reciprocation for the French yachting magazines never, ever having paid him one centime for articles he wrote about sailing.

*** He did, and sent McGinn a postcard dateline: 'Nombre Dios Bay'.

of Army discipline still hanging from his every word and his martinet personality, was not only escaping Spanish taxes but also an irate husband.

They had been at sea twelve hours when the engine blew up. Sam then revealed to them that it was the irate husband, the R.A.F. engineer officer who had kindly volunteered to 'fix' the engine trouble. There was total silence when the engine coughed and died. They were on a lee shore, being carried towards the rocks on the Spanish coast by the current, but Tristan told McGinn to hoist the spinnaker, and in a just-discernible light breeze that blew off the coast, sailed Primarosa into deep water, while Sam, totally unaware of the danger they had been in (he could not sail his own yacht) sighed: 'Isn't she beautiful, wearing her ballroom gown?' (the spinnaker).

Left to steer a set course using the tip of the main mast on a star to guide by, they awoke to find that Sam had been following a sputnik and they were way off course. Then Sam nagged because socks had been left on a bunk, a cup was not on a place-mat, Tristan 'did not wash before breakfast' etcetera. By the time they had suffered his griping and moaning in Cartagena and all the way to Almeria, they decided to say farewell to the Adjutant, and take a bus back to Alicante and leave Sam to order up an Army crew from Aldershot to fly out and sail him to Gibraltar.

Sam had paid just enough to finance a small voyage in Tristan's newly-acquired yacht, for he planned to sell the Cresswell to a British visitor to use as a floating home. When he bought Pancho it was being sold by the German owner for the same reason Sam had scarpered out of San Antonio, to evade the Spanish tax-man. This slight drawback was solved by Tristan painting out the name Pancho and substituting Banjo, risking bad luck, as sailors did not re-name ships, boats or yachts for that superstitious reason.*

Suspicious harbour inspectors paid a visit, so Tristan decided to cast off, reciting one of his favourite sayings: 'First turn of the screw clears all debts.'

First light next day found them approaching Port Andratx, the nearest

---

*A year later, Jones, broke as usual, leased the Banjo to an American visitor to Ibiza, who smashed it up on the rocks at Santa Eulalia where it was stripped of everything by Ibicenco fishermen.

landfall to Ibiza, and Tristan casting a weather-eye regarding with disdain the clapped-out British Seagull motor which had packed in just ten minutes out of Ibiza harbour, and the ancient rags the German owner had called sails.

Just outside the beautiful harbour of Andratx lay the Shemara. Tristan called up to one of the crew: 'Ask Nora if she's coming ashore for a wet, matey.' The sarcastic reply was: 'She's already ashore, *matey*, drinking that rot-gut cognac with the rest of the crew.'

'Thanks for the warning,' shouted Tristan, and turned to McGinn and said: 'Just testing. Right, we're off. If we go ashore here and hit the sherbet with Nora Docker,* it'll be the end of the trip. We'll go through the 'funnel' today and sail the north coast tomorrow.'

Banjo came about and they headed for Dragonera, known to sailors as 'the funnel' because it was a narrow passage-way, a short-cut, but with very high cliffs on either side. McGinn could see that Tristan was nervous about tackling 'the funnel', occasionally looking at the barometer, wary of a weather change. Sure enough, the moment they entered the passage they felt the force of the wind coming from the north right at them as they tried to tack into it. The wind came off the walls of the cliffs and battered the tiny Banjo, ripping the mainsail before they could drop it. They tried tacking on the jib and battled against the wind for an hour and were scarcely half way through Dragonera when Tristan decided they were not going to make it and told McGinn to drop the kedge anchor and wait until the wind dropped. It did not drop, and when they tried to hoist the anchor it was stuck in the rocks on the sea-bed. Tristan tacked again and again until they got the right angle to free the kedge and they came about and went back through 'the funnel' with the wind howling and the sea abaft the beam, as if they were being chased by all the hounds of hell.

They headed up the coast to Santa Ponza, Pagueres, avoided Palma and passed Puerto Campos and Puerto Petra before sighting the beautiful inlets of the tiny village of Cala d'Or. McGinn had been here before, when the beautiful Nana sat on a rock near her father, Bertholet's, house,

* Lady Docker, whose husband owned B.S.A. (British Small Arms), had been banned from Monaco by Prince Rainier for abusive behaviour in the Monte Carlo casino, tearing up the Monegasque flag.

wearing a green bathing costume and looking for all the world like a mermaid with her long, waist-length brown hair slightly bleached by the sun, and the early morning rays lighting her deep tan. Now the French had discovered it, and as McGinn and Tristan spoke French fluently, they were invited everywhere (the French love those who speak their language, scorn those who don't). Tristan had not yet started writing for French yachting magazines so bore no grudge then, and they were joined by the pretty French girls who were there on holiday with their parents. The second most beautiful, Sylvie St. Andre de Perrin, made a bee-line for McGinn and asked if she could read one of his novels. She was almost as beautiful as her sister, who was there nursing a broken heart because her husband Claude Lelouche, director of the film, *Un Homme et Une Femme,* was divorcing her and there was some dispute over possessions because they owned the Biarritz cinema on the Champs Elysees (the BG's and *Va-ta's*** in Sylvie's Sorbonne set pronounced it 'Bee-aye-tz'). Sylvie's mother, a staunch Catholic McGinn had named The Reverend Mother, was extremely annoyed when Sylvie let McGinn sleep in her bedroom, even when her 20-year-old daughter assured her nothing had happened, that it was an act of mercy as Tristan, jealous, had taken the dinghy and McGinn, who had dined well, as the French say (drunk, in English), would have had to swim back to the Banjo.

Nana was now married to a Spaniard, and her father gave a party for all the summer visitors. After two weeks of partying, French girls and drinking sessions, McGinn kissed Sylvie goodbye with heartfelt promises to meet in Paris soon, and Tristan purloined an old bicycle, took it aboard Banjo and, as they set sail for the island of Cabrera, a Spanish army outpost, he wrote in the log: 'Made passage for Cabrera out of Cala d'Or, a picturesque little resort on the NE coast of Majorca. British newspapers can be obtained at the kiosk.' Later he painted the bicycle bright orange with the legend: 'Tender to the yacht Banjo'.

Cabrera was a strange little island, where a yachtsman could actually sail into the rock, moor the boat and spread out lunch on a rock table inside and hide from the heat of the day. The only inhabitants, apart

---

** French upper-class slang, used by girls describing possible future husbands: BG's = *Bon genre* (of a good family). *Il-va-t-a-la Messe* = goes to Mass, a good Roman Catholic.

from a few visiting yachtsmen, were a platoon of slovenly soldiers and a fat Major, who appeared twice a day on the balcony of his house on the harbour, dressed in pyjamas, a dressing gown and his officer's cap. He would take the salute as the flag was raised or lowered and then retire to bed with his chubby mistress. It must have been one of the best postings in the Spanish army.

By now totally broke by the cost of the new mainsail which had been made by a sail-maker in Palma during the fortnight they had spent in Cala d'Or, they headed south to Ibiza, but in the afternoon a storm caught them unawares and they were being battered so hard by the wind and waves that they almost keeled over. The boat was lying on its side in the water, and McGinn managed to drag the jib down before it touched the waves and Jones righted the boat. As the storm passed over they saw that an Italian cruise liner had hove-to and watched them in case they went under. Hoisting the jib again, Jones said: 'You see how it can happen in a matter of minutes if you don't keep a weather eye out? Sailors say that the Mediterranean is like a woman, changeable, impulsive, whereas the Atlantic is like a man, predictable, like the trade winds.'

They sailed around Formentera, a flat, scarcely inhabited island where artists had bought small plots of land at six pesetas a square metre just for a laugh, to say they were landowners in Spain, for the rocky land was worthless at that time. The sons of families inherited the agricultural acres inland in Ibiza and Majorca, and the daughters were given the rocky coast. It was this rocky coast that developers bought in the seventies and eighties making the daughters rich and their brothers envious.*

It was pitch dark when they sailed towards Ibiza harbour, and the American Fleet were in. They passed beneath the prow of a giant American battle cruiser where a sailor, armed with a rifle, was on guard duty.

'Ahoy there,' Tristan called out.

'Yes, sir?'

'Tell your Captain he's on my mooring ground,' he yelled.

'Right, sir.'

* In the early '70s, two sisters who kept goats on the beach, Playa d'En Bossa, were offered millions for their vast tract of land. They refused to sell, explaining that the land had been in their family for generations. 'But you are childless spinsters, and you can make a fortune and retire for life,' said the speculator. 'Ah, that's all very well, but *what would happen to our goats*?' they said, and refused to sell.

Jones chuckled. It was one of his joys to poke fun at Americans. While sailing a small boat across the Atlantic, an American battleship had signalled to him: 'Do you need supplies? Is there anything you want?' and Jones had signalled back: 'We've run out of ice.'

After a few more nights in Ibiza, McGinn received a letter from his sister, and decided to return to London.

CHAPTER 11

Hampstead

McGINN returned to Hampstead to buy an apartment, United Artists paying the lump sum when John Schlesinger said he would direct the film of McGinn's first novel. The solicitor drawing up the papers for the maisonette which was the upper part of his sister's property, asked: 'Is it a nice flat?' When McGinn replied: 'I don't know, I haven't seen it,' he looked shocked and said: 'Oh, I do *urge* you to look at it.' McGinn explained that he was buying it to annoy his sister's neighbours who owned it and had a big dog that attacked his young nieces so that a wall had to be built to split the garden into two, and he would simply let it and keep on travelling.

His first tenant was an American professor from Princeton, who was translating Osip Mandelstam from Russian into English. Jenny had got her M.A. and was about to take a teaching job, and did not like the idea of McGinn's long absences. Elli Theodorakis, who was the niece of Mikis who wrote the music for 'Zorba the Greek', had been living with John Clark for three years and she also took exception to his wanderlust. Two lovely and highly intelligent women in their early twenties were not going to contend with lovers who shot off to the Balkans, the Middle East and Spain, whenever they felt like it, while they sat at home mending the socks. There was a move afoot for Jenny to teach in Uganda where Andrew Cohen had been Governor General. At dinner with the Queen at Buckingham Palace, she had referred disparagingly to Uganda's 'so-called *royal family*' and Andrew had replied: 'Yes, Ma'am, and several generations older than your own royal family.'

McGinn knew that he would do nothing to make Jenny change her mind. He had always let events take their course, let things happen as if by some pre-ordained or pre-conceived plan, and he could not visualize himself 'settling down'. Nor could he see himself walking down the aisle. He had seen his parents' destructive marriage at close quarters. In any case, he had difficulty supporting himself let alone a woman and children, and he was a heavy drinker who preferred the freedom of the road to a nice fireside. They both knew it was about to end. She also suspected, quite rightly, that McGinn was more in love with Ibiza than with her, and would be spending long periods there. They were beginning to have rows. He told her he thought Andrew, at the Ministry of Overseas Development, was pouring taxpayers' money into an unstable country and risking making things worse than they were.* Soon after, they decided to go their own ways...

Meanwhile, there were parties to attend in Happy Hampstead and its environs. Gillian Ronson gave a party. Gillian, along with her friend Pat Arrowsmith, was one of the early women's liberation movement fighters in London, prepared to confront and battle with the police and even go to jail for their cause, and McGinn took along a Russian he had met in the London Press Club and introduced him to the battling women of Britain. McGinn was fascinated by the Russians, for he suspected, from the moment they met, when someone had told Yevgeny (Eugene) Kryukov that McGinn was a friend of Kim Philby's son, John, that he was a member of the K.G.B. He had telephoned McGinn's flat several times while he was away and finally made contact and asked to meet in Hampstead. McGinn directed him to the Three Horseshoes bar. After ten minutes of pleasantries, Kryukov pulled out some five pound notes and made a fan of them, saying: 'It must be very expensive to travel as much as you do.' At that moment, a flash went off on the other side of the darkened bar. McGinn could not see who had taken the photograph: it could be a colleague of Kryukov for a blackmail attempt later, or someone from M.I.5 tailing Kryukov to see where he went and who he met.**

* Idi Amin, an ex-Army sergeant, an illiterate, and a savage, led a *coup* and ushered in a murderous *regime*. He kept his enemies' heads in his office refrigerator.

** All Russians working in London were tailed every night, and there was a five mile radius restriction on their movements. The KGB followed all foreigners in Moscow. McGinn asked John Philby to ask Kim how Penkovsky the spy had been caught, and he said they had followed a British Embassy man to a block of flats where 2,000 Russians lived, and the only resident who had a visa for going abroad was Oleg Penkovsky.

Kryukov was very keen to meet Mikis Theodorakis when John Clark mentioned that his girlfriend, Eli, was going to have a party for her uncle Mikis to welcome him to London after his jail term in Greece. Soon after this party, Kryukov rang McGinn again and wanted to meet in Hampstead. McGinn was bemused by the Russian and fascinated by him. He had the most extraordinary memory of anyone McGinn had ever met, and although he drank heavily, he filed away information and, after consuming a bottle of whisky, could repeat verbatim things that had been said hours earlier. During dinner in Parkhill Road, with Driscoll and Joan Kennedy* he announced: 'The British people eat too much.' He then proceeded to consume the entire contents of a bowl of fruit: apples, oranges, bananas and cherries.

Kryukov telephoned a week later wanting another meeting in Hampstead. This time he brought along a friend, who was the London correspondent of Pravda, a stocky, athletic looking character who looked like a rugby player and had a capacity for strong drink even greater than Kryukov. In The Flask they looked around at the Bohemian crowd and Kryukov said: 'Sheer decadence' (his English was superb).

'Ah, yes, Yevgeny, but they have the freedom to say what they like, which is more than you can do in Mother Russia, and I'll prove it to you.'

He turned to an Irish friend who was well known for his nationalist sympathies and said: 'Tell my friends here what you think of the Queen and the Royal family, Pat.' The Irishman yelled at the top of his voice: 'Fuck 'em all, the bloody parasites. The whole bunch of them can kiss my royal Irish arse. They should be put in a sideshow in Coney Island, and if the Yanks won't buy them – shoot the buggers.'

Kryukov and the Pravda man looked shocked, then the crowd burst into laughter at Paddy's usual drunken Friday night speech and the two Russians waited to see if the Governor would call for the thought police and when nothing happened they decided they were hungry and wanted to go to the fish and chip shop.

While waiting in the queue for cod and chips the man from Pravda recited Shakespeare in Russian, a rendering of 'Hamlet' he claimed, to entertain the customers as they waited, and later the threesome ate their

---

* Joan Kennedy was the first woman in England to be given a mortgage by a local council. As a top copywriter on a regular salary, who could have been a director of S.H.Benson had she been a man, she argued for equality and Camden Council complied.

cod and chips out of the paper with their fingers on the short walk back to McGinn's flat in Denning Road. After giving them a drink, McGinn took a book from his library, one he had mentioned to Yevgeny, and handed it to him, saying: 'Would you like to borrow this?' The Russians looked at the title: *The History of the British Secret Service*. The Pravda man looked sharply at Kryukov as if to ask: 'Who is trying to recruit who?' Kryukov looked worried and handed the book back saying: 'Peter, if I read that, I wouldn't be able to sleep for a month.'

Yevgeny said he wanted to meet John Philby* and McGinn pretended he did not know where he was living and did not know anyone who had a phone number for him. He was beginning to tire of the Russian, who was always on the *qui vive* and was clearly trying to use McGinn for some purpose or other. Whatever it was, whether it was going to be a request to do some travelling on their behalf because of their London restriction,** he never found out, because all he really wanted to do was get back to Ibiza and the sunshine and do some research on a book about the effects of the Civil War there. The blackberries were out again. It was time to leave England. And the trip he and George and Seley had been saving up for, a journey by car to Marrakesh, was in the offing, and his feet were itching to get on the road again.

---

* McGinn had suggested to John Philby that he could be financed by a television agency to film his father in Russia. It would make a good programme. He asked him to ask his father what life was *really* like in the Soviet Union since he had had 'the cure', and they locked him in a hospital ward specialising in alcoholics. He had threatened to commit suicide by jumping out of a window if they did not give him his cigarettes. While filming in Siberia, at a picnic by a lake, Philby had made a crack about the battle of Stalingrad, and one KGB man had grabbed him by the scruff of the neck and snarled 'In Russia, we do not joke about the war.' In reply to McGinn's question John was told: 'Being a vodka drunk in Russia is just the same as being a whisky drunk in England.' Whatever 'the cure' was that the Russians had used, it did not work. And they were always suspicious of Philby, as they were of any man who was a traitor to his own country.

** Some months later McGinn saw a tiny paragraph in *The Times* to the effect that the London correspondent of Pravda, along with another Russian, had been found shot dead in the seats of a car parked near the early warning radar system at Fylingdales in Yorkshire.

CHAPTER 12

To Ceuta – and Back

STORMS lashed the Spanish coast as they called at various resorts down the coast, with Seley sipping constantly from the bottle of vodka he had put in the voluminous pocket of the fireman's topcoat before they left Ibiza. They went inland to Murcia, then back to the coast and inland again, and the further south they went the more primitive it became. In one village *tienda*, George asked for a tomato juice, and the woman could not open the tin. It was clear that she had never opened a tin before in her life, for she started hammering a screwdriver into it until George looked behind the counter and found the triangular can-opener, probably the one her husband or son knew how to use, and opened the tin himself, the woman looking on amazed. The 1970s were not far off but Spain was still primitive. Workmen in restaurants (all single men ate in restaurants because they did not go shopping for food, or cook for themselves), ate with a piece of bread and a knife. Forks lay unused on the table. Many people over 40 were illiterate, for Franco had not wanted the working class to be educated. Some villages were still using the kind of barter the anarchists used before the Civil War, when four million of them scorned the use of money. McGinn recalled his friend Fernando Diaz, who worked for the post office in Hampstead, telling him that in 1955, as a National Service officer, he had to read out letters from home written by a village scribe to men in his platoon, and write letters home to their girl friends or *novias* for them, and that he had visited Estremadura where most of his platoon had come from for their National Service and found that the villagers paid with eggs and potatoes for drinks or meals – there were no forks in sight – and they had never seen a 100 peseta note.

The one good thing about their drive south was that the bars had never heard of vodka, so Steve Primero could not buy a new bottle, claiming, when George complained about his constant drinking: 'I'm not *drinking*, goddamn it, I'm just *sipping* it. *I'm rinsing my teeth.* My teeth hurt.'

The sun had come out in Algeciras, but the trip ended on the Spanish-Moroccan frontier in Ceuta.

Seley had strolled ahead to chat to two red-bands, the Armada police chiefs, all of them speaking in French. Seley, a bag of nerves and worried stiff about entering an Arab country, as he was Jewish, need not have worried because they were thrown out five minutes later, because George had neglected to have his passport stamped with a visa in Ibiza and had been told to go back and do it or he could not leave Spain. No sooner had the police told Steve that Marrakesh was 'a little Paris in the desert', than they saw him re-enter the little car, start to lambast George for ruining the trip, take a swift blast on the vodka, and drive off to the harbour.

The problem now was that the customs officers in Algeciras would naturally assume they had been in Morocco.

'Where's the hashish?' a nasty one asked.

McGinn was trying to explain in bad Spanish how they had not actually entered Morocco, when Seley, his nerves frayed, stepped out of the car, and took a long drink from the up-tilted vodka bottle. The customs officers looked at McGinn, at George, then at Seley, and said: *'Passa'*.

After Tarifa, Steve became more and more aggressive, annoyed because now McGinn was trying to tell him to knock off the sauce, and a verbal battle began. George stopped the car in the main street of a little town, with Seley yelling: 'Nobody tells me what to do,' as he got out of the car. 'You should have been a goddamned schoolmaster,' he shouted. A group of policemen who had been standing outside their police station in the centre of the quiet street heard the noise and ran inside and closed the door.

Seley calmed down in Cadiz, a good drinking town with excellent little bars and restaurants and, as usual, he had his own room at their hotel, George and McGinn sharing, following Tristan Jones's advice: 'It's the same as in a small boat – why pay double?' Seley had already explained his views on this: 'First of all, I only share a room with a woman I'm sleeping with. Secondly, as I told them in New York when they tried to get me in the Army, 'Do you think I'm going to sleep in a roomful of goddamned farm boys farting in my face? Not me!'

Unfortunately the bars of Cadiz and Cordoba had a plentiful supply of vodka* for foreign visitors to their cities and Seley became more and more aggressive and insulting until they decided to split up, with Seley walking off, shouting and threatening to take a train back to Valencia or Alicante. Having booked a room for himself and McGinn in a nearby hotel, George asked the smartly dressed receptionist if he could advise them where to go for *chicas*.

'The restaurant here has very good chicken, sir,' he told George, in perfect English.

'No, no, not chicken. *Chicas*,' said George with a winning smile, placing his left hand inside his right elbow and making an internationally known sign.

Outraged, the prim clerk said: 'Sir, you are in the Hotel of the Catholic Kings – *Los Reyes Cattolicas*. This is a respectable family hotel – not a brothel.'

A taxi driver proved more helpful and took them to the red light district which was always the most interesting part of a Spanish town with more life in one bar than in the whole of Geneva.

'We keep forgetting, George, that we are in Spain,' said McGinn. 'I mean, Seley nicking the altar wine in Seville cathedral could have got us all thrown into jail. I couldn't stop him.' The unconsecrated rough red wine had been in a flask on one of the side altars near the entrance

---

* Seley's original family name was Selig, Russian Jews escaping the pogrom by emigrating to America. This may have accounted for his liking for vodka. His father was the lawyer who handled the divorce for the wife of Vito Genovese, the head of the Mafia in America, on whom *The Godfather* was based, and as a young law student he was approached by gangsters who offered to pay for him through law school if he would work for them afterwards. At fifteen, he had made the grave error of joining the communist party in New York and was a marked man by the F.B.I. for the rest of his life. His father had to plead for a passport for him to live in Europe after the McCarthy hearings on Un-American activities. Divorced three times, his third wife married Oppenheimer, the 'father of the atom bomb', and when she visited Seley in Ibiza on holiday she was tailed by F.B.I. agents. After his first book, *The Cradle Will Fall,* was published, he lived in every art colony in the world: Mexico City, Sauselito, Greenwich Village, Woodstock, Martha's Vineyard, New Orleans, Paris, Menton, Chelsea, St. Ives in Cornwall, and from 1956 until his death, in Ibiza.

to the cathedral and it was not to Seley's liking. 'Let's have swig of this,' he said and then grimaced. 'Ah, a shy little wine, possibly three weeks old. Timid, yet full bodied, and made, one suspects, with iron filings and the urine of an insect known as a gnat.'

'They'll throw the key away if they catch you,' said George.

'Jewish altar wine is much better,' he replied, 'but too sweet. I don't see why these priests don't invest in a decent Rioja.'

After the squabbles and the break-up in Cordoba McGinn and George drove up the coast to Valencia to catch the boat back to Ibiza, but with many hours to fill they headed for the girls again and some of them started to admire the thin quiff of blonde hair George had held on to as the last hallmark of youth, composed of fifteen hairs combed straight back from his forehead. One of the bolder girls asked George for money and he said: 'Really? You'll pay me? That's very nice of you.' She reached into a voluminous handbag, withdrew the longest pair of scissors McGinn had ever seen (no doubt her weapon against attack), and with one swift stroke, snipped off George's quiff at the roots, the fifteen hairs falling to the floor of the bar, to the great amusement of the other girls.

Back in Ibiza on the overnight boat, they found Seley fully recovered and in a very good mood, ready to recount, over dinner in San Telmo restaurant, his little adventure in Cordoba.

Somehow, and he could not remember how, he had lost his shoes, a splendid pair of English brogues he had lovingly polished for twenty years. In his socks he had sat with a group of people near the Cordoba synagogue, drinking coffee and trying to discern what language the group spoke. Eventually he called over to them: 'Hey – any of you guys speak English?'

There were three men and two women. One of the men said: 'As a matter of fact, we all speak English fluently.'

He looked with disdain at the figure in the fireman's coat wiggling his holey socks.

'So what kind of language were you speaking just then? It's not Arabic, and it's not French or Italian or any other known European language. I speak fluent French and some Spanish, but I didn't understand one goddamn word of what you were saying.'

'We were speaking Hebrew,' the man said, flinching.

'Hebrew? Holy shit, you mean that's Hebrew? This is ridiculous,

134

because I'm a Jew myself, born in Newark, New Jersey, and I didn't even recognise Hebrew, my own fucking language. Have you been visiting the synagogue? That Franco's a murdering son of a bitch but he wasn't anti-Semitic, and he didn't burn the synagogue down. How long are you staying?'

'Would you mind keeping your obscene observations to yourself and stop using filthy gutter language in front of the ladies...'

One of the other men stood up and said: 'Come on, let's get away from here...'

As the group paid and left, the first man said: 'And you are NOT a Jew – you are a DISGRACE...'

'Yeah, sure, sure, that's what the critics said about my book, *Baxter Bernstein*, that I was a disgrace to my religion and my flag. The first anti-hero book, promoting PEACE not WAR,' he had yelled at their retreating backs.

Later, in the railway station, the porter had shown great respect for this figure who looked like a member of the Senate down on his luck, and called the station master who saluted him and helped him aboard the train and into a compartment.

McGinn looked around the restaurant. They were eating excellent French food at Spanish prices. He was able to rent an apartment on the sea for five pounds a week; cigarettes were five pesetas for twenty and as Seley had often pointed out, and Brendan Behan had discovered, 'the gargle is fer nothin'.' In the early seventies it was possible to live the whole winter in Ibiza for three hundred pounds, or fifty pounds a month.

'Are you staying long this time?' George asked McGinn.

'Yes, for a long time, George,' he replied. 'It feels like home.'

* * *

Although the weather was hot, Steve Primero wore his heavy black overcoat with silver buttons as he came out of Wauna's bar into the Calle Mayor in Ibiza and looked around with scorn at the tourist trinkets on display in the shops. He was morose.

'I'm not in the best of health. I have a rodent mole. You know what that is? It's a mole that eats its way into your goddamn nose, and I have very bad sinus trouble and my teeth hurt and I have a pain in my chest.

You know my ribs are all wired up. I was crushed by a bus in Majorca and I nearly croaked. I was given the last rites of the Catholic Church, although I'm a Jew. My father came from New Jersey to see me. He's a lawyer, but he didn't manage to get me any godamn compensation for my stoved-in chest. In any civilised country I'd have had a million dollars, but not here. No sir. And a nun complained to my father that I'd touched her up. Anyway...' he paused and hitched his *cesta,* the enormous Ibiza straw bag up onto his shoulder. Peeping from it was the neck of a bottle of brown stone with a stained cork in it. 'Ibiza's not a bad place to live. You can get a litre of gin for nothing. Of course...' he paused again and looked thoughtful.

A little smile played around the corners of his mouth 'Of course you have to eat the occasional orange for your health...'

The buttons on his overcoat had the letters N.F.S. on them. 'National Fire Service,' he said proudly. 'It's a British fire-fighter's topcoat, a present from England, and I'll tell you, it saved my life this winter. My chest. I have to keep warm. And the gin helps. The only reason I drink, really, is to kill the pain...'

A little Ibicenco with a shock of wiry black hair and swarthy appearance came out *of Es Quinques* restaurant.

'Hey, Jaime,' Steve shouted at him. 'Got any *sopa?* Got any *lengua?*'

'*Si, Steve. Hay sopa de legumbres, y lengue tambien.*'

'Jaime's a good guy' said Steve, waving acknowledgment 'and he makes vegetable soup called *potache* with chick peas and cabbage. Keeps the cold out. And it's cheaper to eat there than buy food in the shops and cook it, not that I can cook, except bacon and eggs, but he's a bit mean with the portions. Itty-bitty slices of tongue - that's *lengua* in Spanish. It's on the menu today. You wanna eat there? I'll be in there at one o'clock if you wanna join me. Hey - that's not an invitation by the way. I can't afford to pay for anybody. My electric fire's in hock and Luis down at Toto's bar is holding my gas fire against bar bills, then the goddamn weather had to turn cold again. Leave it open, right? I'm gonna be there anyway. One o'clock.'

He moved majestically down the Calle Mayor, a distinguished figure if it had not been for his clothes - he would often boast later 'I have the best collection of secondhand clothes in Spain' and list the donor of each item.

Suddenly he was hailed by a girl in flowing flowered robes coming out of the restaurant opposite the flower shop. 'Hey , Steve,' a raucous voice called, 'Are you going to Far Out Phyllis's party?' The accent, the tonality, had been transplanted from the streets of Brooklyn to the Calle Mayor. There was an explosion of an expletive followed by the words, '...Far out Phyllis,' lost up in the crevices of the narrow buildings.

'The whole island's going to it, man,' she screeched.

Another roar as the expletive hit the walls of the narrow street and the words...'you too,' bounced off the window panes.

'Yeah? Oh yeah? Get lorst old man,' she shouted at his back. 'You can't get it up anyway...'

The huge black overcoat turned and an angry face glared at her. 'Oh yeah? That's what you think baby. That's what you think. Sure, I may have to thumb it in, but there's no problem on that score, no sir. And stop shouting at me in my street. I *live* here, goddamn it. And I came four thousand miles to get away from that goddamn accent, so leave me alone. Why don't you go jump off the cathedral? Make a proper job of it next time.'

The owner of the George and Dragon bar came out to see what all the shouting was about. The back of the black overcoat was disappearing around the corner in the direction of the Calle de la Virgen followed by a stream of abuse in broad Brooklynese.

'She wants him to give her one, but he won't,' the bar owner said.

'Who is she?' asked Peter McGinn.

'Oh, that's Jumping Susan. She's a right head-banger. She gets acid rushes when she closes her eyes, dancing lights and all that trip. Dropped a few frames too many.'

'What did he mean by telling her to jump off the cathedral?'

'That's how she got her name. In a fit of depression she tried to top herself in Figueretas but she forgot to jump far enough out of the five storey apartment block she was living in and she hit each balcony on the way down and survived, so they call her Jumping Susan. Are you new on the island?'

'No, I was here years ago before they built the new airport. That was in the days when the lights would fail on the landing strip and the 'plane would have to return to Palma. I remember leaving a pair of old suede shoes on the harbour wall as the boat sailed and saying to myself that I would never return. But here I am again.'

'It's a magnet. I came here from Africa and bought the bar with money I made illegally exporting tropical fish in plastic bags sealed with a swift lick of the flat iron and a few bribed airline people. But the real bread was made by exporting parrots. Change the number one to the number twelve on the export form. Parrots worth a bomb in London and New York. You have to get the same typewriter to make the change. Want a beer?'

'I'll pop in later. I have to pick up mail before the post office closes.'

'Best San Miguel in town. And a flush toilet. Pickled eggs and pickled onions made especially by the owner, Pete the Parrot. That's me. Apologies for no toilet seat. Kept buying plastic ones but the soldiers from the barracks up on the hill come in and stand on it and crack it up. They hold onto the bend in the pipe by one finger, like strap hanging, and their big Army boots crack the seat. I swear some of them, from Estremadura have never seen a real bog before.'

What the bar owner said was true, and the traces of primitive Spain lingered on amongst the tourist trappings. Behind each *finca* or small farmhouse was a cactus patch and that was the toilet, the strong roots of the prickly pear cactus acting as a natural sewage system. Ibiza was an island that had been taken by the scruff of its neck and thrown into the twentieth century.

Now the island was a popular holiday place, known and talked about in the bars of New York and the coffee houses of Chelsea and the clubs of Berlin. The Vara de Rey was like a scene from a Paris fashions show, with beautiful girls from Scandinavia and Germany and England and France showing off the latest crazy fashion, often invented there on the island to reach the stores of the capitals the following year. The girls pranced, the men stared, and faces were pushed upwards towards the sun beating down on the terrace of the Montesol hotel. Elmyr de Hory was table hopping and glad-handing. The King of the fake painters who had been involved in selling millions of dollars worth of impressionists to Japanese and American collectors, was echoing Jumping Susan's cry: 'Are you going to Far Out Phyllis's party?' When he came to Nescafe Jack, he paused, pushed his nose in the air and walked past, for Elmyr did not like to mix with losers. Jack took his own tin of coffee to the terrace and spooned it into a used cup, but the waiters were making threatening noises...

A few tables up from Nescafe Jack sat Crazy Hans, and sitting next to Crazy Hans, wearing sunglasses, was a small dead pig. The suckling pig, or *lechon* had been bought by Hans from the butcher that morning but he was entertaining it to a drink in the sun before taking it home prior to roasting it for a group of new acquaintances. The idea had come to him when he had seen an item on a menu in a harbour side hotel which was in Spanish and English:

SpanishEnglish
Lechon Roast pig with spit

Sitting beneath his feet, and clearly resenting the presence of the pig were two Pyrenean mountain dogs, Mister Smith and Sir Edward. Crazy Hans had brought his two best friends in huge crates from Hamburg to Ibiza airport, where, well bred as they were they caused the arrest of Crazy Hans by the Guardia Civil when they deposited on the tarmac two mountainous calling cards they had held in since their Lufthansa flight took off.

'Welcome to Ibiza,' a British passenger had said disdainfully turning his head away from the sight, while the Guardia shouted at Hans as he sought, in vain, the equivalent words for pooper-scooper in his German-Spanish dictionary. It must have been 'be kind to tourists week' for the men with the patent leather hats, for they let him leave the airport precincts for the taxi rank where he discovered to his chagrin and fury that Ibicenco taxis did not take dogs.

'Fleas? What do you mean fleas?' he shouted at the tubby throng of miniature cabmen. 'My dogs don't have fleas. They are cleaner than you.' The cab men guffawed and pointed at his feet and the direction of the town, and Hans set off to walk, with his two suitcases and guarded on either side by Mister Smith and Sir Edward.

It turned out to be Hans' lucky day for Finnish Dora happened to be returning from the airport after seeing someone off to Hamburg and managed to find space in her 2CV for Hans and his huge mountain dogs, but it meant that her dog - one of four - which retained its name, Bullshit, from the original owner, had to run alongside the bouncing little car, occasionally glaring at the two faces of Mister Smith and Sir

Edward who were watching him keep pace at forty kilometres an hour.

'You will have to meet my friend George when he returns from Palma,' Finnish Dora said to Hans over a quick drink in her beautiful villa, painted white and covered with red roses, bougainvillea and morning glory on the D'En Bossa beach. 'I swear to God he can talk to dogs. He actually trained one to sing. Stroppy it was called which is English for Strop-bollocks, whatever that means, and it used to join in at the chorus.'

The result of all this was that Finnish Dora and her friend Lena from Helsinki were the first two invited by Crazy Hans to his party at his newly rented house at Talamanca.

'Come and have a drink' Crazy Hans called from his seat outside the Montesol. In front of him was an enormous measure of *pastis* and tucked beneath a saucer, several unpaid tabs. 'I have changed my name, by the way. I am no longer Hans. I am Doktor Ricard.'

'I have to check for mail,' McGinn called, 'and I thought you called yourself *Jean Baise-a-l'oeil.*'

'That was yesterday. Today I am Doktor Ricard..'

Hans liked to speak French, which he spoke fluently, and he was a jazz fanatic. He loved the French language and New Orleans jazz and would have liked to be French, or, coming back in another life, Django Rheinhardt.

By the post office, a donkey brayed. It kept quiet if Spaniards approached, but brayed loudly for foreigners, who gave it sugar. By now it was probably diabetic and the man with the Golden Arm was Steve Primero who fed it sugar filched from every cafe and packed into his huge overcoat pockets. The donkey would start to bray when it spotted the National Fire Service overcoat a quarter of a mile away.

There was a queue in the post office because Paul George was collecting his monthly remittance from his family in America, and he kept dropping it. Thousands of pesetas fell on the floor.

'Do we have to wait all day while this Greek Geek collects his dough?' an American voice in the queue said.

Having fortified himself with a bottle of Jack Daniels for the ordeal of the trip to the post office for his money, Paul George stumbled as he bent over to pick up the notes. Two girls in *kaftans* bent to help him but he brushed their hands from his money, watchful in case anyone tried to snaffle and secrete a note.

From behind the counter grille, fourteen pairs of Spanish eyes flashed at the sight of the remittance man tottering amongst the falling bills. They hated him. For some years their total monthly salaries did not add up to the sum that Paul George collected. Every time they got a rise they hoped that they would outstrip him, but his family in America augmented his remittance to match the cost of living in the USA.

Finally, amidst grumbles of 'get that asshole out of here,' and 'he deserves to be robbed,' he managed to get together the bundle, which would have choked the diabetic donkey outside, and force it into the pockets of his sagging, old man's trousers. Hitching up his bad trousers with the kind of coloured, striped belt with a snake buckle a schoolboy would have worn, he glared at the queue with one mad, glittering eye, the other closed in a squint.

'Any more lip from you guys,' he snarled, 'an' I'll get a couple of torpedoes over from Detroit to cream you mothers.'

'Get outa here you bum... get lorst... drop dead creep... goddamned juice-head...' came the cries from the foreigners queuing for mail.

A giant negro watched as McGinn went to Finnish Dora's Apartado box. She had let him use it for mail as he was about to rent a flat on top of her villa. As he opened the box and took out a letter for Dora from Helsinki, a postcard for George from his son in Wales, and a letter from his bank, the negro voice said: 'Yeah, man, you have to be some kind of *official* round here to get a *box*.'

The hippy queue stared at McGinn convinced in their paranoia that he was from Scotland Yard Drugs Squad at the very least, perhaps working for the FBI and the Drugs Enforcement Agency or all three. McGinn had discovered on this visit to the island that the great division was not between the Spaniards and foreigners or between nationalities or between age groups, but between juice-heads and pot-heads. The smokers of pot operated their own little secret service of where to get supplies, who was dealing, who would make the next run to Morocco and risk six years jail to bring supplies back to the island, and who were the police spies and undercover drug squad team from Madrid. The drinkers only became paranoid when they stopped drinking, but the pot-heads spent their lives slithering around corners, whispering in their own code or slang.

With the young heads fresh from the States, the giveaway was often a bag of cakes they carried to assuage the raging hunger that a smoke brought on: sticky doughnuts and sweet biscuits and that Spanish delicacy *ensemada*, light puff pastry dusted with icing sugar and known to the literary fraternity on the harbour as 'fried air'.

The old heads never ate. The intake of sugar alleviated the effect of the *kif* and if the pangs could be resisted the high lasted longer.

"Like, what brought you to the island, man?' a girl was asking the big negro.

'Ah dunno. Ah heard about the scene, y'know, like where it's at. Ah guess what ah really want, man, is to get back to mah *roots*.'

'Yeah, right.'

'Ah mean, like where it all started.'

'Right.'

A bluebottle battered itself insensible trying to get into the post office window. Outside the sun was getting hotter. There, on that ground, Hannibal had recruited his army of Ibicenco slingers before he set off to cross the Alps with elephants. The Punic invasion had left behind the corpses of Phoenicians on the hillside behind the Cartega cinema and also the Ibicenco or *podenca,* the dog that is depicted on the frescoes and sarcophagi in tombs in the Middle East. There, Roman statues guarded the entrance to Ibiza old town, headless; a practical people, the Romans changed the heads on the extant statues as power changed hands; under Nero a week in politics was a long time.

'Like Ah also wanted to walk on the *moon.*'

'Right.'

February was the month for moon walks.

The first blossom of the winter was the mimosa, closely followed in January by the almond blossom when the whole island turned white and by February there were valleys that could have been covered with snowdrifts, and the combination of this scenery and the full moon of February caused the most eerie effect all over the island. Kids came from Canada and America to drop acid on the night of the full moon and say later that they had actually walked on that great orb of glass marbles shining with a glow that made the fields of almonds appear to be lighted by neon strips.

Sin Zapatos was from Sweden. He walked much and talked little and was always barefoot. Hence the name: without shoes. His conversation was limited to the sketchy vocabulary picked up from popular songs and the few phrases needed amongst young people to converse: Hi, OK, Far out, Right on, Turn on, With it, Uptight, Laidback, Strung out, Great, See you...

No one had discovered his real name, for the small income he had came in a monthly cheque from the Swedish vice-consul who cashed it and gave him the pesetas.

Cherokee Frank passed Sin Zapatos in the entrance to the post office.

'How,' said the Swede.

'How,' said Frank, smiling. In the movies American Indians also had a limited vocabulary, and the Big Swede had picked that up. Frank, a full-blooded Cherokee Indian took the greeting in good humour. Cherokee Frank was waiting to die. He was an Infantry Captain in the US Marines in Germany, invalided out with a weak heart, and he knew he had not long to go, but accepted his fate like a true Indian. He bought paintings, at will, bought Jack Daniels whisky and good French wine from the Post Exchange on the mainland and he chased girls. Not only chased them, but thought about them every waking moment of the day and then dreamt about them.

Frank was proud of his reputation with the girls. The girls would laugh and advise a newcomer: 'You gotta lay the Cherokee. Frank's the greatest.' Everyone knew that Frank had not long to go and the flower girls were determined to give him a good time.

'I've been thinking about it,' said Frank when McGinn greeted him. 'It wouldn't work. No way. Imagine those guys in Washington going for an idea like that? They'd freak, man.'

Frank had been contemplating McGinn's suggestion that he approach the Army Chiefs of staff in Washington DC with an idea in keeping with the moves towards national identity: that as a full blooded Cherokee and son of a Chief, and a Captain in the United States Marines who still had his uniform and attended reunions with his old regiment in Germany, he should be allowed to wear the eagle-feather headdress with his uniform. Frank had looked skeptical when McGinn had tried to persuade him to wear the Cherokee Chief's headgear with his khakis at the next reunion, imagining the look on the faces of the military when he turned up and said 'How' to them and pointing out that Russians wore their fur hats, Aussies their bush hats and Sikhs and Indians their turbans, so why not ?

'It's a good idea though,' McGinn said to Frank.

'Sure. They'll do it someday, too, when pigs fly.'

'This is the age of protest, Frank.'

'You don't know how long it took them to get round to giving an American Indian a commission in the Armed Forces.'

'How did you swing it, Frank? You must have put your civilian occupation down as *brave*.'

Frank laughed. 'Actually it was *teacher*,' he said.

An American voice, piercing as a well sharpened stilletto, but without the same nerve-shattering qualities of the eldritch screech of Jumping Susan, brought the conversation to an end. 'Hi, Pete, Hi, Frank. Are you going to sign?'

It was Pot Peggy. She had with her another petition, an annual effort to persuade the authorities not to deport her. Green-eyed Peggy liked a smoke. She was valiantly trying to bring her children up on a tiny income from her parents, and the authorities did not like her presence because her husband had been involved in a crime on the mainland upon their arrival in Spain and was still doing time.

The latest petition, to be presented to the judge along with Peggy's plea that her children were now almost Spanish, settled in school, etcetera, was the result of an unfortunate little mistake that Peggy's children had made, understandably, when their teacher had asked all the children to fill in forms for school meals with the line: NAME OF MOTHER: and they wrote: 'Peggy', but to the question: NAME OF FAMILY they wrote: 'Pot'.

The children explained to the startled teacher that that was the only name they knew their mother by, and everyone on the island called her that, so that must be her real name.

A quick glance at the list of those who had already signed, the lynx-eyed flash down the page being noted by the suspicious and ever-watchful Peggy, like a snake eyeing a mongoose, revealed who was on the island, and who was out of jail. It even revealed the surnames of those who went by one name only, or by nicknames. Newcomers about to settle on the island were warned: there are two questions you must never ask in Ibiza: what's your surname, and what do you do? The first might just elicit a reply like 'Just Mike' or 'Just Jacob' but the second would bring forth various replies: 'I mind my own business.' 'Inspector of blind alleys', 'I wind eight-day clocks' 'Coronation programme salesman.' 'I export dolls voices', 'Man ah doan do, ah am', 'You mean for an encore?', 'I'm just a gigolo,' and Steve Primero, asked once by a sarcastic militarist what he had been doing in Mexico during the war, replied: 'I was spying for the Japanese.'

The owner of a harbour side bar, who was about to sell it, told the prospective proprietor that various customers owed considerable sums of money to the bar and a list of these absent debtors who would, of course, pay their tabs on their return to the island. As an example of this mutual trust on the island the bar owner mentioned the case of Deaf Henry, a retired English solicitor, who had a *'cuenta'* for seven years and they had never once asked him to pay up, trusting his story that a rich aunt would die in Eastbourne and he would inherit her house and settle his account.

The list read:

Nescafe Jack
Peter the Book
Jill the Pill
Anna Banana
Rick the Prick
Kamikaze Schmidt
Too Much Tommy
Gordon the Flute
Hairy Pat
Charlie 103
Wanted John

Alongside each *nom de plume* or *nom de guerre* was written an amount in pesetas and the total came to a sum that made the prospective buyer's eyes glitter. But then he frowned.

'Wait a minute. Wait a minute. There's not a name on here. Who the hell is Kamikaze Schmidt? I know who Nescafe Jack is. I've seen him in action.'

'Kamikaze Schmidt is a German yachtsman. He left here just before Christmas to join the flotilla that leaves the Azores around New Year's Day every year on the trade winds that take them to the States.'

'Not that rotting hulk that lay next to the 'Tagomago' last year with bilges full as a family po?

'And who the hell is Wanted John?'

'Well... they don't actually call him that now. He's known as Unwanted John.'

'What's the difference? Wanted John, Unwanted John, it's still not a name. Not a name you could go to court with.'

'He's always kept his name secret here. You see he came here because he thought he was wanted on a murder rap in the States. He'd been involved in a bar fight and had hit a guy and he thought he'd killed him so he fled the country. We all knew him as Wanted John, then he got a telegram saying his mother was dying so he had to go home, so he thought he'd better face the music and go to the cops and confess, but they said, 'Oh, we got a guy for that. He's doing life. It was nothing to do with you.' So when he came back here everybody called him Unwanted John.'

'So where is he now?'

'Oh, don't worry. He'll be back. They all come back eventually. This island's a magnet...'

Back on the Vara de Rey the lunch time crowd had thinned out, and the fashion parade was almost over. Some of the hard drinkers were still at the tables outside the Alhambra, and the long-haired hippies of the island were there in force, having eschewed the more bourgeois *milieu* of the Hotel Montesol. The waiters were banging glasses down and rattling saucers when they served them, for they did not understand that they were to give tips to the waiters.

'They hate us,' one of them said to McGinn.

'No they don't. You should give them a small tip. There's a rule in Europe about that: if a guy is using shoe leather to serve you, tip him, but if someone is just standing behind a bar, it's not necessary. The waiter who banged the chair down has seven kids, and he lives by his tips"

'Seven kids? If he bought condoms he wouldn't need tips.'

The hippies stared. Across the Vara de Rey, entering the main square was a magnificent horse and rider. The horse had had its chestnut coat groomed to perfection and its hooves shone with black polish. On its back, chin upheld and cap firmly on head, was a Captain in the Spanish Army, sword dangling from his hip, spurs glittering, riding boots like mirrors, pistol in polished holster, medals glistening in the sun, and on his face, a look of extreme *hauteur*.

As he came around the main square, the hippies began to jeer. The horse pranced and the officer glared, his black eyes flashing hate at the bearded, tattered throng on the terrace at the Alhambra. His hand strayed momentarily in the direction of the holster holding his service revolver, and then back to the reins.

'Ooh, look at her - isn't she lovely?'

'Make LERV - not WAR!'

'Ass hole.'

'Give PEACE a chance...'

'All you need is LOVE, man.'

'Scheisser."

'Espece de con.'

'Connard.'

'Arriba Espana!'

That was a mistake. The officer might have swallowed his pride and continued his spectacular ride down the Vara de Rey but he reined in his horse and stopped. The members of the 'penal colony' as the hippies were called by the sailors on shore leave there, had insulted his country. A photograph at the time of the Civil War in Spain captured an old man with a hesitant hand stretching out for bread being distributed from the back of the ration lorry to a scrambling mob, and on his face was etched for ever the pride of Spain, the shame of having to beg, the loss of face. That same look came over the face of the Captain as he dismounted and surveyed the hairy, bearded group on the terrace.

The hippies stopped their catcalls, and a silence seemed to fall over the whole main square. Even the hundreds of linnets from the D'en Bossa marshes that feed on the square's plane trees were silent for a few seconds as the officer began to draw his sword. The hippies, now silent, hastened to leave their terrace seats and moved into the interior of the bar, a dark and gloomy cavern. Sunlight had never filtered into the subfusc corners of the main bar and to enter the nether regions, a potholer's lamp was recommended to penetrate the gloom. This was the bar famous for its row of hole-in-the-ground toilets where a very small Ibicenco fisherman had received a urine shower-bath from a tall American who failed to see his tiny crouching form in the dark, and the punch-line was that the little man did not even protest, believing that all foreigners behaved like that.

The half-drawn, shining sword was replaced in its scabbard. The hippies had taken seats in the main salon, waiting to see what the officer would do. A few stood at the bar near Pepe the waiter at his serving place, and Pepe said, over and over again: '*Cuidado eh? Cuidado*,' - 'careful... careful' believing that there was safety in numbers. The bearded throng held fast to their seats as the officer regarded the entrance to the cafe where the enemy had taken refuge, and then came to the quick decision on what tactics to use to revenge the Honour of Spain against the hirsute mob within. The very act of wearing a beard was a sign of aggression to Spaniards at that time, suspecting the wearer of hiding his true identity and associating him with piracy and crime. A red-bearded man walking down the Ramblas in Barcelona would be followed by the call 'Me-e-eh-h-h...' imitating the sound of a goat, and the Guardia Civil eyed a bearded man as if he had hidden a *cache* of hashish near his Adam's apple.

The Captain took his mount firmly by the reins and led it into the cafe, the horse having to bow its head to get under the architrave. He did not hesitate but took the horse to the very centre of the big room and, with a call which only the horse could have understood, he turned his steed with practiced skill, so that the horse's rump sent tables, chairs, hippies, guitars, glasses, cups, saucers, sugar bowls, bottles, straw bags, leather hats, *ensemadas* and unfinished drinks scattering in the direction of all four walls. In seconds there was a clear circle in the centre of the salon and the shouting, protesting clientele had been washed up like the tide against the skirting boards and the foot rail of well-worn brass that lined the bar.

Honour was satisfied, and leaving Pepe and Jose to sort out the chaotic scene, the Captain returned to the street and rode proudly away.

In the Vara de Rey, Crazy Hans, who had left the company of his lounging pig to watch the action from the doorway of the Alhambra, returned to his seat.

'Hoo, hoo, hoo - Did you see that? Now the hippies vill fire-bomb the barracks, you will see.'

'I don't think so.'

'Did you see what that officer did? He must have broken two guitars at least.'

'Worse than that,' McGinn said, 'he spilt Nescafe Jack's half-finished tin of coffee powder. Now he'll have to shoplift another.'

'Never mind, anyway. Do you want a drink from Doktor Ricard?'

'I thought you were giving a party this afternoon, Hans. Are you sure you'll be able to cook?'

'Don't worry. I have the charcoal ready. I just put General Franco here' - he indicated the pig with sunglasses sitting next to him...

'Not so loud,' McGinn said. 'The last person who insulted the Caudillo sitting right where you are now, was an Irish writer called Brendan Behan. He was popping champagne corks, shouting 'gargle is fer nothin'', at passersby and managed to hit the Guardia Civil in the eye. The cops were just waiting to get an excuse to throw him in jail anyway because when the Spanish Press asked him at the airport what sights he wanted to see in Spain he said he said the only sight he wanted to see in Spain was Franco's funeral.'

Hans stood up, and Mr. Smith and Sir Edward stood up with him, looking expectantly at their master. They clearly could not wait to get back to the countryside and hunt for rabbits. 'Sit,' said Hans in English and they obediently sat. If he wanted to call them in from the hills he put a cassette in his portable tape recorder and played, very loud, the opening bars of Beethoven's Fifth Symphony. The dogs responded and came running to the villa Hans had rented, to eat the food he had prepared for them. To put them to sleep he played 'All the Things You Are' or some music by Coleman Hawkins, but their favourite was by Ella Fitzgerald singing 'No, You Can't Take That Away From Me.'

'OK we all go to my car now,' said Hans, clipping a lead onto Sir Edward's collar. He proceeded to drag the pig, still wearing its sunglasses, across the road, through the traffic, followed by Sir Edward who had started to sniff at the little trail of blood that oozed from the pig's hind quarters as the procession made its way to where Hans had parked his 2CV. He had not reached the halfway mark in the centre of the square, however, when the dogs of every shape size and colour seemed to emerge from every side street running towards the Vara de Rey and make for the trail of blood that stretched from the Montesol to where Crazy Hans was now running towards his battered car. The pig's sunglasses were abandoned on the tarmac as Hans hurled himself and Mr. Smith and Sir Edward into the little car and dragged the pig in after him. In seconds the 2CV was surrounded by barking dogs, jumping up at the windows while Hans was trying to shut the sunroof in case any of the dogs tried to effect a rooftop entry.

George, the English barman, who had been walking down the pavement by the Alhambra, stopped and said:

'Blimey, look at that! There's Otto from Santa Eulalia, Tita from D'en Bossa, Tikky from the Pena and Schnuffy from Talamanca.. And look - there's Hardcastle, and Stroppy and... and TYKE... how did he get into town? Must have followed me in... and there's Fatty... amazing.'

Fatty was a much-hated dog in the fraternity of foreign bar owners, inhabiting whichever hostelry took his fancy at night and spreading himself over the soft cushions as if he owned the place and refusing to budge until the irate owner whose seats were being occupied by this nonpaying customer, would drag the cushions out into the street with Fatty sprawled on them, snapping, and give it a quick toe in the rear to send it on to the next bar.

Fatty waddled along behind the yelping, growling pack, now joined by a few strays who haunted the meat market who had fine noses for a piece of fresh meat and were desperate to get the pig's carcass, having suffered all their lives from an old Spanish saying: 'Why do dogs eat bones? Because nobody gives them any meat.' Hans revved up and shot past the rank of taxis, with the little taxi drivers yelling at him and Mr. Smith and Sir Edward glaring at them from the back seat as they shot by with a howling pack of dogs bringing up the rear.

'There's never a dogcatcher around when you want one,' said a languid English voice.

'Look there goes No-Name,' shouted George.

A little dog with brown, black and white patches shot past the Alhambra and tried to catch up with the fleeing Hans and his yelping entourage. No-Name was a dog that frequented the harbour. No one knew where he lived or how he survived but he had a good leather collar and a brass plate on it. The trouble was he was so quick that no-one could ever catch him to see the name on the brass plate. This little Sin Zapatos of the dog world shot off like greased lightning as hands reached out from cafe tables as he went by.

As Hans disappeared in the direction of Talamanca the little posse of assorted dogs seemed to lose interest as they arrived at Pen and Ink

Corner. This was the corner of the harbour where effluvia from the nearby slaughterhouse was deposited causing an aroma which distracted dogs but sent casual visitors hurrying past, gagging, until they reached the fresh air beyond. It was an Australian's remark: 'Cor - wot a pen-and-ink' that had given the corner its name, and he added a rider: 'It'd kill a brown dog.'

'Why 'brown'dog?' someone asked Aussie Tony.

'Why not' was the laconic reply.

The sound of barking, yelping dogs died away in the distance and the Vara de Rey returned to its normal noisy, bustling ambiance. In the middle of the square, the sunglasses lay where they had been abandoned in flight, George picked them up. 'Here - you'd better give them to Hans this afternoon.'

'Aren't you coming to his party?'

'No. Dora and Lena are going, but I'm working. I'm running three different bars again to try and get some money together for a trip to Greece with Tristan, if he'll take me as crew.'

'How do you manage it?'

'I do a shift in Wauna's, open the bar up at ten a.m., then stand in for the owner of the Taverna while he has a long lunch and siesta, then in the evening I do the Whisky-a-Go-Go.'

'Gawd George, how does your liver stand it?'

'I don't know. I think I need a spare, especially for the weekends - and for tomorrow.'

'What happens tomorrow?'

'A tourist boat comes in. A Mediterranean cruise taking in the Balearics, lots of Brussels and Septics.'

George was in the habit of reverting to Cockney rhyming slang in his speech, but he was not a Cockney. He was a Welshman who had moved to South London.

'I'm going to have a couple of games of bar billiards when I come off duty to get the old liver back in trim,' said George.

'Steve Primero tells a story about his liver. One night in his apartment in New York he had a twinge...'

'Don't tell me,' George interrupted. 'My doctor told me never to joke about the liver.'

'So did mine. He was about to inject me with cortisone for tendonitis in the elbow and he asked when it hurt, and I said every time I lift a pint of Guinness. He said one more joke and he would send me for a biopsy.'

'That's nasty. Very nasty,' said George, who had been what is known as a Sick Bay Tiffy in the Royal Navy which qualified him as a male nurse in Civvy Street, and he was often called upon to give injections of Vitamin B12 or cortisone by foreigners who did not want to pay the fees of the local *practicante*. A favourite story often told by George was of a sailor who was given a little bottle by the Medical Officer aboard ship for a urine sample, then asked to provide a sample of his stool for further examination. George swore that the rating returned the next morning with a turd balanced on the bottle top, explaining that he couldn't get it inside because the neck was too narrow.

'They take a small section of your liver for examination,' he added with a grimace. 'Of course it doesn't do any hard drinkers any good on this island because the bar owners sell *corriente* gin and vodka and *hierbas.* The draught stuff costs a quarter of the real stuff, so they top up the vodka and gin bottles with *corriente* and charge the full price. When its mixed with tonic or tomato juice or orange or lemon you can't taste the difference, but you feel it the next morning when you feel as if the winner of the Grand National has been kicking you in the liver all night.'

'You don't do that, do you George?'

'Everyone does it. Except Merlin.'

'You mean to say Merlin sells the real McCoy. All those bottles are genuine? No *corriente* ?'

'That's right. Merlin is an officer and a gentleman.'

The English bar owner George referred to was a former advertising copywriter who had held a commission in a Guards regiment and, like many in advertising, dreamed of writing a best-selling book, and could often be seen sitting in the sea, knees awash with salt water, scribbling on a large pad. The bar he had bought, 'Merlin's', on the harbour, was an insurance against the precariousness of his new vocation, but had unfortunately become a fixation, so that if anyone refused to pay he would threaten them with a lead-weighted wooden cosh, and could sometimes be seen pursuing Ibicenco fishermen out of his bar and along the harbour, waving his cosh, if they left without paying.

'He also pays his barman properly,' added George.

'In fact, Joachim is the best paid barman on the island. That's to stop him stealing'

'Did he steal?'

'All barmen steal,' said George. 'What do you expect? Long hours working for peanuts, having to face all those drunks, especially on a Sunday night. Can you imagine the trouble on Sunday nights?'

'It's a bad day generally in Spain. Franco was clever. He kept down the price of telegrams, travel, *Celtas cortes* and cognac. That meant a workman could contact his family cheaply, visit them, smoke himself silly and get slaughtered every Sunday night. There are one million industrial accidents a year in Spain. Most of them occur on Monday morning.'

'Steve Primero says never walk under scaffolding in Spain on Monday morning, if you don't want a club hammer or a friggin' brick on your bonce.'

'Yes I've seen him make a detour into the middle of the road to avoid scaffolding or a ladder.'

'Maybe that's the origin of that old superstition about walking under ladders. You might get a tile or a hammer on your bushel.'

'So Merlin sells the good stuff, eh? That's worth remembering.'

'Yes and he never puts two bits of foreign crumpet in his doorway to attract customers, either. As I said, Merlin's a gentleman.'

Many of the bar owners would pay two English or Dutch or German blondes to sit just inside the doorway of their bars where the passing men could see them. There was a law in Spain that a policeman had to be able to look into a bar, hence there were no closed doors, only, in winter, glass partitions. The blondes showed a bit of leg and toyed with soft drinks as bait for the passing trade.

'Two girls came round to Wauna's for a break Sunday night,' said George, 'and the Ibicenco sniff-hounds followed them. You should have seen them. They could smell a cat on heat from here to Formentera. Then the fighting started. I had to punch three of them out of the bar but they came back every time. One freak actually jumped from that balcony, what Wauna laughingly calls her Minstrel's Gallery, onto the heads of the squabbling, throbbing mass below. So I put the music on.'

George had a special trick to deal with passionately aroused, agitated, jealous, fighting fishermen and others. He would put on *El Concierto de Aranjuez* by Rodriguez and after a few bars the noise of bickering would die down, then silence would reign in the bar while the beautiful music lilted and soared amongst the plains and mountains of Spain their Fatherland. There would be an occasional sob as a plasterer from Andalucia or a tiler from Toledo broke down. Thinking of their Poor Old Mums in the family home on the Peninsular, in the villages of Estremadura or in high rises in Badalona and Alicante, and brushing away furtive but manly tears, they would sidle out of the bar and seek consolation in cognac elsewhere.

'Got a light, George?' McGinn asked him.

George looked furtive. He looked away and then looked back to see if McGinn was serious or attempting to wind him up.

'You smoking now?' he asked.

He looked at the packet of *Celtas Cortes*, the second cheapest brand of cigarette in Spain, and said scornfully: 'Those things? Here -' he dug into his pocket and produced three lighters of different colours: blue, rose and black. He tried all three. Only one of them worked.

'Keep it,' said George, handing McGinn the black lighter of the French throwaway type called Bic. 'Times must be hard if you smoke these.'

'Abel Matutes smokes Ideales,' McGinn said, referring to the old millionaire banker of the island, who could often be seen shuffling down the harbour, wearing faded clothes and staring at the ships, most of which he owned. Once McGinn had looked up the meaning of his name in a Spanish-English dictionary and found that *Matute* meant smuggling.

'Steve Primero says when Ideales went up by one peseta a packet, he started to roll his own.' said George.

He pocketed the two empty lighters. Later, during one of his shifts in the three bars he was working in, they would be replaced by full ones. Innocent tourists would place their cigarette packets and Bic lighter on the bar only to find, minutes later, that their lighter had run out of gas. George had twelve different colours of empty lighters under the bar and it took only seconds to switch the old one for the new.

A cloud of linnets rose in a chirruping, cheeping cacophony from the plane trees in the square. They came in twice a day from the salt marshes of the Playa D'en Bossa to feed on the round clusters of seeds in the trees.

'There he goes again,' said George.

'Who?'

'The Deputy Mayor. He's shooting at the birds with an air rifle. You might as well sling one baited hook into a shoal of herring.'

'Why is who doing that?'

'Because the Mayor has refused permission for his idea to chop down all the plane trees in the Vara de Rey.'

'But why should he want to do that?'

'To stop the birds shitting on his car.'

'Why doesn't he park in another street?'

'What? And walk fifty yards in the hot sun? Besides, the other streets are only in the shade for half of the day, and he'd have to change sides and re-park.'

'But if they chopped down the trees in the Vara de Rey he wouldn't have shade.' 'Shhhhh... don't anticipate him. Let him work it out for himself as he did with that other tree-chopping idea.'

'What was that?'

'Just before you came back someone wrote to the *Diario de Ibiza* suggesting a solution to the problem of motor car accidents, mainly on the San Antonio road. British tourists got a bit Oliver Twist and started driving on the left and hit a couple of trees and that began swelling the accident figures for Sunday driving. The reader suggested chopping down all trees on the island so a car would go into a field rather than dent a tree. This stroke of genius was quashed by the Deputy Mayor's mother who likes her shade on her Sunday drive. Otherwise he would have gone ahead with it.'

'Catch you later, George, I'm walking back to the house.'

'Have a good time this afternoon.'

'A thought has just occurred to me, George. About Hans.'

'What about him?'

'On this island he ought to be called Normal Hans.'

CHAPTER 13

An Aperitif

CRAZY Hans had dug a hole in the ground in front of his rented villa, lit a fire in it and was slowly rotating the little pig over the hot coals. 'Dora! Lena! Peter!' he shouted. *'Wilkommen in mein haus.* You are the first to arrive. I have whisky, gin, vodka, wine, beer, schnapps, porto, sherry, *hierbas*, cognac, cointreau, green Chartreuse, *pastis...'*

'I'll have a *pastis*,' McGinn said.

'Oh, sorry, you can't have a *pastis*. No water. When I dug the hole for the fire I didn't know the bloody water pipe was in the ground there and I cut through it. Don't you see how wet the ground is?'

'You can get water from the well with a bucket,' said Dora.

'I tried that, but the cord slipped out of my hand and I let the bucket and the cord fall down the well.'

'But you've got to have water, Hans,' said Dora.

'Why? I can get a coffee in town.'

'But for washing.'

'Paper plates.'

'No, I mean washing yourself.'

'I do like Hemingway. Rub myself down with alcohol. Hemingway never washed. It's bad for the skin.'

'But the dogs?'

'Ah. OK, I get a plumber in the morning. Today they can drink beer. They like San Miguel.'

Hans decided to invite Sir Edward and Mr. Smith to the party. Two figures moved amongst the rocks and bushes on the side of the distant mountain as the dogs followed their Pyrenean instincts and hunted rabbits in the gorse and scrub of the hillside. In the kitchen of the villa, by the open window, Hans placed his transistor and a tape of Beethoven's Fifth Symphony. He put the tape on and watched the two dots in the distance as the opening bars rang out: Da-da-da-da... Da-da-da-da... The dogs came to a halt as their call-sign came to them, and suddenly they came running down the hill as the soaring music brought them closer and closer to their master. Hans gave them both a big welcoming kiss as they dashed into the kitchen and jumped to greet him. He took two bottles of San Miguel beer from the fridge and poured them into bowls marked Sir Edward and Mr. Smith.

By four o'clock in the afternoon, with Hans becoming sadder and sadder, it became clear that no one else was coming to his party. Hans tried to do the Spanish chef's trick of cutting the suckling pig into portions by using the edge of a china plate, but somehow missed the divide in the vertebrae and broke the plate instead. He hurled the two halves of the plate into the rocks by the side of the house and divided the roast pork with a large knife.

'Is there anything else with the pork, Hans?' Dora asked.

'Yes I have whisky cake.'

'No, I mean vegetables or salad.'

'Merde!' shouted Hans. 'I left my straw basket full of vegetables in Wauna's bar when I went to pick up the *lechon.'*

'Don't worry,' said Lena, 'It will still be there - along with half a dozen others that have been forgotten.'

'You take the vegetables for your house, Dora,' said Hans. 'I won't be cooking for some time. Give me the basket when we meet next.'

As they drove off Hans was sitting by the dying embers of his fire, head in hand, closely watched by the alert brown eyes of Mr. Smith and Sir Edward.

The basket was there in the bar along with four others, whose owners sat on the bar stools or the cushions of the seats in various stages of intoxication. They had been there since opening time, when they had finished their marketing and had stopped in for an *'apertif'*. It was not unknown for one or two of them to be drinking their *'apertifs'* when the barman started to close up, and the baskets of food to be abandoned until next morning when those containing ham or steak would have been an attractive target for the cockroaches and other night prowlers of the insect and rodent world.

'Hi, Dora,' shouted Mad Mike, who sat with another Finnish resident. Urpa, who had clearly been trying to match Mike drink for drink, much to her detriment, for her eyes seemed to be swivelling in her head.

Mike was something of a war hero, having been blown up in a tank in Vietnam, and had a full disability pension from the United States Army. This necessitated him visiting Germany once a year for a medical checkup, when Army doctors would inspect the metal plate in his skull, the pacemaker in his heart, his false rectum and his wired-up bones, every one of which had been broken in the explosion. This walking miracle of modern science was sometimes called Mechanical Mike and sometimes 'Mad' Mike. He preferred the latter sobriquet and would frequently introduce himself: 'Hi. I'm Mad Mike.'

When Dora introduced Lena from Helsinki to him that is exactly what he said, in his resonant, deep, attractive American voice: 'Hi there, Lena. I'm Mad Mike.' The swivelling eyes of his newfound friend Urpa, a painter of some considerable ability, failed to focus on Dora and Lena, but when Lena told her that she had especially brought a bottle of *Korskinkova,* the ultra-strong Finnish vodka from Helsinki for her, the heavy eyelids lifted in recognition of the word.

'Ah, *Korskinkova,'* she breathed.

A family of British tourists, probably visiting the town from one of the package-tour holiday hotels in San Antonio entered the bar and took seats in a corner. 'He's here again,' said the man, nodding in the direction of Mad Mike. 'Maybe he sleeps here,' said the woman, settling into the seat and making an attempt to straighten her son and daughter's hair with a quick brushing movement. 'He certainly looks as if he does.'

'Oh, look out,' said Doreen, another painter, Irish and amply proportioned with a Colleen's jet-black hair with the sheen of a raven's feathers on it. 'The 'watch-your-language' brigade are back.'

A look of hatred was cast in her direction, where she nursed a gin and tonic sitting on the corner barstool.

Dora and Lena had begun an animated conversation, trying to communicate with Urpa.

'They're at it again,' said the British tourist to his wife. 'I won't 'ave it.' He stood up and walked over to Dora, a rotund and formidable blonde even more amply proportioned than Doreen.

'Would you mind watching your language,' said the tourist.

'What are you talking about?'

'I said 'watch your language,' - there's women and children present 'ere.' He pointed to his wife and children.

'But what has that got to do with me?'

'We've had enough of it. That feller there -' he pointed to Mad Mike, 'was effing and blindin' last night when we were in 'ere. You should moderate your language when women and children are present and stop swearing.'

'But I wasn't swearing.'

'It sounded very much like it to me.'

'We are speaking the Finnish language together. Urpa, Lena and I are from Helsinki. Urpa is a painter, Lena is a journalist and I teach music and art.'

'Oooh, I'm very very sorry, Madam, I'm sure. I do apologise. Can I get you a drink to make up for my mistake?'

'Three vodkas and a whisky for Mike.'

'What? Oh no, I'm not getting the Yank one. 'e should be locked up.'

'He was locked up. He was a prisoner in Vietnam before he was rehabilitated.'

'Was 'e now? It's not my day, is it?'

'No it's not,' called Doreen from her perch in the corner of the bar. 'Why don't you go to a tea and cake shop where they cater for pricks like you?'

'Right, that's it, then. I'm not staying here to be insulted by rubbish. I know that accent. Irish.'

'Half,' said Doreen. 'I'm half Irish and half pissed and I came to Spain to get away from twats like you.'

'Come along, dear,' the man said to his wife. 'Lets get out of here. I've had enough of them and their filthy language.'

'What are you talking about?' Doreen said. 'I haven't even said fuck since you came in. Has anybody here heard me say fuck?'

The visitor and his wife put their hands over their children's ears and hurried them out of the bar.

'I didn't even say maternity ward or sanitary towel or French Letter or anything...'

'Thanks a lot, Doreen,' said George the barman when the family had left. 'You just cost me three vodkas, a beer and three cokes.'

'You'll recover from it.'

'And when are you going to pay your *cuenta?*'

'Watch your language.'

George laughed. 'OK, OK, but you've got to pay your bill, Doreen. Wauna is doing her nut about all these unpaid *cuentas* and she's instructed me to collect or refuse service.'

'I'll pay her when Uncle Ted sends his cheque.'

'He hasn't sent you one for months.' Doreen had a long-lost 'uncle' in London who would occasionally send her small amounts through the post.

'Another cheque that never arrived,' said George.

'I'll have a vodka and tonic until it gets here,' said Doreen.

'You what?'

'I'll buy that, darling,' said Fortune, who sat in the other corner of the semicircular bar, bright red hair flaming, gold bangles and ornaments jangling and dangling from her neck and wrists, a tall, handsome woman who had some vague connection with a firm in the United States and had a private income from a large sum of dollars her husband had left her in his will.

Fortune, one of those rare creatures, a millionairess with a heart of gold (birthday and Christmas presents for every child in sight) had arrived in Spain in a ranch mink (a bargain at £12,000) and mink hat to match (another bargain at a mere £500), and, with her beautiful teenage daughter, a merry-eyed blonde, had taken a horse-and-carriage ride up and down the Ramblas in Barcelona, while some of her 36 pieces of luggage were loaded onto the Ibiza boat.

Back at the hotel, Fortune had cried: 'Darling, I've lost my hat.'

'Forget it, Mum, the boat's leaving soon. It's gone forever now.'

Their finca in Ibiza had no water and no light, but even then they had not realised how primitive Ibiza was in the 60's.

The *'carniceria'* or butcher's shop displayed one local sausage, called *'sobresada'* They asked for lamb chops or a *'gigot'*, a leg of lamb. Strange sounds came from the garden and 20 minutes later the woman slapped down the leg of a sheep, the wool still attached, and they became vegetarian for several years afterwards.

An Aperitif

It was four years before the ladies again saw the lights of the Ramblas and slept in soft beds in the Orientale hotel in Barcelona, and as they stepped from the foyer and began to join the evening *paseo,* they saw, coming towards them at a brisk trot, the very same miniature cabman with his big whip and empty carriage touting for trade.

The horse was wearing Fortune's £500 hat. The cabman had cut two holes for the nag's ears. Hailing the cabman Fortune said: 'That's my mink hat your effing horse is wearing.' And the cabman, remembering the pair, gallantly offered to buy Fortune another hat.

In Wauna's bar, Fortune called: 'I'm buying today.

'Put it on my tab, George. Ah - hello there sailor... this calls for another drink, George. What are you having darling?' Fortune swiveled on her barstool to greet a short, wiry, fierce-eyed, bearded sailor who had entered the bar, dressed in filthy dungarees and a torn jersey.

'That's very nice of you, Fortune,' said Tristan Jones, who had a small former lifeboat, a solid clinker-built Lloyds A.1. oak-on-teak vessel that had once grazed the rocks of the Northumberland coast and now bore the legend: Dunkirk 1939. Neatly coiled snakes of expertly spliced rope on the deck denoted the skipper's proud seamanship.

'I could do with a wet me darlin'. I've bin tryin' to repair my diesel engine with bits of string and sealin' wax. My poor old boat looks like a Bulgarian sewage inspector's office, and my galley looks like the inside of a Worthington-Simpson bilge pump. I'll have a San Mig.'

A loud grumbling came from the corner cushions in the bar as Mad Mike clasped Urpa in his arms and she said: 'I lerv yoo...' and Mike's deep, broadcaster's voice replied: 'And I love you, too, baby.'

'And tonight,' Urpa said, 'Vee vill make zee bootiful lerv my darlink...'

'Right on, baby...'

'Jesus' said Tristan Jones. 'Look at them. Shall I compare thee to a summer's day?'

'Make love?' said Fortune Ford, 'They don't look as if they will make it to the taxi rank.'

'It's all right,' said George, polishing a whisky glass, 'I've ordered the ambulance for them.'

A small cockroach appeared over the edge of the bar, took one look at Doreen, and started to flee. She banged her handbag down hard on it.

'Now look what you've done,' said George, inspecting the tiny corpse. 'You've killed Ermintrude.'

'Friend of yours?' asked Doreen, sipping her vodka and tonic.

'I've been training her up all winter for the circus. Poor little Ermintrude.' said George, flicking the remains into an ashtray and then into an refuse bin.

'There are plenty more where she came from,' said Doreen.

'Oh are there, sarky? You try keeping a Spanish bar free of cockroaches. Old Wauna goes potty if she sees one. I spray the place every morning but it's no good. You know the way Sandy in Santa Eulalia beats flies out of his bar with a tea-cloth if one dares to enter - well, that's the way Wauna feels about *cucarachas*.'

'That's the answer,' said Doreen.

'To what?'

'Where do flies go in the winter? They come here - to Ibiza. And talking about flies... look at yours.'

'Oops,' said George looking down and then zipping up. 'Sorry about that.' 'Don't worry about it,' said Doreen. 'As old Churchill once said: 'A dead bird can't fall out of its nest.''

'Oh yeah - and I've had enough of your lip. You need a zipper on your mouth. If music was bullshit you'd be a brass band...'

'Now stop it, you two,' said Fortune from the other corner. 'I know you really love each other...'

'What?' Doreen coughed, choking, and her loose tooth fell onto the floor of the bar. She eased herself off the bar stool and bent down to pick it up. She was about to pop it back into the gap.

'Don't put your tooth back, Doreen. It's been on the dirty floor...'

Doreen paused with the crown between thumb and forefinger.

'Wash it first, darling, for God's sake.' said Fortune.

'Oh, yes,' said Doreen, and absentmindedly swished the crown around in her vodka and tonic and then fixed the molar into her gap. George and Fortune watched, fascinated, as she then took a sip from the glass.

'Bloody 'ell.'

'What's wrong now?' asked Doreen.

'Your notions of hygiene are, to say the least, bizarre...'

'That's funny - coming from you, the Cockroach King of the Calle Mayor...'

'Right, that's it, Doreen. I've had enough insults from you for one day. Piss off.'

'I will. Don't worry. I'll take my overdraft elsewhere,' said Doreen, standing up and adjusting her skirt. She opened her voluminous handbag and took out a screw-cap jar, opened it, poured her vodka and tonic into the jar, screwed on the cap, and pushed her empty glass towards George.

'Go on - OUT!' shouted George.

'When he escorted your Mum to the plane, Fortune, you said how sweet they looked, George walking with your Mum hand in hand. It was actually hand in handbag.'

'OUT!' shouted George making to come around the counter and reaching for an Irish Shillelagh that hung on a leather strap behind the bar and sometimes used by Wauna to curb the ardor of Spanish building workers on their Sunday night binge.

As Doreen scuttled out of the bar she almost knocked over a tall, skinny, bespectacled Dutchman.

Hank, aged nineteen, was a draft dodger from the Dutch Army and was employed by one of the tourist hotels to call out the numbers in the Tombola game on Saturday nights and to operate the film projector in the hotel cinema. Seeking advice from Tristan Jones on the mysteries of the Tombola he had been told: 'It's called Housey-Housey in the Royal Navy, Hank. It's simple, like all the numbers have a name, such as Number Ten is either Bacon and Egg or Downing Street...'

'Bacon and Egg?' said Hank.

'Yes. Like the slice of bacon is the number one and the zero is an egg.'

'An egg.'

'Yes. Don't you see? It's easy. You've got Legs Eleven, then thirteen is Unlucky for Some, and Twenty One is Key of the Door, then you've got Doctor's Orders, Top of the House, Clickety Click all the sixes...'

'Hang on a minute, hang on a minute, Captain, my head is going for a swim. You write it all down please,' Hank had said, bewildered.

Now, as he entered Wauna's bar, Tristan Jones called out to him: 'How's it going Hank? You still doing the Tombola?'

'Yes, It's good, no problem. The British tourists come up to me after and ask me where I learnt my English which is so fluent, so colloquial.' Hank signaled to George with his hand pulling down on a pump, indicated that he wanted a draught beer. 'So I say all Dutchmen speak English like that, and other languages too, like French, German, Spanish, and they say 'That's amazing,' and I say no, we have to because nobody speaks Dutch.'

'But you got the hang of the Tombola slang, Hank?'

'Sure Captain. Number Ten - Sailor's breakfast. You got it wrong, you said bacon and egg, but a tourist put me right.'

'You're right Hank, but a sailor's breakfast is a cigarette and a cup of tea, the cigarette being number one, and the zero the cup of tea.'

'*Doppferdommer,* Captain, don't start again. I have already problems with German tourists at the hotel.'

'They don't understand the slang?'

'No it's not that. They don't play Tombola. It's the English films they don't like. Before it was all English in the hotel. Now some Germans get Neckerman package tours here. One big fat bastard came up to me last night and said: 'Hey, Dutchman what the hell do you think you are playing at? Three night I have been on holiday in this hotel with my wife and two children. The first night you show 'The Heroes of Telmark', the second night you show 'Where Eagles Dare' and the third night you show 'The Longest Day'. Every night we watch Germans being slaughtered. What kind of holiday do you think this is for us?''

'I don't know who chooses those films, Hank, but I did hear some package tourists went home complaining that they had battle fatigue,' said Tristan Jones 'and talking of battle fatigue, how are things going in Holland for you?'

'The bloody army are still after me. They want to put me in a monkey suit and cut my hair off.'

'Are you working tonight?'

'No, Captain. Night off. Why?'

'Deaf Henry's boat's in trouble. He tells me it took a bashin' against the harbour wall in Formentera during that storm last week. Wants me to sail over and take a look at her. I'm lookin' for a couple of likely lads to sail with me. I've got my writer friend here that I'm teaching to sail. That's one volunteer. I need another.'

'I'll sail with you, Tris,' said George who had been listening.

'I thought you were working three bars.'

'Only two today. I just heard the cops came round and ordered the boss of the Whisky-a-Go-Go to smarten the place up ready for this tourist boat that's coming in tomorrow, so I'm off tonight.'

'Can you sail a boat, George?'

'Sure, I was in the Royal Navy, you know.'

'Is that right? Well, I'll be handcuffed to a chicken's prick, I never knew that, George.'

George turned to serve a customer and Tristan Jones finished his beer. 'Right, then,' he said, banging his glass on the small, oblong bar towel advertising English beer, 'that's three crew aboard. I'm off to tinker with that engine. We'll have a wet before we cast off, mates.'

When he had gone, George took a jug of cold tea out of the refrigerator and reached up the shelf behind him and took a Chivas Regal bottle and uncorked it.

'Getting Wauna's sherbet ready, darling?' asked Fortune, laughing.

'Shhh... nobody's supposed to know about this,' said George, topping up the bottle which already contained a small amount of tea.

'You pee in that, don't you, George?' Fortune laughed.

George looked hurt. 'Now, then, darling, we'll fall out if you spread wicked rumours like that.' George chuckled as he poured. 'And I don't want to lose my best customer.'

Fortune winked at him and took out a small mirror and snapped her expensive handbag shut. George replaced the bottle and said to Fortune: 'How's it look today?' as she applied a little lipstick.

'Don't ask, darling. As Tallulah Bankhead said: 'They just don't make mirrors like they used to."

A mountain of flesh, her hips almost as wide as the door posts, appeared and paused on the threshold. It was Wauna, the owner of the bar, blonde hair thinning, bright blue eyes flashing as they regarded her customers within.

'Bit quiet in here, isn't it darling?' she called to George, who was putting on his coat, preparing to leave for his next stint at another bar. 'I'm getting a bit worried about this place. Business is dropping off. There hasn't been a good fight in here for three weeks.'

She placed her huge straw bag on the counter, nodding to Fortune's greeting. Bottles clinked in the bag. They contained cheap draught spirits - gin, vodka, cognac and even draught *cointreau* - which she would use to top up the bottles on the shelves. Only old regulars could detect the rot-gut booze when mixed with tomato juice in a 'Bloody Mary' or when bitter lemon or tonic was sloshed onto it in the glass. Regulars didn't drink *corriente* spirits, but pointed to the real bottles which were kept for discerning customers who knew the tricks of the trade. Wauna had once placed a notice on the door of her bar, proudly proclaiming:

OUR ICE IS MADE FROM REAL MINERAL WATER

Someone had written underneath:

SO IS YOUR GIN

'Any money in the till today, darling?' she asked George as he took the straw bag and Wauna squeezed her huge frame through the gap between the counter and the wall. 'Or are they all doing a Deaf Henry?'

George laughed as he slipped her the book containing a record of all the drinks that had been charged that day. George liked to tell visitors the story of Deaf Henry's *cuenta*.

Henry's tastes were modest. He lived aboard his tiny ketch in the harbour when it was not in Formentera harbour, and took a *cafe con leche*, an *ensemada,* the famous 'fried air', in the morning, sipped an *apertif* at noon, ate aboard his boat, and took a cognac as a *digestif* before returning aboard for a siesta. A few beers in the evening would also be marked up by the bar owner, who had complete faith in Henry's promise to pay, and had not once asked him about the very substantial account during the seven years he had kept it in an exercise book marked *'Don Henri, Ingles'*. It was also doubtful if he had ever asked Deaf Henry, or anyone else, for his customer's surname. If anyone had the temerity to mention the Seven Year Cuenta, they would be told: 'Don Henri is an English gentleman. He has promised to pay and I trust him absolutely.'

It was Henry's boat, a battered little unseaworthy construction of rotting, leaking planks that Tristan Jones had been asked to check on that night, for Deaf Henry had a fantasy that one day he would sail his wooden sieve up the Nile and drop anchor and visit the Temples of Abu Simbal. It was a fantasy worthy of the island of Ibiza.

Tristan Jones also had a fantasy: that one day he would sail on every major lake in the world by ballooning overland to reach them, in a small, lightweight yacht acting as the basket. His other, more practical, ambition was to sail on the Dead Sea 1,310 feet below sea level then take his boat to Lake Titicaca, thus entering the Guinness book of Records as the sailor on the lowest and highest water levels in the world.

The grizzled skipper had another reason for wanting to go to Lake Titicaca in Bolivia: a French yachtsman had boasted in Le Havre that his new boat had the highest mast in the world, and Tristan Jones wanted to send him a postcard from Titicaca claiming that *his* mast was the tallest, and giving the height, 12,506 feet, to prove it.

George the barman also had a fantasy: that one day he would be slim enough to go up Piss Alley, the short cut between the Calle Mayor and the Calle de la Virgen where his next bar was located. This fetid alley, a tall tunnel between the walls of the houses, could be used as a short cut by average weight men turning sideways and holding the breath as they ran up or down towards the fresh air. Men staggering between bars in the Street of the Virgin would pause to use it as a public toilet, making it dangerously slippery, especially on Sunday the Spaniards day of rest, recreation and pub crawling.

Wauna flicked her ash into her favourite 100 Pipers ashtray, advertising the Scotch whisky which held stage in the centre of the bar and looked with approval at George's work for he had polished it ready for her arrival and above it lay an array of sparkling glasses.

'Has that old bull-dyke Pat the Rat been in here today, George?' Wauna asked.

'No way,' said George, putting on his coat and hitching his straw *cesta* onto his shoulder. Wauna moved closer to him, trying to see if there was anything in the basket that should not be there. 'She wouldn't dare set foot in here, Wauna,' said George, watching Wauna watching the gap in the *cesta*. 'She knows she's barred for life for what she said to you about there being 'many a slip twixt...''

'Dykes? Dykes?' said Fortune from her corner, jangling her gold bracelets. 'We call them ditches in England.'

'That old bat should be put in a ditch and the ditch filled in,' said Wauna, perusing the Credit Book and working out how much she was owed for that day. 'They should have kept her in the slammer where she belongs.'

Wauna was referring to the prison sentence passed on Pat the Rat in South Africa. As an aggressive and vociferous campaigner against Apartheid she had discovered that the city planners had built two sewage systems, one servicing the black community and one for the white community, the pipes separate so that white waste matter would not mix with black. Her scornful denunciation of the architects of this scheme brought a heavy prison term during which she attempted to commit suicide by drinking rat poison. The attempt failed because Pat the Rat - hence the name - had the metabolism of a uranium burner and survived the attempt on her own life.

'And what about that farter-buster?' said Wauna as George made for the door, 'has he been in here?'

'What, you mean Doris Karloff?' said George, 'She wouldn't dare, not if she doesn't want a mouthful of signet rings. Besides, she's hanging out with Ewald the Hamburg Iron, they're hoping to open up a men-only bar in the old town. They said it's going to be the only bar in Spain where men can dance with men.'

'Ha,' laughed Wauna shortly. 'If they get permission for that, my name's Franco.'

'They got a third partner - Youssef.'

'What - Florence of Arabia? That little Salamanca. And who's keeping the books? Heinz?'

George laughed at Wauna's referring to Ewald's long-suffering dog. In April, when a group of old Nazis living in Madrid celebrated the birthday of Adolf Hitler by attending a requiem mass in a church cordoned off by *Guardia Civil*, a chalked notice had appeared on the door of the Taverna bar: HAPPY BIRTHDAY HEINZ. Ewald had arrived, dragging Heinz behind him and protested 'But it's not Heinz's birthday.'

It was explained to Ewald that the general consensus of opinion was that Heinz, who gave currency to the expression 'hangdog look' was in fact a reincarnation of *Der Fuhrer*. The punishment for Hitler's early crimes - not the bigger ones, for which he would be punished later - was to be sent back to earth as Ewald's dog.

'But it's not his birthday,' said Ewald, failing to see the point of the sarcasm. 'I think he was born in August.'

George vanished through the doorway in the direction of the Street of the Virgin, and within minutes of his disappearance Doreen returned. She had been watching from Juanito's bar on the corner until the coast was clear.

'Hello Wauna,' cried Doreen, 'you're looking very nice today.'

'When are you going to pay your tab?' Wauna asked.

'I'm getting my uncle's cheque next week,' said Doreen.

'Blimey,' said Wauna. 'Where have I heard that before?'

'The cheque's in the post. Do me a favour, darling. My name's Huggins, not Muggins.'

'Yes, and my name's Craft, not Daft. I've talked him into doubling my allowance because the cost of living is going up in Spain.'

'What's that on your hat?' Wauna asked, pointing to a little bunch of violets Doreen had pinned to her black straw cartwheel hat.

'Violets, dearie... lovely violets... a little present from Speedy Gonzales in the flower shop opposite. He likes to pinch my arse.'

'Well, there's plenty of it.'

'Listen to who's talking.'

'Here - stop it you two - you're always bickering, but I know you really love each other...'

'Georgy-Porgey can't get up Piss Alley and with a bum as wide as yours, you can scarcely squeeze down Avenida Espana,' snapped Doreen, referring to the wide main road that led out of town.

'There's a rumour,' said Wauna, staring hard at Doreen's flower bedecked hat, 'that you wear a corset on each thigh.'

'Now stop it. Wauna - give everyone a drink, on my tab. What are you having, Doreen?'

'Gin and Tonic, Fortune, thanks.'

Wauna, who was still staring at Doreen's hat, noticed that Fortune was also beginning to look curiously at the little bunch of violets that the shopkeeper had pinned on. Wauna flashed a look of warning to Fortune not to say anything, for they had noticed a little snail had crawled out of the bunch of violets and was starting to make a tour of the cartwheel hat, leaving a little trail of glistening slime in its wake.

'And what about that other farter-buster - or is it the other way round - tee hee - Bonnie Ronnie. I bet he hasn't dared show his face here. Where's he working now? Pretty Pat's?'

'No,' said Doreen, 'He got the tin-tack.'

'So what did Pat sack him for?'

'Same reason you barred him - graffiti on the netty wall,' said Doreen. 'Same slogan, too. Funny though isn't it?'

'I don't think it's funny at all - I think it's disgusting. I mean, I have respectable English visitors coming in here, and if they see that kind of filth on my toilet wall, I'll lose customers. I'm in business, darling, after all.'

'Those arse-holes wouldn't understand it anyway,' said Doreen, 'They'd think the cook had written it up.'

'Enlighten me, girls, for Chrissake,' said Fortune. 'What did he write?'

'Too Many Cocks Spoil the Breath,' said Doreen.

'Ha Ha,' laughed Fortune. 'He's a caution that Ronnie. Did you hear about him with the French tourist when he was helping George out in the Whisky? I can't remember the details of the prices and everything but this French gang ordered a gin and tonic, a Cuba Libre, two San Miguels and a hierbas, and when the Frogs asked *'Combien*?' Ronnie said: *'Soixante Neuf pesetas, s'il vous plait.'*

'George nearly choked. He pulled Bonnie Ronnie aside and said: 'Ronnie, you berk. What do you think you're playing at? A G.T., a Cuba Libre, two San Miguels and a hierbas... that's... are you out of your mind? You only charged sixty nine pesetas.'

'That's right, *soixante neuf*,' Ronnie said. 'It's the only French I know.'

'Do you think it was Ronnie who sent that porno parcel?'

Wauna's question to Doreen and Fortune was interrupted by the arrival of a neatly dressed Spaniard, with a neat collar and military tie, neatly clipped moustache, highly polished shoes and well-creased trousers.

'Buenos tardes, senoras y senoritas,' said the dapper little man, looking around and flinching slightly at the sight of Mad Mike and Urpa asleep in one corner and Fatty the dog asleep in the other.

'Hello, mate', said Doreen.

'Muy buenos, senor,' said Wauna, smiling her best businesswoman's smile.

'Hay Chivas?' said the Spaniard.

'Certainly, sir,' said Wauna in English, her smile widening as she reached for the bottle of Chivas Regal on the shelf behind her.

'Un doble, por favor.'

'A double? Certainly sir.'

'Colonel. I am the new Colonel of the barracks here. Colonel Fernando Martinez Hidalgo Diaz, tenth regiment of the Cavalry, at your service, Madame.'

Wauna flinched at his calling her 'Madame'. She had lived with

and loved an Indian princess called Indira, a Brahmin high-caste who
was the 'Madame' of the union, for many years and Wauna was proud
of her butchness and toughness. She had laid out Tristan Jones with a
right hook when he was being naughty in the bar (he had returned an
hour later with a swollen jaw and hurled a bicycle through the open
door, scattering customers and fleeing as he yelled: 'Unfair to British
Seamen.'

'Have one yourself,' said the little Colonel, and Wauna's big wide
smile returned as she reached for the other Chivas Regal bottle on the
shelf below.

Fortune and Doreen watched as Wauna poured herself a measure
from the other Chivas Regal bottle - 'I'll just have a small one, darling,
my figure, you know,' she winked at the smiling Colonel and moved
her hands over the shape which was the female version of the Michelin
Man. Fortune and Doreen exchanged glances as she sipped and made
a face.

As Fortune made her slow and stately passage to the toilet she
whispered in Doreen's ear: 'That's not *Darjeeling* it's *George darling*.'

'What are you two whispering about,' said Wauna, accepting the
Colonel's proffered note and giving him her full attention while he
exercised his vocal chords, showing off his deep, masculine, sonorous
voice and Castilian Spanish.

A sudden wind battered the half open door.

'There's a storm coming,' said Wauna. 'Shut that door, Doreen,
there's a pet.'

'What's the point?' said Doreen, looking at the doorway. 'There's
more than a storm coming - here's Steve Primero.'

'Oh, shit,' said Wauna, then put her fingers to her thin lips: 'Sorry
Darling, I mean Colonel. Excuse my French.'

'That fucking Jaime is going to be a millionaire soon if he keeps on
giving me itty-bitty portions like he gave me today,' shouted Steve,
thrusting towards the bar in his British Fireman's overcoat. 'I asked for
lengua and he gave me two slices of tongue the size of this goddam
purse,' he flung his leather purse onto the counter and took some coins
out of it.

'Gin,' he said shortly.

'I don't know why you go there, darling. I cook at home, it's much better. Why don't you do the same?' said Wauna, chinking glasses with the dapper, smiling Colonel who was regarding, with supercilious scorn, Steve Primero's appearance.

'Cook at home? Me?' he called. 'Why it takes me all my time to make bacon and eggs, and then there's the washing up. Me? Cook? Can you imagine me gutting a fish or taking the entrails out of a chicken. Ugh. Anyway, by the time you'd bought the food and wasted time shopping, you may as well go to the restaurant. You know what I saw in a shop today? Wall safes! Wall safes! Can you imagine this lot? When I came here they didn't have a pot to piss in. They couldn't afford a *Diario* to wipe their asses on. Now they're hunting for scented toilet paper and investing in wall safes.'

'You can buy take away food and heat it in the oven.'

'Heat the oven - in the stove? I don't know how the goddam stove lights. I'm not a practical man, Wauna. I have to get a man up to my place to change a light bulb or mend a fuse. I have a guy come up and change my typewriter ribbon.'

'How often's that?' Doreen asked. 'Every ten years ?'

'Smartass,' said Steve. He smiled a little smile. 'You know that's funny. It's about right, as well. The rarest sight in the world must be a used typewriter ribbon in the garbage can in Ibiza.'

'I know a rarer sight,' said Doreen, 'you buying a round of drinks.'

'Why you black faced bog-Irish bitch...'

'Hey, cut it out you two, will you. This is a respectable bar.' She turned to the little Colonel who was on his second double whisky, and smiled at him. 'Just high spirits, Colonel, don't you take any notice of them.'

'Oh, she's right, of course,' said the Colonel in perfect English. There was a moment's silence in the bar while it sank in that he had understood all that was said.

'You speak good English, Colonel,' said Wauna.

'I spent a year at Sandhurst in England.'

'With the Coldcream guards?' asked Steve.

'You can't expect a Jew to buy a drink,' said the Colonel, 'or to buy a bar of soap. This one looks as if he needs a good wash. Like most of his race...'

'Hold on a minute, Mister,' said Wauna, noting that Steve was about to let loose with a stream of verbal abuse, 'you can't say that about the great Jewish people.'

'Oh can't I?' said the Colonel. 'I am the Commander of the Garrison here. Who's going to stop me?' He looked expectantly at Steve Primero.

'I am, darling,' said Wauna, and she picked up the empty Gordon's Gin bottle (she drained it into Steve's glass for good measure) and brought it down smartly on the Colonel's head, the pieces of glass scattering over the floor. In the deadly silence that followed, only the muffled tones of the Beatles singing: 'She loves you, yeah, yeah, yeah...' could be heard from the record player behind the bar.

The Colonel stood, stiff with dignity and hurt pride, as a trickle of blood ran onto his beautifully laundered shirt. His pride as shattered as the gin bottle, he stood for a moment, flicked a little pink tongue out to taste his own blood, then turned on his heel, as if on a parade ground, and walked stiffly out of the bar and into the street.

'Holy shit,' said Steve Primero, breaking the silence, 'now you've gone and done it, Wauna.'

'All that injured pride,' said Doreen. 'Did you see it? You better skidaddle, Wauna, before the Old Bill come charging down here to nick you for assault and battery.'

'Yes, go on, Wauna, go home, before there's trouble. You can't hit a Spanish officer like that and get away with it.'

'Not me, darling,' said Wauna, finishing off the Chivas Regal the Colonel had left in his glass. 'He won't do a damn thing. Do you think a Spanish Colonel is going to go down to the police station and complain that a woman hit him? It would hurt his macho pride more than that cut on his head, darling, believe you me.'

Just then the door opened and Tristan Jones came in, shaking rain off his oilskin cape.

'Force nine and blowing up,' he said, making for the bar. 'Where's my crew?'

'Here they come now,' said Doreen. 'I'm off,' she added swallowing her drink quickly and sidling out past a glaring George and bespectacled Hank, looking like two drowned rats.

'You mean to say you're still going? In this!' said George, aiming a kick at the retreating behind of Doreen as she made her hasty exit.

'It's a bloody storm out there, Captain,' said Hank.

'Look at them,' said Tristan Jones, scornfully, pulling at McGinn's elbow. 'You should put them in a book. They've got all the moral fibre of a broken legged grasshopper.'

'Here...' George started to protest at the insult.

'I thought you said you were in the Royal Navy?'

'I was.'

'Well cast off , mate, and don't listen to Van Trompe's pipe cleaner here,' he sneered.

'No need to be rude,' George said, smiling.

'Van Trompe? Van Trompe?' queried Hank.

'Yes. Heard of him, have you? The Dutchman's Pride?'

Tristan Jones pointed to the slumped figure of Mad Mike, arm around Urpa's shoulder, just coming back to life and murmuring deeply: 'Lessgohomebaby. We gonnaballallni' baby...'

'If you don't watch out, you'll end up like that matey. Now what were the words again to Van Trompe? I forget.'

''Van Trompe was an Admiral, brave and bold, the Dutchmen's pride was he...'' McGinn said. ''He cried Yo-ho and away we'll go...''

'No that's what the British sang, 'So he cried yo-ho, and away we'll go, come aboard Merry Men with me... and we'll drive this Dutchman down below, to the bottom of his Zuider Zee... to the bottom of his Zuider Zee. Van Trompe attached a whip to the top of his mast to whip the British off the seven seas, but Drake attached a broom to his mast to sweep the seas clean of the lot...''

'I'm ready when you are, Captain,' said Hank, wiping the steam from his spectacles.

The little Cresswell, with its FOR SALE sign, was battered by the harbour swell, the board announcing to all the world that she had been at Dunkirk rescuing British soldiers was made slightly askew by the wind.

'Cast off me hearties,' yelled Jones, starting up his engine.

'Jesus, where's his parrot?' muttered George, slipping the green plastic mooring line and jumping nimbly aboard as the Cresswell's bow was pointed seaward.

Black, ominous thunderheads crashed in over the old town outlining the cathedral tower and a wind battered driftwood against the rocks by the Mole. Rain slashed across the boat almost obscuring the light of Talamanca lighthouse off to the left. A Spaniard who had been battling to put out an extra anchor shook his fist and yelled: *'Locos. Ingles locos.'*

Jones glared with wild dark eyes and gave him the prongs.

The Spaniard responded to the two-finger insult with his own country's insult, left hand smacked inside raised right arm with clenched fist.

'Marinero della tierra.' Jones shouted the gravest insult to a Spanish seaman - calling him a land-sailor.

'I keel you when you corm back, *cono.*' the sailor shouted.

'You and whose army, mate?'

The last cry was flung away with the wind as the little Cresswell's bows raised as the first big wave hit her.

'Steer two-nine-six,' shouted Jones.

'Aye-aye,' McGinn called trying to keep the compass needle straight on the bearing.

'Coming about....,' Jones yelled.

'You're not putting bloody sail in this are you,' George cried.

'We're going across on the jib, mate. You don't think I'm going to waste good diesel fuel, do you?'

The little boat calmed as he put her into the wind and then he went fo'ard to pull up the jib and sent her scudding in the direction of Formentera.

'Come on, you little beauty,' Jones called. 'Show 'em what you can do, me darlin''

'Jeez - look at us go,' said George.

'Like a bat out of hell, mate,' shouted Jones as the Cresswell tore into the waves and battered forward through the wall of water, sending spray over the cockpit.

By now they were skimming over water beneath which lay a sunken Roman road, visible in daylight, but now all was black with the occasional flash of the Formentera light and Es Palmador lying ghostly and dark in the distance.

George hung on to the security rail, his face poking out of the dripping Sou'wester that Jones had issued to his scratch crew. Hank was below, clinging onto the sides of the Captain's bunk staring myopically at the rattling teacups on hooks above the little galley and groaning at each shudder of the Cresswell's timbers.

Jones glanced at the needle. He would not take the wheel, having been paid for sailing lessons, and he would insist that his pupil, McGinn, got practical experience no matter what the weather or conditions were like. He had boasted that he had trained his cabin boy to take apart and reassemble a diesel engine while blindfolded so that he could do repairs at night in an emergency.

'George, don't sit there like a spare prick at a wedding, lash the boom. I don't want any accidents. I once took a boat across the Atlantic with three officers as crew - two Americans and a Dane. The two most useless things aboard a sailing boat are a wheelbarrow and a naval officer. The Dane took the boom across his head when we were two days out. On the third day he was actin' kind of funny, but I knew he was round the twist on the fourth day when I awoke to find him varnishing my socks.'

George guffawed as he made the boom secure.

'It's not funny, mate. We had to heave to in the Azores and the American Air Force flew him back to a funny farm.'

There was a crash below and Hank slithered from the bunk and fell amongst the pots and pans rolling around on the floor of the cabin.

'What's that noise?' shouted Jones, peering down the open hatchway at the sprawled figure below.

'The bloody tin of biscuits, Skipper,' shouted Hank.

'My biscuits? Pick 'em up then, and put them back in the box.' Hank scrabbled around picking up the Crawford's varieties.

'That's it, Captain,' shouted Hank.

'Right - now make a cup of tea.'

'A cup of bloody tea?' Hank choked on the words.

'No, mate, a cup of good tea - three spoonfuls and one for the pot. Tea you could trot a mouse on. Tea you could sail a flat iron over. Tea you could stand the bloody spoon in. Get on with it.'

Hank busied himself below, filling the kettle and placing it on the gas burner in its swaying cradle.

'And don't forget to warm the pot' yelled Jones into the hatch. He turned to George who still clung to the safety rail stanchion looking miserable in the heavy weather gear. 'Once I was trying to get back to Le Havre in a storm, George, with two Frenchmen charterers aboard when suddenly a giant wave hit us and all hell was let loose. The 'oggin came pouring down the hatch onto these two Frenchies below. You should have seen the state of that galley, mate. Everything in it had fallen onto the Frogs and it was awash below, knee deep in sea water. It was a filthy night, black as a guardsman's boot, and the storm was knocking seven bells of shit out of us and the Frogs thought they were definitely en route to Davey Jones's locker. 'What do we do now, Captain?' one of them shouted. 'Make a cup of tea,' I yelled back. You should have seen their faces, George, you'd have thought I'd asked them to sign the pledge.'

Miraculously, a few minutes later Hank produced four mugs of tea and passed three of them up through the hatch.

'Blimey,' said George, looking at his watch, 'do you realise we're making better time than the Formentera ferry?'

'I should hope so, mate. I'll outrun that floating plastic soap-dish anytime. Aah...' he shouted, slinging the tea over the side, 'You call that tea, Hank? That's gnat's piss.'

'You said one for the pot, skipper.'

'Three plus one for the pot - that's four you nit. Bloody useless Dutchman. The only thing the Dutch ever invented was the Dutch cap.'

'Oh?' shouted Hank below, 'and what about our cheese?'

Suddenly the shrieking wind drowned the laughter of Tristan and George and tore the jib to shreds.

'Start the engine, Hank,' yelled Jones.

'Aye, aye, sir,' Hank called back and there was a rumbling and a shuddering as the ancient diesel sparked briefly into life and died. Jones swung himself below. 'I don't believe it. We're out of fuel. There's a blasted leak. Damnation, I've got no jury rig, no spare jib. George - get your arse down here and help me. There's a British Seagull in the for'ard dodger. Best little engine ever made. Coming about,' yelled Jones, 'take her off the wind, this is no good, she's abaft the beam and we'll be on Formentera rocks in a minute.' He grabbed the wheel as George went below and she keeled over, sending George and Hank flying against the bunks as Jones brought her round and faced her to the wind.

'Get that engine up here or we'll never get to San Francisco harbour tonight.'

'It's fallen on my leg,' shouted George, struggling beneath the weight of the engine.

'Leg? Leg' called Jones, 'you don't need legs. Yachtsmen don't need legs, only arms, to pull up a sail and an anchor. Go on, pull Hank,

P-U-L-L - like you're pulling a storm trooper off your mother.'

They struggled up and fixed the little engine to the beam and with one swift pull, George started the motor.

'Coming about.' said Jones at the wheel.

'Lee-o,' called George.

'Put your change in your other pocket,' yelled Jones, as the Cresswell turned and dipped, her mast almost in the water as she righted herself and Jones pointed her bows at the entrance to the harbour. The little engine spluttered away and they chugged with the wind into the shelter of the harbour, where Deaf Henry's boat, which looked as if he had made it from discarded orange boxes, lay with its clinker-built hull in splinters.

'What are we going to do about that?' George asked, looking sorrowfully at the little wreck.

Jones tapped the barometer. 'Nothing, mate. Get your heads down and kip. This storm will abate by morning. You get the boat back to the Holy Island tomorrow and I'll stay and get her dragged up and caulked for Henry. Look at her timbers, mate - rotten. Sail to the Nile with that? You might as well try an' strike a match on a bar of soap.'

'Poor Henry,' said George.

'By the way, I meant to ask you - what did you do in the Navy, George? You weren't in Boats*, were you?'

'No, I wasn't in Boats. Most ex-submariners are head-bangers, aren't they? I was a sick bay Tiffy.' **

'A sick bay Tiffy? You tell me now? I've got a scribbler-johnny, a sick bay Tiffy and a Dutch draft-dodger as crew on a night like this?' Jones looked skywards. 'I'll say one thing: somebody up there likes us.'

*Boats: Submarines   ** Sick bay Tiffy: Male nurse

CHAPTER 14

Fakers

MOST of the foreign bars in the town opened at eleven in the morning, but the George and Dragon, also known as the *Jorge y Dragon*, opened at ten thirty. Being a British-owned bar, Spanish law insisted on the name being in Spanish, or in special cases, both languages. A bar owner called Jack put up a sign JACK'S BAR but the police made him change it to JUAN JACK'S BAR, but they could do nothing about WINSTON'S as there was no Spanish equivalent to the name.

George popped his head into the George and Dragon where the new English barman was filling a straw bag with empty bottles. 'We're not open yet, mate,' said Olly the barman. 'I've got to go and get the *garrafa* plonk in these bottles - but you can have a drink while you're waiting.'

'Waiting for what?' asked George.

'Waiting for me to open,' said Olly.

'OK, I'll have a *hierbas*,' said George. 'Seen Pete the Parrot?' he asked, settling on a bar stool, 'or his sexy, Scandinavian wife?'

'No, they're out of town today. Funny you should ask 'cos I just heard a funny story from his brother Paul. You know Pete has a parrot in his flat? And Paul lives in the flat above? Well the parrot learned to imitate the wife while Pete was on the job, but even better, it started to imitate the bedsprings, a perfect reproduction, squeak, squeak, squeak. Parrots are amazing birds, really.'

'Yes, true. I know a few stories about parrots,' said George.

'Anyway, Paul woke up, or was woken up by the sound of squeaking. He tried to get back to sleep but he couldn't. He knew his brother and his wife were away in Barcelona for a shopping trip and there was no one in the flat below. It was impossible to get back to sleep so he tried to work out what the squeaking could be. Finally he got up about three thirty a.m. with a torch and went out with an oil can and oiled all the hinges on the shutters, the *Persianas,* that had been left open and were swinging in the wind, then closed them all up. As soon as he closed his eyes the squeaking started again. He got the key to his brother's flat and went in and there was Onan the parrot squeaking away imitating the bedsprings.'

'Is that its name? Onan?'

'Yeah, quite a few parrots are called Onan because...'

'They scatter their seed upon the ground, I know. I've read the Bible too. A long time ago, mind you...'

'Mind the shop, George, I'm just popping round to the *Bodega.'*

A few minutes after Olly left to fill his bottles Madrilas came down the steps, wearing paint-spattered trousers and stained shirt. He shook hands with George and asked if the boss was in, explaining that he had been commissioned to paint the bar, whitening the walls and staining and varnishing the beams ready for the tourist season starting. When Olly returned and confirmed that Pete was away, Madrilas said he could do the job that night, working till dawn, but he had to have the key.

'I give the key to you, Madrilas, there's no problem. You start work when I close at three a.m. and you finish by eight.'

Madrilas nodded acquiescence, looking furtively at the array of bottles on the shelves, a pink tongue flicking nervously over parched lips.

'Drink?' Olly asked.

Madrilas brightened. *'Si, si cognac, por favor.'*

'Are you sure this is wise?' George said to Olly.

'What, giving him a drink?'

'No. Letting him paint the bar.'

'Pete's the boss. He's getting the work done half price.'

'Oh, that's all right then. Expect he'll drink the other half off those shelves. Don't you know about this guy?'

'Sante,' said Madrilas, affably toasting Olly and George.

'Cheers mate,' said Olly, wiping the bar and listening to George with cocked ear. 'He does love a sherbet, for sure.'

'Love sherbet? Giving him that cognac is like giving him a loaded revolver, mate. One is too many and a thousand is not enough. I came to one morning in the alcoholics ward of the *Beneficencia* and he was chained to the bed next to mine. Handcuffed and in leg-irons, matey. The nuns had done it to restrain his ardour. He'd tried to jump the *Madre Superiora* the night before and took eight of them to bolt him to the bed frame. He saw me in the next bed and asked what time Wauna's bar was opening. I hadn't the heart to tell him he was barred. After all, there he was, chained, handcuffed and manacled. I didn't want to hurt his feelings.'

'How come you were in there, George?'

'Oh, that was all to do with Speedy Gonzalez - you know the little dwarf speed-cop they had on the island last year? Well, you know how you hear things in bars? Some Ibicenco told me that Speedy didn't have a driving licence, that he'd never passed the driving exam, but he fancied himself in big boots as a speed cop, so they gave him the job. Trouble is he got too big for his boots.'

'What happened?'

'He came in just as I was closing, about five to three in the morning. I could see he was as pissed as an owl. You know, his boots looked as if he'd borrowed them from Action Man and they were covered with mud. I refused to serve him, so he waited outside until I closed then he arrested me. He pulled his gun on me, the lot. Mind you, I'd had a few behind the bar, naturally, but I wasn't as bad as him. They made me walk the line, touch my toes, touch my nose, balance on one foot, all the usual bullshit, and I passed with flying colours.

Then the little rat said I'd insulted his boss. I said I thought Heinrich Himmler was dead, and he did his nut, raging on about foreigners. So I told them he was drunk and they should test him and furthermore he was riding a police motor cycle without a driving licence. They loved it, of course. You know how coppers love to drop each other in? Well, he failed all the tests and couldn't produce a licence so they nicked him.'

'What's he doing now?'

'I dunno. Probably modeling for a garden gnome manufacturer or something. He's out of the police force, anyhow.'

Madrilas was addressing Olly in rapid Spanish and Olly asked George what he was saying.

'He's inviting you and me to eat with him today. *Poulet Basquez,* chicken Basque style with green peppers, onions, etcetera. Here in the bar.'

'He wants to cook it here?'

'No, eat it here. He prepares it on a big tray and puts it in the baker's oven around the corner. He's a good cook.'

'It's OK by me. What about you, George? Will you come?'

'Not on your life, mate. You asked me how come I was in the *Beneficencia* in the next bed to laughing boy here - I attended one of his Basque noshes and he produced a cocktail in an aluminium cooking pot consisting of every drink on all three shelves. I was arrested trying to get aboard a Russian cement boat in the harbour. The Guardia Civil thought I was trying to defect to Moscow, but I told them I just wanted a glass of vodka and some caviar with the Captain so they let me go. After they nicked Speedy I went on a bender, then they nicked me and they took me to the nuns' hospital to dry out.'

'OK, Madrilas - but NO DRINKING! OK?' Olly said.

'Madrilas looked pained. He put his hand over his heart and looked as if he were about to cry. *'No possible, senor. Mucho trabajo,'* he made the action of painting the ceiling and varnishing the beams and George gave him a sideways look.

'Anyway, have a good nosh - I'm going to open up next door. You might have a busy day, Olly. There's a tourist boat due in at midday with a few Yanks aboard, cruising the Med. So fill your ice trays up.'

George had been open only five minutes - just in time to take the cash out of the freezer box in the fridge - when he had his first customer. It was Urpa the Finn, looking bedraggled and unkempt, as if a platoon of infantry had marched over her by mistake on her way into town. Her hairstyle was what was known as the Cairn Terrier look - she peered through the light blonde tresses that obscured her vision, occasionally putting lower lip over upper lip and blowing upwards to get a better view of the bottles on the shelves. Her upper eyelids were heavy through lack of sleep and her mascara looked as if a little spiders had got into it by mistake then run off in several different directions.

'What can I haff to drink, George?' she asked in a voice like sandpaper being rubbed on a rusty gate. 'Anything you like, darling. You look as if you need an eye-opener. Had a rough night?'

'I haff a date here with a guy at eleven. I am early. Giff me a Ricard, George.'

'One Ricard, coming up,' said George, turning to put a tape on to liven the bar up. He knew of old that a lone foreign woman in a bar would attract young Spaniards in for a drink, especially as they could only see the back view, blonde hair, a fur trimmed tweed coat and kinky boots. The music was loud and George missed the faint thump as he reached to turn it down, then carefully poured a good, stiff measure of the *pastis* and filled a bowl with ice cubes for the water jug.

When he turned round to serve Urpa the bar was empty.

'Hello?' George said to himself, 'Where's she gone.'

He looked at the toilet door, but it was ajar. She wasn't in there. 'Urpa?' he called. 'Funny. She was here a second ago. Must have nipped out for some cigarettes. Ah, well, pity to waste a good drink.'

George topped up the drink and raised it to the notice board which held a dozen photos of customers. One, Cherokee Frank taking a great lump of steak from a grill with a two-pronged fork, looked as if he were about to do a heart transplant. 'Here's to us all,' said George. 'And here's to you, Georgie-boy, and may the skin of your arse never cover a banjo.'

As he finished off the Ricard he heard a groan from the other side of the bar. He would have had to climb onto the sink to see over so he went around by the open hatch.

Urpa lay in a heap of tweed, fur, hair and handbag between two bar stools and alongside the one she had fallen off when the first blast of music drowned out of the noise of the thud as she fell.

'Blimey, Urpa, I hope you're not driving,' said George, helping her to her feet and dusting down her coat.'

'Sorry, sorry, George, the bar stool slipped, they are not very good, these bar stools, you know.'

'Yes, I've told Wauna about that. It's this Spanish wood, you know, gets all wobbly, especially when you've had a few drinks. The old metal stools were much better, but she changed them. Are you sure it's a good idea for you to have a drink? You should have a Fernet Branca. That would pull you round.'

'I haff to meet a guy at eleven thirty. I think I am in luff, George, with this guy I met. Oh, it was so wonderful, George. OK, give me a furry banker.'

'It's a Fernet Branca, Urpa, not a furry banker. That sounds like one of the Gulbenkians. I like that, a furry banker. ''Ere 'oo's that over there, then? I don't know, looks like a furry banker to me...'

'George, you are talking to yourself.'

'Yes, it's a habit, darling. A habit acquired by most bartenders in Ibiza in winter. One Fernet Branca coming up.'

Urpa took Doreen's usual corner seat and hooked her handbag to one of the hooks placed on the underside of the bar.

'Have you been doing any painting recently, Urpa? Been to your studio this week, or last week?'

'No, I'm sick of it, painting, painting and nobody buys it anyhow. I'm sick of art, George.'

There was a sound in the open doorway and Mad Mike stood there, gazing into the interior of the bar, looking at first at Urpa, then at George, then at the bar stool in the far corner, the one usually occupied by Fortune. He shuffled towards it, lank shoulder length hair swinging over his G.I. Army shirt, flip-flopping as he made his slow way to the far corner stool and hauled himself up onto it. He glanced once again at Urpa, who was looking for something in her voluminous handbag, then beckoned to George with his right index finger and motioned him to lean closer.

'Jessurrs, George, what the hell happened yesterday? Man do I need a drink.' said Mike trying to keep his resonant voice down to a whisper.

George, attempting to lean towards Mike, had cringed back as a waft of breath like dragon's halitosis hit him in the face.

'Something to put the goddammed fire out, George, you know? Man, I've got a mouth like seven rows of rat-shit.'

'I dunno about that, mate. I think a couple of them stayed in there and died.'

'What's that, George? You gotta come closer, I can't hear you. What time have you got?'

'Twenty minutes past eleven, sir. Now what would you like to drink?'

'Thazz OK, I'm not late anyways. Hows about a Bushmills George, on the rocks with just a leetle beet of charge water to soften it up? Lissen - ' Mike lowered his voice 'has anybody been askin' for me this morning?'

'No, you're my second customer today and...'

'Thassalri' George, just gimme that mother-stompin' Bushmills before I die of thirst here.' He looked over in the direction of Urpa, staring at her. She looked back and averted her eyes, continuing to search her handbag. 'And George,' Mike called 'could you put the Stones on - after this tape, of course. Don't get me wrong, George, I like what you've got on now, but I'd just like to hear the Stones thassall.'

There was a loud shout in the doorway: 'Hey, George - has Fortune been in yet?' Steve Primero stood framed in the doorway, chromium N.F.S. buttons shining on the fireman's overcoat, waving a letter in the air.

'Not yet, Steve.'

'I've just had some amazing noos from the States. I've got a daughter! Would you believe it? They tell me after all these years. She's seventeen years of age, and her mother just broke the noos to her that I'm her father. She's living in Brooklyn. I'm going to post a letter'. He walked down the Calle Mayor in the direction of the post office, rereading the letter as he went.

'George,' Urpa called from her corner of the horseshoe bar. 'How much do I owe you for the drink - I can't remember its name.'

'That's all right, darling, it's on the house. No charge to regular customers for a hangover tonic. You spent enough in here yesterday, anyway.'

'I was in here yesterday? I'm afraid I had a lot of drinkie-winkies yesterday, George. Here's the money. I'm leaving.' She lowered her voice and said in an urgent whisper to George: 'That man keeps staring at me.'

George pushed the coins back across the counter, and Urpa pushed them back towards him, saying: 'It's a tip, for being kind.'

When she was gone, Mike called: 'Hit me again, George, with that magic Bushmills. Man, I dunno what's happening, but I'm supposed to have a date here this morning with some Skywegian broad I shacked up with last night. You know, through the rose coloured mists of time, I do believe I got engaged to be married last night and we planned to honeymoon in Florida, I think. Or was it Morocco?'

'What was her name?'

'Now George, don't ask me complicated questions. How would I know a thing like that?'

'Was it Urpa?'

'What? What kind of name is that? It sounds like something a baby would say when you smack it on the ass. Urpa... urpa...'

'Well, the lady you were with in here all yesterday afternoon and evening and the one you were necking with outside the Montesol and the one you were seen falling into a taxi with last night and asking the driver to take you to Grand Central Station and the driver said 'OK, Mike I know where you live' is the one who just walked out of here. She's called Urpa, a Finn, a painter and I suppose that would classify her as Skywegian as Tristan Jones calls them. Furthermore, she had a date in here with some guy..'

'Holy shit,' said Mike, putting his hand on his forehead.

Fortune Ford entered the bar laden down with straw baskets filled with fresh vegetables from the market, meat from the butcher, fresh flowers from the flower shop opposite, beads and bracelets and bangles jangling as she plonked herself on the barstool next to Mike.

'I'm exhausted, darling. What's everyone having to drink?' she said, hooking her handbag under the bar.

'I gotta get off this island, George,' said Mike, getting down from the barstool. 'Sorry I took your usual seat, Fortune. I gotta go.'

'Have a quick one, darling.'

'No, I'm off home. I think I've seen the light.'

'He staggered out of the door, followed by the anxious gaze of Fortune Ford.

'What's wrong with him?' she asked George.

'I think he's just had a broken engagement.' said George.

'Oh, the poor love. I'd have bought him a *cafe consolo* if I'd known that. I had to buy one for Doreen last night, darling. She was in tears when everyone was taking the Mickey out of her because of that snail crawling around her hat all evening and everyone knowing but her and laughing behind her back.'

'She was in here again, was she?'

'She comes in as soon as you leave, darling.'

'Did I see blood on the counter over there?'

'Yes, Wauna whacked some Spanish colonel with a gin bottle for making nasty cracks about Steve Primero. You should have seen the look on his face. We expected the Guardia or the Armada or the local cops to come charging down here but nothing happened, as Wauna predicted. Actually the police did come in here much later but it wasn't for that. They were checking everybody's papers. Nobody had any, of course. So they told us all to go home and return with our passports. No-one came back, of course and they waited in an empty bar until closing time.'

'Why should Doreen cry because a snail crawled around her hat?'

'That wasn't the reason she was crying. She was crying because a Spaniard stamped on the snail. You know how she loves snails.'

'Yes. She worked for a veterinary surgeon in London, didn't she? I seem to remember her telling me she got the sack over something to do with a dog swallowing the top of a detergent bottle...'

'No that was something else. A woman said her dog had swallowed the top off a Domestos bottle and the vet operated and found a piece of leather lead but no bottle top. When he told her she insisted that she had seen the dog swallow it and insisted that he open up the dog again and take a second look. The vet knew there was nothing in there so Doreen suggested she went out and bought a bottle of Domestos and give the woman the top and say he'd found it, but the vet said that would be unethical so he operated anyway and told his client the dog must have coughed it up or rejected it somehow.'

'So why did she get the sack?'

'That was because she was supposed to be minding a valuable chinchilla rabbit which was under sedation while the vet was out and she went to the pub instead, and a ferret that was being treated for 'flu got out of his cage and ate the rabbit on the operating table.'

'Well she'd better stay out of range today. There's a posh tourist boat due in and she's a regular little beer bandit when there's some strangers around, especially if they've got poppy!'

On the Vara de Rey Steve Primero had just called out to Cyril MacTavish: 'I don't need you today, Cyril. I got my mail' when a fight broke out on the terrace of the Montesol next door.

It appeared that one of the waiters, new on the job, had tried to charge Nescafe Jack one peseta for hot water and Jack had thrown a wobbly and threatened to take his custom elsewhere. Chairs had been knocked over and a glass broken in the dispute. Jack had run off to Dirty Domingo's where he knew his custom would be accepted without sordid commercial haggling.

'Good news?' Cyril MacTavish shouted at the retreating back of Steve Primero.

'Fantastic news. I've got a daughter. In Brooklyn. Imagine that? After all these years? I'll tell you later...'

Cyril MacTavish turned to his wife Molly, a silver-haired quietly spoken Scots woman who wore the same orange waist-length cape as her husband, made to her own design, so that they looked from a distance like two butano gas bottles sitting side by side. 'How did he manage that?' asked Cyril, swinging the ball of ivory he held on a string. 'Artificial insemination by post?' Molly tittered politely behind a small, gloved hand. 'I've heard rumours about the length of his equipment,' said Cyril, 'but three thousand miles would be a slight exaggeration, don't you think?' Molly burst into fits of giggles.

'I've heard of P.L.O.T.O. - y'know, Pipe Line Over The Ocean. That's it. El Ploto, that's what Steve calls himself, and that's the plot of his next epistle: G.I.'s, Sailors, Airmen: why leave your sperm in the States when you can send it by El Ploto, the pipeline that keeps you in touch with your loved one...'

'Stop, stop, Cyril, or I'll die laughing,' giggled Molly.

Cyril stopped swinging his ivory ball.

'Well, you told Steve yesterday that there'd be mail today and it would be good news.' said Molly.

'That's right. The ball really swung around yesterday, my love. I'm quite pleased about that.'

Several of the island's residents who lived in the town and were getting lazy about the walk to the post office, including Steve Primero, whose only physical exercise consisted of an occasional game of bar billiards, would stop to ask Cyril if they had any mail. Cyril placed the ivory ball over the proffered wrist, left hand only, and, depending on which way the ball swung, Cyril would announce: 'No mail today, Jack,' or 'There's something for you Doreen, it could be your uncle's cheque,' or 'Waste of time going today, Jimmy.'

'No point in telling him,' said Molly, pointing at a tiny figure in cravat and cashmere sweater glad-handing his way down the serried tables outside the Montesol.

Everyone knew that each week a warrant arrived from the French police for the arrest of Elmyr de Hory, the Hungarian confidence trickster who had lived on the island for several years in a splendid villa above the hill that contained the Phoenician graves above the Via Punica. Elmyr had been lucky for several years because the Spanish police wanted certain Basque terrorists extradited from France and would not give up little Elmyr until they got their wanted men on the other side of the frontier. The French had labelled Elmyr *'Le Roi de Faux Peintures'*, but most of the fake paintings he had sold with his accomplices to Japanese and American millionaires and galleries had been painted by students at the *Ecole des Beaux Art* in Paris who were clever copyists.

Elmyr was good: he could knock out a Modigliani in under an hour, but the students were better, and worked, unknowingly, for a small fee. Better than any of them was the English forger who made perfect copies of French experts' certificates of authenticity which went with each painting, and it was the certificate, not the painting, that convinced the rich collectors and the galleries.

Elmyr had kept the same name, de Hory, throughout the 60's and 70's, as he could no longer leave the island. Before his arrival in Spain, while using his glib tongue to divest the elderly rich of their unearned incomes in the expensive hotels and clubs of America and Europe, he had been known as Count Philippe de Joxe, Sir Justin Foxe-Rivers, Prince Emile Plesch, Le Duc de Chambertin, and, the name he liked most of all, Louis Butane which he had taken from the orange butane-gas bottle sold in Spain.

'Are you going to Far Out Phyllis's party, Elmyr?' someone called out to him as he tablehopped.

'Oh, Gawd, I think if I hear that again I'll scream,' said Elmyr petulantly. 'Yes, dear, of course I'm going to Far Out Phyllis's party. I was the *first* one she invited. Anyone'd would think it was *the* social event of the year...'

He came light-footed towards Cyril's table. Elmyr had shaken hands with them all on the Vara de Rey over the years, the celebrities and the stars, the personalities in the news, the pop singers, the famous summer visitors and men from the Mafia and the Union Corse that he feared might one day kidnap him and hand him over to the French authorities for a ransom.

'Going to the Post Office, Elmyr?' Cyril called as he approached.

Elmyr glanced with disdain at Cyril and Molly in their 'going steady' orange capes. What was he doing mixing with these minor artists, Elmyr wondered, remembering the good old days when he was conning in England as Sir Percy Brett and had actually shaken hands with the Queen at the Royal Garden Party and it had been on the tip of his tongue to say 'Hello sailor' to Prince Phillip but had thought better of it, and drinking with those faggy footmen in that pub near the Palace and loving all the Palace gossip, calling them Phil the Bubble which was cockney rhyming slang for Bubble and Squeak - Greek, and her Majesty referred to as Brenda all the time, and Prince Charles as 'Wales' and Princess Anne's army officer husband they called 'Plank' because they said he was as thick as two short planks. And then New York, how wonderful it had all been when they had money in the good old days and Dag Hammarsjold, the head of U.N.O. was chasing Elmyr's accomplice in crime, Fernand Legros, calling him 'my little Egyptian', it had been a fairy tale, in more ways than one, he smiled to himself at the thought and looked at the people on either side of the Scots couple, ensuring that there was no one of importance within earshot. His shifty, guilt-ridden eyes strayed away from the faces above the orange capes, for Elmyr rarely looked at the person or persons he addressed.

'Why don't you go and piss up your kilt and play with the steam,' he hissed, and walked quickly on.

'The con-men are in town,' said Cyril as Elmyr slithered around the corner in the direction of the bullring and the Ibiza town police station where a duplicate of his police file was kept, where they had almost pulled his fingers out of joint fingerprinting him when he applied for a renewal of his *permanencia*, his residence permit.

'Cliff's been offering to lend or give Steve Primero some money,' said Cyril, watching the tall man striding towards them.

Molly followed Cyril's gaze and saw the American with big leather boots and the smooth face heading in their direction.

'That's unusual,' said Molly. 'I wonder what that's all about?'

'He's up to some scam or another,' said Cyril.

'Hello Cliff,' said Molly as the American stopped in front of their table.

'Hi Cyril. Hi, Molly. Seen Steve?'

'You might catch him at the post office, Cliff,' said Cyril, and the

American hurried off, straw bag swinging from the shoulder of his suede jacket.

'Steve says he claims to have persuaded some famous American millionaire to let him ghost his memoirs - worth a fortune to a publisher. He's already asked the British consul if she'd type the manuscript.'

'Do you suppose it's true?'

'Who knows? I never believe anything I hear on this island. They say England's a lump of coal surrounded by fog, and Jersey is two thousand alcoholics clinging to a stormbound rock. Well this place is full of fantasists living in a dream world. Cliff isn't a writer because he's interested in literature or because it's a vocation or an obsession but because he wants to be a celebrity. He insists on showing Steve chapters of a book he's writing. Steve said: 'Listen Cliff, the first chapter is Hemingway, the second is Thomas Wolfe, the third is F. Scott Fitzgerald - when are you going to write your chapter?"

'And what did Cliff say to that?'

'Oh, he just smiled and said: 'But Steve, these are people I admire."

'Here's Steve Primero now.'

'Right, we'll get all his news.'

'Cliff's looking for you, Steve,' said Molly as he approached the table.

'Thanks. I saw him from a distance which is a good place to be. He's sitting there eating a chocolate bar and drinking a milkshake and smoking his goddam pipe. You know, I can't stand people who don't drink.'

'Is it true he offered you some money ?' Cyril asked.

'He's up to something. Something to do with writing the memoirs of an American millionaire. I'll believe it when I see it. He'd better watch out or he'll end up in jail. Poor Cliff. All he wants to be is famous.'

'So what's this news about a daughter?' Molly asked.

'Yeah, isn't it great? Would you believe it?'

'Sit down and have a coffee,' Molly said, 'and tell us all about it.'

Steve sat down with them and the waiter hurried up. Steve was popular with waiters, always treating them as equals and tipping correctly. 'No coffee for me,' he said to Molly, 'I've had four this morning. Hey Jaime - gin *con gel*,' he called to the waiter.

'So what's her name?' Molly asked.

'What's her name? Wait for it - Rebecca. How Jewish can you get?

Her mother's Jewish, of course. We used to drink in the same bar on Bleeker Street when I lived in the Village. It was a brief affair, one of those things. Before I went to Mexico.'

'What did you do in Mexico, Steve?'

'As a matter of fact, I was spying for the Japanese,' said Steve, contemplating his melting ice-cube.

'But that's terrible...'

'For God's sake, Molly, I was dodging the *draft*.'

'And how many times have I told you, dear,' said Cyril nudging the orange cape next to his, 'there are two questions you don't ask in Ibiza: what's your name and what do you do.'

'Sorry dear.'

'All right, then.'

'But don't get me wrong, I came back to face the music, yes sir. Went right down to the recruiting office in New York. There was this big sergeant behind the desk. 'Hi, Steve,' he says to me, looking at my papers. 'What do you mean, Hi Steve?' I shouted at him. 'Who the hell gave you permission to call me Steve?' 'You won't shout at me like that when you're in uniform, boy,' he said. 'Oh yeah? So you're going to put me in uniform, are you? And give me a gun? You know what I'll do if you give me a gun? I'LL SHOOT YOU, you asshole. And furthermore, I'll put a uniform on when I get certain guarantees from the United States Government. The first guarantee is that nobody makes any *money* out of this war. Like the bastards who became millionaires in the First World War, selling barbed wire and weapons to the other side. The second guarantee is that you call up the women - all those who like handing out white feathers to men, and put them in uniform and see how they like getting their asses shot off instead of screwing men on leave and other guys while their husbands are away.'

'Blimey, Steve, it's a wonder they didn't arrest you and put you in jail on the spot.'

'Boy, they sure as hell were angry.'

'What happened next?' Molly asked.

'They put me down as nuts,' said Steve, sipping his gin.

'What? You mean they certified you?' said Cyril.

'No. They sent me to a shrink. He was their top man, the head of the Army psychiatric department in New York, and I told him exactly what I'd told the recruiting sergeant, that I didn't see why a lot of fat-assed businessmen became multimillionaires by profiteering and selling armaments - sometimes to both sides. No more Sir Basil Zacheroffs stopping the shelling and bombing of German munitions factories because Allied money was invested in them. No more factories like Vickers, England, selling firing pins to Germany which were used to kill British Tommies. No, sir. I'll put a uniform on when I get those guarantees.'

'Jesus, Steve, I'm surprised you're here to tell the tale,' said Cyril. 'So did you end up in the laughing academy?'

'Not at all. Exactly the opposite as a matter of fact. He made a date with me.'

'Made a date?'

'Yeah. He asked me to meet him after work in a little quiet bar around the corner from his office where we could talk. I thought he might be a faggot, you know? But I wasn't sure, so I met the asshole anyway. He bought the drinks then put a proposition to me: he asked me to work for him.'

Steve looked at the letter in his left hand.

'How did we get into this? I was rereading these letters...'

'Read that after. My curiosity is aroused,' said Cyril. 'Did you go to work for him?'

'Sure,' said Steve. 'He said I was the only honest man he'd ever met in his whole life. He asked if I'd be interested in working in his office interviewing guys trying to dodge the draft posing as nuts. He seemed to think I'd be able to spot them and wheedle out the fakes from the real thing. He knew I'd been a law student and had a book published and he seemed to think I had a good insight into human nature. So that's how I did my bit, as they say. 'Dear Steve... I'll start again...' he held the first letter up to the light and read:

'I'll bet you're surprised to hear from me after all these years, but the other day was my daughter's seventeenth birthday...' he broke off. 'Imagine that ? She waited seventeen years to tell her daughter who her old man was? Do you know I've forgotten what she looked like. I'll have to ask for a picture. Err... on second thoughts... that might not be a good idea,' he lifted up the letter again: '... and I'd promised to tell her who her daddy was when she was seventeen,' he broke off again.

'Daddy! Imagine that? Me?' then continued with the letter: 'She took the news very well, considering,' he broke off. 'Considering? Considering what? What the hell's she mean she took the news very well. What am I? Some kind of outcast.'

'*Calma,* Steve, *calma,*' said Cyril, 'read on, McDuff.'

'McDuff? MacBeth, more like. Lady MacBeth, that's me. 'Is this a dagger I see before me...' he took out his nail file and looked at it, holding it up before his eyes, 'the handle towards my hand...' '

'The letter, Steve, the letter...'

' 'Come, let me clutch thee...' '

'*Steve* - the letter...'

'Sorry. OK. To continue... Sorry about that as the Army say when they blow your fucking house up...'

'The letter, Steve.'

'Right, right,' he started to read again, 'No, kidding apart, Steve, she *was* thrilled...' he broke off again, 'I should hope she was thrilled, finding out her old man is published and had his picture in Time magazine. Did I ever tell you about that? They said my book, about the draft dodger in Mexico should be hurled - phff - into the cuspidor, that was their very words. So I wrote to them and said if my book should be thrown in the cuspidor and if they had any guts which I *doubted* they would reprint what their critic said about James Joyce's Ulysses when it was published in America. I'll say this for them: they did it. They reprinted their review of Ulysses and they had said it should be thrown into the garbage can or words to that effect...'

'The letter, Steve.'

'Have I told you that before?'

'Yes, Steve.'

'OK, OK. '... she was thrilled. She will be writing to you and putting her letter in the envelope with this and her name is Rebecca and she's a great girl and doing well at college, but she'll tell you all about that. I'm still teaching school'... hey this isn't interesting for you, Cyril and Molly, just chat. But I'll say this, she's a good woman. She brought up that kid without coming whining to me for financial help. She did it on her own. Any woman who does that - works to support her own kid *without* depending on some guy is a *real* woman, yes sir. Not that I could have sent her any...'

'So what does Rebecca say?' Molly asked, interrupting Steve's customary monologue.

'Rebecca? Oh, yes.' He lifted the other sheet of paper to the light. 'Dear Daddy,' he broke off again, 'Hey, I like that. Dear Daddy. You know that's the first time in my life I've been called that?' 'You can't imagine how knocked out I was when Mom told me my Dad was famous - well, pretty famous, your picture in the paper and all when you were young...' he broke off. 'When I was young? What does she think? I'm *old* now? Is that what she thinks?'

'Steve, to a kid of seventeen, everybody over twenty five is old.' said Cyril.

'Yeah, yeah. OK. 'It must be wonderful to be a real writer, Daddy. I'm taking English Lit. at the U. and my favourites are Nathaniel West, F. Scott Fitzgerald and William Faulkner..." Steve broke off, 'that's good, not bad. But I wouldn't agree with Faulkner. Dixie's Dostoyevsky, I called him. Did I ever tell you I cut him dead once on Hollywood Boulevard?'

'Yes, Steve, but you were reading Rebecca's letter.'

'Hey, Cyril. You know sometimes you sound like a fucking schoolmaster. Read the letter, Steve, read the letter, eat your salad, Steve eat your fucking salad, sometimes you sound just like a Jewish mother, Cyril, you know that?'

'But you've got more sidetracks than the Amazon river, Steve. Going off at bloody tangents. What do you call it? Parenthetical interruption? Just read your daughter's letter.'

'Don't tell me what to do. I'm not reading any more. Go screw yourself. This is a private letter anyway. OK, one more line from it: 'I wanna come to Europe, Daddy. I *dream* of coming to Europe to visit you.' You know what that means? Yeah - she wants money. She wants me to pay her goddam fare. Well, I can't. I'm broke. Don't these people know what broke means? I could live for six months on the price of a round-trip ticket to the States. I can't even afford to get my teeth fixed. All summer long these fat-assed German tourists sit under my window eating lobster and I'm up above them eating a can of sardines. How's about that for broke?'

'You don't need teeth to eat sardines,' said Cyril.

'Oh don't I? Well, do you mind if I gnaw on a crust of bread maybe?'

He picked up the gin and drained the glass.

'You don't need teeth to drink gin, either,' he banged the glass down. Cyril and Molly watched him manipulating the flaps on his little leather purse while the waiter waved him away, giving him a drink on the house. They shook hands and Steve took off in the direction of Dirty Domingo's.

'He's worried. That means he's going on a bender,' said Molly. 'You shouldn't have said that about his teeth. It made him angry.'

'Yes, you're right. I haven't seen him so angry since Hal Bloomstein gave him one shoe for Christmas.'

'Hal did that?'

'Yeah, stole it from outside a shop, on display. One shoe, suede, with lace, and leather sole, in the box, tied with ribbon, sprig of holly, the lot. A Merry Christmas Steve, from your old pal, Hal, the card said.'

'What did Steve do?'

'He didn't do anything. He thought for a while of sending another shoe to Hal, but couldn't bring himself to steal one, he's too honest. Then he thought of sending him a Philadelphia Biffy, but he couldn't bring himself to do it.'

'What's a Philadelphia Biffy, Cyril?' Molly asked.

'You don't know? Steve never told you about Philadelphia Biffies, in show business in the States? They send them to each other. You take an empty shoe box and you... well, do something nasty in a black fishnet stocking and put it in the shoe box and post it to the recipient you wish to annoy.'

'How horrible.'

'Steve wouldn't do that. He's not the type. Besides, where would he find a fishnet stocking?'

'Elmyr could have lent him one of his.'

'Now, then, Molly, no bitchiness... '

* * *

George's first customer off the boat and into Wauna's bar was not one he could welcome. He had a bullet head, hair cropped short, and wore a Canadian lumberjack's shirt.

'Hey Buddy,' he called to George when he was three feet from the bar, looking bleary-eyed in George's direction, and swaying on his feet in reverse rhythm to the music on the sound system. 'You gotta Bourbon? Gimme a Bourbon will ya, buddy?'

'Gawd, look at the state of him,' said George, *sotto voce* to Too Much Tommy, who sat in the centre bar stool.

Aloud, he said : 'I'm sorry, sir, I can't serve you.'

'Waddyamean you can't serve me? Wasswrong with me? I got money. You wan' travellers cheques? I got dollars...'

'The police will close me if I serve you in your condition sir. Why don't you go back to the boat and sleep it off and come back later.'

'What kind of bar is this, don't serve gaddam drinks,' the little man muttered and turned suddenly on his heel to do a swift reverse kneecaps out of the door and into the street.

'Is that true, George? Can the cops close you?' asked Too Much Tommy in his soft South Kensington borders-of-Chelsea drawl. Tommy was a failed gambler, a former croupier, having won and lost several large sums at the tables. His one and only conviction in the Criminal Records Office was for the crime common to many gamblers: embezzling. His short, sharp shock in prison had cured his habit, acting as a kind of Gamblers Anonymous course. Women found his voice charming. Some, after listening to Tommy's troubles for ten minutes, felt guilty for not immediately handing over their life savings.

'Sure they can,' said George, 'and they've done it to several foreign bars in town. They even closed down old John Candyfloss at Winston's one night when he was the only one in there. Imagine that? The owner himself serving, nicked for being drunk and serving a drunk, namely the proprietor. He was most distressed. Somebody told me that when he woke up the next morning he found his false teeth under the pillow and his hearing aid in a glass of water.'

'Yes, I heard that. I was at his funeral you know.'

'Were you, Tommy? I don't remember seeing you there. Of course, there was quite a crew, half crying and half celebrating wiping off their tabs. They were very good about the car keys, though.'

'What car keys?'

'Didn't you stay for that - at the end?'

'Actually, I left a bit early. I needed a phlegm cutter.'

'Yes, Swedish Cristina's friend Manolo dropped his car keys into the grave and then they lowered the coffin and started to fill in when he let out a yell, and they had to dig it out and raise the coffin for him to get down there and find his keys. In any other country they'd have said: get another set from the garage. Oh. look out, get your backward facing seats, ladies and gentlemen, fasten your seat belts...'

Too Much Tommy turned round to see why George had suddenly become flustered and there in the doorway stood Paul the Greek, shirt hanging out of his trousers, the wad of thousand peseta notes making his trousers sag from the belt, hands akimbo as if reaching for two .45 Colt revolvers. Small, chocolate-drop Greek eyes staring fixedly at George and Too Much.

'Anybody wanna fight?' he snarled.

'Hello, Paul,' said George, reaching behind for the Chivas Regal bottle, ready to pour his favourite drink.

Too Much Tommy put on his dark glasses as Paul took a seat next to him at the bar, but before doing so he winked at George.

'I may not look tough, but I am,' drawled Paul as he eyed the whisky bottle. 'And that had better be the good stuff, the real Chivas, not that special bottle of cold tea that tub of lard keeps for herself. You tried that on me once, boy...'

'That was a joke, Paul, you know that,' said George.

'I knew that straight away, didn't I? You can't pull a fast one on me. I bin in bars from Shanghai to Acapulco. Did I ever tell you I was a racing driver, George? I raced at Daytona Beach, Ohio, a great track. I love your English Jaguars. Some day you and I are going to England and I'm going to buy a Jaguar and you're going to drive it back for me, George, and I'm going to get back in training on the island here.'

'Yes, Paul.'

'You know if the Mafia hadn't put out a goddam contract on me I'd have been racing now. I was winning too much money and not giving them their cut. My problem was I was too good. They wanted their share of the winnings. You know like they made a basket case out of Joe E. Brown when he wouldn't tip up half his show biz earnings and they threatened to do the same to me. So I split to New York for a while but those guys got button men everywhere. Somebody told me this would be a safe place to hide and I've been here ever since. But I sure would like to get back behind the wheel. Of course I raced under a different name then.'

'Sterling Mouse, wasn't it?' George asked.

Too Much Tommy almost choked on his drink, but Paul appeared not to have heard and was about to continue with his tale of self agrandisement when Tommy said to George:

'*Senta lei. Una bicchiere di agua, per piacere.* A glass ice water pliz *cameriere.*'

'*Si, signore.*' George snapped, playing up and polishing a glass and cleaning the moisture off the mineral water bottle and putting an ice cube and a slice of lemon in the glass and placing it on a coaster and pouring just a little.

'*Grazie,*' said Tommy.

'*Prego,*' said George with an obsequious bow from his hips.

Paul George looked from one to the other, his mouth open. He nodded his head sideways, looking askance at George, who looked very serious but ignoring the silent request for information about the customer with the dark glasses, he continued to polish a glass and cast his gaze towards the ceiling. George was a gift to Central Casting.

'It's a pity,' said Too Much Tommy out of the corner of his mouth, so that only Paul George heard it.

'What's a pity, sir?' Paul asked quietly.

'You seem a nice guy.'

'Are you off the boat, sir?'

'No, plane.'

'Are you from Italy, sir?'

'Sicily.'

Paul's face, normally ashen grey, turned a paler shade of white and his hand trembled as he reached for his scotch.

'Sicily... Sicily... that's a beautiful island, sir,' he choked.

'You got till midnight,' said Tommy sideways.

'Midnight, sir?'

'I'm sorry. As I said, you seem a nice guy. But you know how it is? Your birth certificate expires at midnight.'

Tommy stood up, fumbled with his jacket as if a heavy weight lay under his left armpit, and sidled out to the door without looking back.

George, suppressing a sob of mirth, had to turn his back on Paul, whose chin was almost resting on the counter.

'George,' he squawked, 'that's a Mafia hit-man, I swear to God.'

'A what, Sir?' said George, scarcely able to keep his cockney face straight.

'Don't be dumb, George, for Chrissake. The guy just threatened to kill me if I don't split before midnight. Where can I go?'

'He's an American tourist off the boat, Paul.'

'He's not, for Chrissake. He's from Sicily. You know what that means? He was speaking Eye-talian to you. He's an Eye-talian hit-man from Sicily. He's just the type. The quiet voice, the mineral water, the dark shades and he had a gun, I swear to God.'

'You wouldn't want to let the Italians worry you, sir. If you're fighting them in a war all you have to do is surround the barbers shops - you got 'em all trapped.'

'STOP JOKING, you asshole. This is serious.'

'Language, language, Paul.'

'I'm going to the police. I want protection. I live here, for Chrissake. Never mind the friggin' barber shops, the cops will surround my house so that maggot doesn't get near me. How much do I owe you? I'm going to the cops now.'

He flung a note on the counter, the biggest tip George had ever had on the island, and hurried off to Headquarters.

CHAPTER 15

A Haircut

DENNIS the Menace loomed large in the doorway of the bar a few minutes after the now sober figure of Paul George had been seen hurrying in the direction of police headquarters. 'George,' Dennis boomed from the doorway, 'I've decided to put Strop-bollocks in a TV show. I mean - what a character, a singing dog called Stroppy. Hello Fortune.' he added, taking a seat next to her.

'Drinkie, darling?'

'Thanks, Fortune, I'll have one of George's specialties.

'Not the Shillelagh Snapper?'

'No, the bullshot.'

'Coming up, Dennis,' called George taking a can of iced consommé from the fridge and pouring a large vodka, sprinkling a little black pepper and lemon juice on the mixture.

'Good choice, darling,' said Fortune. 'Also, it solves the problem of lunch.'

'Right.' said Dennis Vance, known as 'the Menace' when on his annual holiday in Ibiza. 'Now George,' he called in his loud film-producer's voice, as if ordering a change of set, 'I want you to recommend a barber to me. You know I heard about Steve Primero in the old days here, having the barber come out to the terrace of the bar on the waterfront to shave him. That's style, man.'

'Yeah, and I remember the barber told Steve he'd had a five-dollar tip from an American tourist, and Steve told him he'd live to regret that day because when tourists start splashing money around all the prices go up and places get ruined.'

'Well, it hasn't happened yet.' said Dennis Vance.

'It will.'

'Stop being a misery and recommend a barber to me, will you?'

'OK. Tipperary.'

'Who? What?'

'Tipperary. That's the barber, the one who used to shave Steve on the harbour. He's in that little side street near the church of San Telmo, just round the corner. He speaks a bit of English. Well, a little bit. What he actually does is sing in English.'

'What's he sing?'

'He sings 'It's a Long Way to Tipperary,' - that's how he got his name.'

'Do you think he'd sing for me?'

'Try stopping him. If you tell him you're a TV producer he'll do a backward somersault through a flaming hoop and end up with a headstand in his shaving bowl.'

'But has he got bad breath?'

'All barbers have bad breath. Have another bullshot and you won't notice.'

'True. True, George. Boy, this does the trick, eh? What a drink. As you say, Fortune, lunch and drinks all in one glass. Beauty. The world is turning from grey to purple.'

'Sounds like my mother's hair,' said Fortune.

'Life takes on all kinds of new aspects. The rosy glow.'

'You had a rosy glow on last week when you drove me into town,' said George. 'Remember?'

'No, what was that?'

'You said 'How high can a Spanish policeman jump?', and I said 'How the hell should I know?' and you said: 'Let's see shall we?' and proceeded to drive straight at No Way Jose who was on point duty opposite the Montesol.'

'Dennis laughed. 'Did I really?'

'Yes. Good job he knows me. Wauna gave him his bottle of Chivas at Christmas.'

'Did you see all those parcels No Way Jose got on Christmas Eve, George?' Fortune asked. 'He almost disappeared under the pile. Mountains of parcels.'

'They're not all for him of course,' said George. 'They are for the police, from the shopkeepers, bar owners, business people and sycophants in general. Everybody who's got something to hide, in fact.'

'Is that true that one parcel was a Philadelphia Biffy?' asked Dennis.

'I don't know about that, but there's some cop somewhere looking for a right shoe to match the left one he got for Christmas from Steve Primero.'

"Yes, I heard about Hal's shoe. Maybe the cop passed it on to the Chief of Police. 'The shoe stops here,' you know?'

'Steve should have given it to French Ferdinand. You did say it was a left shoe, didn't you, George?'

'You know, that's brilliant, Fortune. Who'd have thunk it except you? The only trouble is in might have been the wrong size.'

'Who's French Ferdinand?' Dennis asked.

'The feller with the tin leg. Drinks in the Taverna. Lovely man. Former school teacher who lost his leg in an accident and gets good compensation, a monthly cheque. Boy, does he hit the sauce when he gets it.'

'Poor Ferdinand. That leg's never been right since.' said Fortune.

'Since what?' asked Dennis.

'That was a tragedy, wasn't it George?' Fortune said, looking sad, 'when he lost all his money out of the hole in the pocket of his trousers that month and he had to run tabs everywhere till the next cheque arrived.'

'Yes, the poor bastard. And he's always generous with it too, splashing it around town. A lovely man. I'd trust him minding mice at a crossroads.'

'Fancy putting a wad like that in his trousers pocket,' said Fortune.

'Paul George does.'

'Yes but Ferdinand had a hole in his pocket. Paul has a hole in his head.'

'Will you for Chrissake tell me what happened? What about his leg?' Dennis hollered.

'He was so distressed at losing his month's money that he went and jumped in the harbour,' said Fortune.

'They fished him out and somebody drove him back to his finca in the sticks and he slept it off,' said George, 'but the trouble was that he slept so long his leg rusted up.'

'I supposed if he'd oiled it it would have been all right' said Fortune.

'He was in no fit state to think about oiling legs,' said George.

'Anyway, it's never been the same since,' said Fortune.

'Direct me again to Tipperary's emporium, George, I'm off,' said Dennis finishing his second bullshot with a gulp.

'Did I hear that Pete the Parrot has commissioned Madrilas to paint his bar?' Fortune asked when Dennis had gone.

'Yes. Olly's giving him the key to work tonight.'

'That Olly's a bit naive isn't he? What did he do before he came here?'

"Oh, he loves it here. He's from London. Stands there with a drink saying: 'Two o'clock in the morning, large gin and tonic in hand, can't get that in the Smoke, can you?' and he's picked up the island phrase: Another shitty day in paradise. He sits in the sun outside the Montesol repeating it to himself: another shitty day in paradise, can't be bad, can it? The Ibos look at him as if he's nuts. He's trying to get a bit of a suntan of course. He did the whole summer season in a Hamburger joint in Marbella, with a Jock and a Geordie. Did you notice how white he was when he came here?'

'Actually, George, I did. But I didn't like to comment on it. Sometimes they've just come out of chokey you know.'

'No, he wasn't in the nick, it was a bet. A bottle of Scotch for who could stay the whitest. The three of them did shift work. They'd sidle down side streets, staying out of the sun from June to September, staying white, just to win a bottle of scotch.'

'Well, I hope he enjoyed drinking it.'

'He didn't win it. The Jock did. He had a plastic bag with eye-holes in it for walking across sun-drenched streets. The locals also thought he was nuts. National pride, I suppose. He just had to win.'

'What do they think of us, George, the Spaniels?'

'They think we're from another planet, Fortune. They tolerate us, that's all. I mean, where else would Steve Primero have got away with the strokes he's pulled here? That time he was jilted and his girlfriend ran off to Paris, and he took every chair from outside the Montesol and the Alhambra and threw them into the middle of the Vara de Rey, then took one last chair and walked across to the old Post Office which used to be there and flung the chair through the plate glass window. Then he went in and shouted: 'What do you think of that then?' The little clerk looked up and said 'Thank you Senor Esteve' - the call him Esteve in Spain - 'we needed some fresh air in here'. They respected him of course. That was because he had a friend in Rome who posted letters from Vatican City post office. They thought here that Steve was somehow connected to the Pope. There was the Pontiff's picture on the stamp. They almost crossed themselves when they handed the mail over.'

'Today they'd probably charge excess postage.'

'Excess postage?' came a shout from the open doorway.

'Oh no,' said George.

"Hello, Steve. We were just talking about you darling. Your Vatican Stamps impressing the post office. I was saying nowadays they'd probably charge excess postage.'

'The country for that Is Mexico,' said Steve Primero. 'Did I ever tell you about the excess postage in Mexico?'

George groaned and Steve looked quickly at him.

'OK, maybe you've heard it but Fortune hasn't. Just give me a gin. Gin *con gel*, you know the way I like it.'

'This is on me,' said Fortune. 'Go on, darling. What about Mexico?'

'I sent a letter to New York from this small town in Mexico and the guy weighed it and put a one peso fifty stamp on it. When I got back to my hotel I realised I'd forgotten to say something I wanted to say, so I wrote a second short letter, put it in the envelope, bought a one peso fifty stamp at the *tabac* and gave it to the clerk who weighed it and said: 'One peso seventy five' I said an hour ago I sent the same envelope, same sheet of paper and it was one peso fifty, how come it was one peso seventy five now? The first one weighed less, he said, you hadn't put the stamp on it. Can you believe these people?'

'You sure there weren't a couple or three marijuana seeds under that second stamp, Steve, sending them to a New York grower?' laughed Fortune.

'Not me, baby. This booze has always been enough for me without that other shit. And talking about booze, I just came from Dirty Domingo's and do you know that bastard has put the price of gin up again? He put it up last year.'

'Put what up?' said a bearded figure in a yellow PVC cape in the doorway.

'It's Tristan Jones himself. Have a drink darling,' said Fortune.

'You're back early,' said George.

'Left Deaf Henry's boat in the safe hands of Pepe the Caulker. He's doing it. Had a nice sail back, mate. How's the leg?'

'No problem. Beer?'

'Who's put what up?' Jones said to Steve Primero. 'I hope you haven't been trying to get your leg across at your age,' he added, grinning as he took the beer bottle.

'Oh yeah? What do you mean 'my age' Jones, you sawn-off seafarer. I'm not that much older than you.'

'I thought you said you had to thumb it in?'

'Now stop fighting you two. It's too early in the day for squabbles. We had Wauna and Doreen yesterday, not to mention George and Doreen scrapping. What Steve was saying, darling, is that Dirty Domingo has put the price of gin up.' Fortune said, taking her little compact mirror from her handbag and adding just a touch of lipstick.

'I'll tell you something, boyo,' said Jones, after taking a large swig of beer. 'Two thousand years ago there were two Roman soldiers sitting just outside there on what is now the Calle Mayor and one turned to the other and said: 'That Spanish bastard has just put the price of wine up by two soldi - I'm not drinking there any more.' They stayed away then drifted back to the bar. And I'll tell you something else: two thousand years from now there'll be bloody Martians sitting on the Calle Mayor and one will turn to the other and say: 'That Spanish bastard has just put the price of wine up again.'

Jones paid for a drink and said: 'I don't like running up bar bills when I'm ashore.'

George gave him an old fashioned look. 'But there's an old saying in the Navy and in boating circles: 'First turn of the screw clears all debts.''

'Talking of debts, said George. 'Heard anything of Kamikaze Schmidt?'

'Gone down, boyo, no doubt about that,' said Jones.

'Do you know that for sure, 'cos I'll cross him off.'

'No, but he cast off from here bound for Gib. and the Azores in a rotting hulk that I wouldn't sail from here to Talamanca.'

'But you don't know for certain.'

'I had a dream about him. I saw a mast snapped, decks awash, sails in shreds, a body, floating, bloated...'

'Stop it, darling, please.' cried Fortune.

'I'll leave him in the book, anyway,' said George, closing it and putting it under the counter. 'You never know, his ghost might walk in here and pay his tab.'

'Talking of ghosts...' said George. 'Look who's here.'

'My God, it's Jill the Pill,' said Fortune as a skinny girl in hippy clothing, skirt reaching down to her ankles, entered the bar.

'Hello, Jill, long time no see,' said George. 'Where've you sprung from?'

'I was back in England. Went to see Joe the Blow in the slammer.'

'Where is he?' asked George.

'Strangeways. He was worried about his boat lying off Figueretas.'

'He can forget about that, love,' said Tristan Jones. 'It's a pile of match wood now. There was a bad storm last week.'

'Oh, no. That's terrible news. I'll have to send him a telegram. Can it be salvaged?'

'We might grill a chop on it, when the wood dries out,' said Jones.

'He's insured isn't he?' George asked.

'No, it had run out just after they felt his collar.'

'Did he tell you where the shit is hidden?'

'No he bloody well didn't George, and I'll thank you to be careful what you say...'

'Come off it, Jill. He was caught with only one kilo. There's nine more on this island and you know it.'

'WILL YOU ALL SHUT UP FOR JUST ONE MINUTE,' shouted Steve Primero, turning the bar to sudden silence so that they could hear the words of the song on the tape:

'Even the Bad Times were Good... la-la-la-la...'

'I HAVE A DAUGHTER!' he continued, waving a letter in the air, 'and I've been trying to tell Fortune about it ever since I came in here, interrupted by you ass-holes with your homespun Welsh philosophy about Roman soldiers and goddam hash smugglers in the slammer where they belong. I can't get a word in edgeways here.'

'Blimey, that makes a change,' said George.

'Shut up, George. Just tend bar, will you? I'll thank you to keep a civil tongue in my ass.'

'No need to be nasty,' said George, grinning and polishing a glass.

'A daughter, darling?' said Fortune.

'Her name's Rebecca and she's seventeen years old, and she's proud of her old man, showing my picture around to her friends in New York. She says she wants to come to Europe soon. She wants to work on a kibbutz in Israel for a couple of weeks and then visit me here.'

'Did she send you a photo, darling?'

'Well, er... er... yes, she did, but...'

'Come on, Steve, let's see what she looks like.'

He shyly took a photograph out of a worn leather wallet and presented it to Fortune who looked at it while the rest of the clientele gathered around.

'She's... very attractive, Steve.'

'Well, she's no oil-painting,' said Steve as Fortune passed it from hand to hand.

'She's very pretty, Steve,' said Jill the Pill, ' and she's got your eyes.'

'You think so? She's got my eyes? Really?'

'Better than having his teeth,' said George.

'Shut up, George. Hey - did I tell you I was on the harbour with the old fishermen and I was telling them in my bad Spanish that my top set keeps slipping, and they said I had to eat a toffee and then the toffee would stick the plastic molars to the roof of my moth. GREAT! That's Spanish medical advice for you. Eat a goddam toffee!'

'GEORGE,' came a shout from the open doorway and there stood Dennis Vance with his face covered in bits of sticking plaster and cotton wool. 'WHERE DID YOU SEND ME?'

'Blimey, Dennis, he shaved you. Tipperary's not supposed to shave people. The police took away his shaving license years ago.'

'You tell me now.'

'I didn't know you were going to ask for a shave. I thought you wanted a haircut and maybe a shampoo. He's allowed to do that.'

'Oh, is he? He was as pissed as a rat but I didn't realise it until he got the cut-throat out. I thought he was a nice little feller, singing away. He gave a rousing rendering of 'Tipperarary' and chatted away, said he liked the English.'

'I'm sorry, Dennis, I should have warned you. If a barber becomes an alcoholic in Spain they take his shaving licence away.'

'They should take his breathing licence away from him. Look what he's done to me. See that one there?' He pointed to a cut on his left cheek. 'That's when he got to 'Sweetest Girl I know', and see that one on the other cheek, that was when he yelled 'My Heart's Right There'. He shouldn't have a barber's pole outside his shop he should have an oversize Stiptick pencil. I tell you there was claret all over the bleedin' place, all over the apron, on the floor. Sweeney Todd wasn't in it.'

'Did he apologise?'

'Did he buggery. He tried to charge me for the elastoplast. The Demon Barber strikes again. The insolence of the man. He plays noughts and crosses on my boat race and then wants to charge me for it.'

'Lovely letters, darling,' said Fortune to Steve Primero, handing back the two sheets of paper he had shown her. 'Do write and tell her she'll be welcome here and to come soon. You're very lucky to have a daughter.'

'I've already written to her and her Mom. I just sent the letters off this morning.'

'Could you ask her to bring me some speed?' said Jill the Pill.

'No I certainly can not. What the hell do you think I am, Jill? I just discover that I have a daughter and invite her to meet me for the first time and you want her to bring drugs from America? Because she looks straight, eh? A good Jewish girl. Nobody's going to search for junk, eh? Like Joe College with his tennis balls full of cocaine, swinging his racket through Customs. No sir. You want to stop popping those pills. There's nothing you won't take, Librium, Valium, uppers, downers, inners, outers. One of these days somebody's going to slip you a cyanide pill and you'll drop it for kicks. You're not doing your health any good, you know.'

'What should I do? Drink a litre of gin and a litre of vodka a day like you? With the occasional orange for my necessary vitamin intake?'

'No, get yourself a square meal now and again. Where are you living, anyhow?'

'Joe the Blow's gaff in *Casa Baratas.*'

'What that old dump? I thought he'd paid two guys to rebuild it, fix it up a bit, put a new door on and mend the roof.'

'He did. Dutch Dick and Gordon the Flute are going to start building soon, put a new roof on. Most people get into bedroom slippers when they get out of bed. I slip into a pair of gum boots when it rains. I need an umbrella to read in bed. It's cold, too, especially when the wind blows from the north, the Tramontane, and there's a big gap under the door. You could get a herd of buffalo under there.'

'The Garagal,' said George.

'Is there something wrong with you?' said Jill.

'He's got a sore throat,' said Dennis. 'He's been drinking out of damp glasses.'

"The wind from the north is called the Garagal, and it comes exactly from the opposite direction to Xaloc which comes from the Sahara.'

'That's called the Mitjorn,' said Steve, 'from due South, and occasionally covers these white fincas with fine red sand giving lots of lovely work to Maria the Whitewash.'

'What happened to Maria the Whitewash, by the way?' asked Jill the Pill. 'I haven't seen her around for ages.'

'Maybe she died,' said Dennis.

'No. She's around,' said Steve. 'I heard her screeching outside my window the other morning. What a squawk. It's called an eldritch shriek, like a witch makes.'

'Like a what makes?' said George.

'A witch.'

'What witch?' said Dennis.

'Belt up. You know what I mean.'

'Wordsmith. Eldritch, eh? I like that. I'll try that on the wife sometime.'

'I hope she ain't got a voice like Maria the Whitewash. She can talk to her sister in Madrid without using the telephone.'

'Anyway,' said George, 'It's the Garagal, not the Tramontane.'

'Who gives a big rat's arse what they're called,' said Steve 'Just give me a gin *con gel*. I gotta go soon, anyhow. I gotta see my doctor.'

'What about?'

'About everything. I've got a rodent mole in my goddam nose, and I've got sinus trouble and trouble with my teeth and my chest aches where I was all sewn up after my accident in Majorca.'

'Crikey,' said Dennis, 'You make Mad Mike look like an athlete.'

'Isn't that Gordon the Flute going by now?' Fortune said from her corner barstool with a full view of the street.

Jill the Pill went running out of the bar and down the street in the wake of Gordon the Flute, who wore sports coat, flannels, Army tie, brown brogue shoes and looked as if he had stepped off a bus in a London suburb.

'She won't have much joy with him,' said George. 'When Gordon's drying out he's a nervous wreck. It takes him all his time to hold a newspaper steady.'

'Poor Gordon,' said Fortune.

'I don't know if he's what you call poor,' said Dennis. 'When he can hold the newspaper still enough to read it, he's always scanning the stocks and shares page.'

'He has a few little investments,' said George, 'from dough he made as an oil man in the desert, selling years of his life on an oil station in the Sahara just for a little nest egg which dwindles as the pound goes down.'

'Yes, he shouldn't have put it in Sterling,' said Dennis.

'He's a very loyal Britisher, you know,' said Fortune, 'an ex-serviceman and all that, loyal to the crown.'

'Mine's in Swiss Francs,' said Dennis. 'Anything I make over and above my immediate needs goes into Swiss Francs. Not much return in interest, mind you, but the hardest currency in the world.'

'Thank God mine's in dollars,' said Fortune. 'It's all safe with Uncle Sam.'

'Don't be so sure about that, either,' said George, 'the dollar sometimes goes up and down like a fiddler's elbow.'

'They say the Belgian Franc is very strong' said Steve Primero. 'America bought all their uranium from the Congo, of course, and a few minor wars were started in the process...'

'What about you, George?' Dennis asked. 'Where's your investment?'

'Oh, all my money is in pesetas,' said George.

'*Pesetas*?' chorused Dennis, Steve and Fortune in harmony.

'Yes,' said George, delving into his trousers and producing some coins. 'I have twenty six.'

When their laughter abated, Dennis said: 'Give me a strong drink, George, for medicinal purposes.'

'Give him a Shillelagh Snapper, George,' said Fortune.

'What is that goddam Shillelagh Snapper he serves here?' asked

Steve Primero.

George took the electric mixer from the shelf behind him and poured a measure of whisky, avocat and Campari into the container and set it to whirr for a few seconds, then served the drink to Dennis.

'That's on the house. Don't tell Wauna. It's compensation for damages to your boat-race by Tipperary. But don't you lot laugh about pesetas. The kids in this country have been kept down for too long. When they surge forward and get real education, watch out the rest of Europe.'

Jill the Pill returned, saying: 'I can't get through to him. I tried to shake hands with him but I couldn't synchronise the trembles. He should switch to hash.'

'His Sunday bender,' said George. 'He gets paid a minuscule amount for playing the flute in the town band - he's quite a good musician - and the band get paid on Sunday after playing in town once a month. They all head off to the nearest cheapo bar and get slaughtered on cognac. Then he hits town. He appeared once in drag. Dunno where he got it, a red dress and stiletto heels. Honestly, he's a lovely guy, but I don't think he knows whether he's Arthur or Martha.'

'No wonder with his background,' said Fortune. 'I mean, the cruelty to children in earlier times was abominable. He was taken out of an orphanage at the age of ten and was a boy sailor aboard H.M.S. Ironside. He was actually aboard the Ironside at the Spithead review in 1936 at the age of twelve.'

'British sea power,' said George. 'We'll never see the like of that again. Ships as far as the eye could see.'

'All those golden rivets,' said Dennis.

'Doahn you guys ever do any work?' came a shout from the open doorway.

'Come and have a drinkie, darling,' called Fortune.

A lithe, handsome black man came into the bar, walking with the agility of a panther. On his head was a Catalan beret, pulled low over his eyes and he wore a faded, blue United States Navy issue workshirt, a black leather waistcoat and American Army fatigues tucked into cowboy boots. He bore a close resemblance to the boxer Sugar Ray Robinson.

'You know, Fortune, you are a generous lady, but you be careful now. When your dough runs out, doahn expect these cats to buy for you the way you buy for them, 'cos that just ain't the way of this world, no Ma'am. In any case, I ain't drinkin'.'

He slipped onto a barstool with one lithe movement, and continued: 'I'm still in training because a nigger like me's gotta defend himself. Now doahn all look shocked 'cos I know everybody here call me Nigger Nick behind my back, but I doahn mind, no sir. I'm big enough, I reckon, to take that sheet. But seein' you guys here, sittin' around doin' nothin' reminded me of how I came to join the United States Navy, because we wuz sittin' aroun' shootin' the sheet like that when the cop comes in and hollers: 'Ain't you niggers got any work to do?' That's what he hollered, standin' there swingin' that night stick.'

'So you told him to stop swearing.' said George.

'You know, George, you are nice people, and you are a very funny feller, but there's somethin' you don't know - you don't give no lip to a redneck cop in the snake-eyed South, 'cos those cops are mean mothers.'

'Did I ever tell you about the time I was in the South...' Steve Primero started to say.

'Yes, Steve,' said Fortune.

'Yes, Steve, several times,' said George.

'They are just waitin' to put on their Ku-Klux-Klan robes after dark and have a little necktie party, or go out and plant a fiery cross in the name of the Lord Jesus and then shoot a nigger, 'cos that's what that sound means: a rifle bolt being drawn back and put in place, Ku-Klux-Klan. Anyways, so here's this cop tellin' us all to get work where there ain't no work, an' he knows this. So he says: 'If you niggers ain't workin' you're stealin', an' Ah's comin' back in here tomorrow an' if you-all are in here Ah'm puttin' you-all in jail.' So that's how I came to join up. He was a good recruiting officer, yes sir, 'cos we all joined the Navy and the Army next day.'

'Come on, you've got a log of wood on your shoulder,' said Steve. 'You had it good in the Navy because you were a boxer. Sixth Fleet champion middleweight, weren't you? You didn't have a race problem in the Navy.'

'Oh yes I did, yes sir,' Nick laughed. 'Now you jest imagine the scene, man, in Norfolk Virginia when I was detailed to take a white prisoner downtown, both of us in uniform and me with my Shore Patrol armband an' truncheon an' I was armed. This guy was handcuffed to me. We get aboard the bus to go downtown an' it's a segregated bus. I sit on the white side with my prisoner. The driver looks in his mirror, comes back up the bus and says to me: 'Git to your own side of the bus.' 'Ah says: 'Hey, man, cain't you see Ah'm handcuffed to ma prisoner?' He says: 'This bus don't move till you get to your own side of the bus'. I said: 'Man, like use your haid, if I move to the other side I gotta take my prisoner with me, an' this white gentleman ain't goin' to like that.' Man, this driver weight about two hundred an' forty pounds an' he jest looked as if he wuz goin' to kill me. 'You heard me, nigger. Now git,' he says, glarin' at me. So I pulls out my Colt .45 from its holster and shoved it right up his nostril an' I says: 'I got a Forty Five here that says I don't move. Now you go and drive us downtown before I blow your haid off."

'And he did,' said George.

'He sure did,' said Nick, chortling at the memory. 'He sure as hell did.'

There was a sudden commotion in the doorway and Too Much Tommy, in handcuffs, was thrust into the bar by three Guardia Civil, two of them with machine guns and the third holding a pistol.

'George, for Chrissake, tell them it was a joke. Paul George denounced me for threatening to kill him, the silly-born little shit heel.'

The officers started muttering amongst themselves and pointing at George behind the bar. Tristan Jones edged away from the pistol, which was a little too close to a big hole in his seaman's jersey.

'What's the Spanish for joke?' asked George, looking for the little pocket dictionary he kept under the bar. His sudden movement caused the policemen to spring into action, cocking the pistol and machine guns and pointing them at George who gave a sickly smile and held up a little green dictionary that said: DICCIONARIOS UNIVERSALES MATEU - Ingles-Espanol Espanol-Ingles.

'Joke,' said George. 'Humour *Ingles. Momentito.*'

'It's something like *jocos,*' said Jones. 'Or try *humoroso.*'

'*Jocoso,*' said George looking at the hard, unflinching stern faces of the three Guardia Civil. He turned back the pages: '*Complacer,*' said George desperately, '*humor,* capricho. *Mi amigo Tommy humorista.*'

The Guardia looked at George and looked at Tommy in his dark glasses. Tommy certainly did not look like a humourist at that moment.

In a stream of rapid Spanish they beckoned to George to come out from behind the bar.

'You're a witness, George. You'll have to come with us.' squawked Tommy.

'I can't go anywhere, mate. I've got to open up the Tavern in a few minutes. Where the hell's Wauna? Late again as usual.'

'Saved by the bell, darling, here she is now,' said Fortune from her observation post on the corner barstool.

The Guardia Civil stood back respectfully as Wauna sailed in, looking from left to right, at the guns, at Too Much Tommy in handcuffs, at Steve Primero standing silent for once, at Nick crouched on the stool, like a cat about to spring into action, at Dennis's Shillelagh Snapper on the bar, at Jill the Pill's flat chest and hippy beads, at Fortune's handbag hanging on the hook under the bar.

'What's this a holdup?' she said, then turned on her brilliant smile and accosted the police officers: *'Buen dias, caballeros. Que passa con mi amigo Tommy acqui?'* She pinched Tommy on the cheek and there was an immediate relaxation all round. She had called the Guardia Civil 'gentlemen' and they liked that and she had referred to Too Much Tommy as her friend.

Luckily Wauna spoke fluent Spanish and within minutes George was on his way with Too Much Tommy to Talamanca for the confrontation with Paul. Curious eyes followed the jeep with its occupants along the harbour, past the slaughterhouse on Pen and Ink Corner and past the yacht club to an area of small, single storey houses near the lighthouse.

'So you got him, huh? Nice work fellas. *Muy buenos.'* said the little man with the big bottle of whisky in front of him. The Guardia looked curiously at the table where Paul sat. Apart from the huge two-litre bottle of whisky there was a cardboard box containing two hundred small combs, all brown. Next to it was another cardboard box containing over a hundred French *Bic* lighters of various colours. A green plastic bucket nestled by his slippered feet.

The Guardia became animated when he made a move to supply glasses for everyone to have a glass of Scotch to celebrate the quick arrest of Too Much and indicated to George the bartender to start clearing up the situation.

'Are you out of your bleedin' mind, Paul? It was a joke. Tommy is a mate of mine. He was only winding you up.'

'He threatened to take my life,' said Paul with dignity. 'He gave me till midnight to get out of town or my birth certificate would expire. I knew he was a hit man...'

'He's not a bloody hit man, he's a tourist, for Chrissake. He's had a row with his wife in London and she's divorcing him and he came here to escape from it all and he was just having a little joke with you. Now you've got to withdraw that *denuncia.*'

'He said he was going to kill me. He's got a gun.'

'He hasn't got a bloody gun. Open your coat, Tommy.'

'I can't. I've got the darbies on.'

'Con permisso,' said George to the Guardia and opened Tommy's jacket to show that there was no Walther PPK hidden there. 'See? Now I guarantee he's OK. He's a friend. I know him. Now withdraw the *denuncia.*'

'Would you fellers care for a drink?' asked Paul, spreading out an array of small glasses, six in number, having included the handcuffed prisoner in the round.

'No, no, no, for the love of Mike, withdraw the charges against Tommy and we can all go and have a drink in the Tavern. Tommy's got a contact with a garage in London where you can get a cheap Jaguar and get back into training for your racing career.'

'Is that right?' One slightly crazed droopy eye gazed at George and Tommy and back again to George. 'A Jaguar? Are you sure you fellers won't have a drink?'

One of the Guardia pulled out the papers that Paul had signed denouncing Tommy and scanned them.

'Will you please, please withdraw that *denuncia* now, Paul. We can have a drink afterwards.'

'You're sure about a Jaguar? You can get me a good deal? And you'll drive it back for me?'

'Yes, yes, sure.'

'I ain't payin' good dollars for a heap of junk.'

'No, no, you'll get a good bargain.' said George reaching, tentatively, for the papers with a polite *'con permisso, senor'?*

He gave the papers to Paul who looked at them through bleary, half-closed eyes, then tore them into four quarters and threw the pieces

216

into the green plastic bucket.

The senior officer motioned George and Tommy to leave the premises and when they were outside and about to walk to the jeep with the other two, the older man said: *'Momentito.'*

He stepped quickly back inside and there was the sound of a single pistol shot followed immediately by the sound of shattered glass and a great waft of Johnny Walker Red label came through the open doorway, accompanied by the strangled cry of a deprived child within.

At the corner of the row of houses the Guardia, having muttered amongst themselves, suddenly stopped the jeep, bade George and Tommy descend, took the handcuffs off Tommy and drove off.

'Shit,' said Tommy, 'It's a long walk back to town.'

'Think yourself lucky you're not being deported.'

'All coppers are bastards.'

'They don't like a lot of paperwork for nothing.'

'Why's he got all those combs and lighters on his table?'

''Cos every time he goes out he loses his comb and his lighter in the bars, so he buys them by the gross now to save shopping at the chemists and the *tabacalleria* all the time. Actually he doesn't buy the lighters by the gross. He has some contact in town who sells them to him by the dozen.'

Tommy looked furtively sideways at George.

George coughed.

'I had an idea like that once,' said Tommy. 'It was looking at Nelson's column in Trafalgar Square gave me the idea.'

'Idea for what?'

'A business based on perpetual motion. Supposing the column were hollow, and supposing you had trained those pigeons to fly with a pea in its beak to the top and deposit it in a little tray which comes down inside the column to where you wait and tip the trays of peas into the paper bags and sell them to the American tourists. All those pigeons would be working for you.'

'They'd eat the peas.'

'No, they'd be fed before starting work.'

'A pigeon has to land six times a day or it starves to death. If you can keep 'em in the air for long enough with scarers they croak.'

'There'd be special feed times, six meals a day, but every other pea goes to the boss. Or you could mark one pea in every packet with a cross, and that's the one the worker-pigeon can eat.'

'What if it was short sighted and couldn't see the cross?'

'We could get it spectacles. Wasn't there a guy once who invented smoked spectacles for pigeons and made a fortune?'

'I don't know if he made a fortune. To make a fortune you'd have to sell smoked pigeons to spectacles, you know, grilled outside French football stadiums and sports events.'

'You don't think it would work? Not even in St. Mark's Square in Venice, hire an empty building for the little lift?'

'It's an idea anyway.'

'I got it from you, George. Those lighters.'

'Oh, I only do that with rich tourists. The Germans have so much money here they don't know what to spend it on. And what's a new lighter to a German tourist?'

'Nothing. A burnt match.'

'Right. Hey, that's not bad. Did you hear about Steve Primero and the German tourist last year? "Excuse me, sir, vell, vell, see doctor has given me suppositories for the stomach troubles, but zees Spanien suppositories have tin foil - how you say, silver paper - wrapped around them. Vot I am askink is: do I take zee tin foil off?" "No," says Steve.'

'The poor bastard,' said Tommy. 'That's Jewish medical advice - keep the tin foil on.'

'Look out, we're coming to Pen and Ink Corner soon. Keep your face mask on. What a pong.'

'One whiff of that and you say to yourself: why go to Ibiza? You can equate it by going through a sewer in a glass bottomed boat.'

'He's selling that glass-bottomed boat.'

'Who? Sixto?'

'Yes, he's married now to an English girl and they have a baby son and he's fed up with tourists and the island being ruined, so he's selling it.'

'Funny name, that. Sixto.'

'There was a Pope Sixto.'

'Is that right?'

'He was embarrassed on the beach once, all these English kids coming up and looking at his feet. He heard one say: 'Does he really have six toes, Mummy?'

'There's a rumour that he called his son Sevento.'

'Isn't that the Cresswell? Tristan Jones's boat?'

'That's the good ship all right.'

'He moors it here?'

'It's free here.'

'No bloody wonder. What about the smell?'

'Oh, the sheep got used to it. Besides he had a shower last year.'

'You sod, George. I hope he can't hear. He'll knock seven bells of shit out of you.'

'Here's where we part company, Tommy. I've got to go and open up the Tav.'

'Oh, I'll come up with you and...'

'Err, well, I'd rather you popped in later, Tommy. I've got to sort things out first, get the beer barrels arranged for new delivery and clean the graffiti off the netty wall. There's a new graffit... graffito, isn't it, singular, yeah, graffito artist in town. Not bad, either, I suspect Mad Mike.'

'Why Mad Mike?'

'The graffiti has an American flavour to it. It's American – more American humour than British.'

'Like what?'

'One I scraped off yesterday said: "The girls in Ibiza have TB or VD. Only screw the ones who cough".'

Tommy laughed: 'Any others?'

'"To be or not to be, Shakespeare. To be is to do, Jean-Paul Satre. Do-be-do-be-do, Frank Sinatra." That sort of thing.'

'So how do you compare that to British graffiti?'

'British is basically more vulgar and infantile. You know on the French letter machine: 'Buy me and stop one,' or 'Don't throw your cigarette ends in the urinal' to which they add: 'It makes them soggy and difficult to light.' or 'My mother made me a homosexual,' to which they add 'If I give her the wool, will she make me one?' Tommy - I've got to go.'

'See you later, George, and thanks for all your help.'

'I'm at the Whisky a-Go-Go tonight if you're in town, that's my third shift.'

'That's a date.'

'No it's not, it's an apple.'

'No it's not, it's a pear.'

'A pair of what?'

'A pair of bloody nut-cases standing here in this pong.'

'See you.'

George cut through the side streets, past the bar on the harbour where they sold the Green Fairy, the genuine Spanish *Absenta,* the drink that had been made illegal in France. He was tempted to stop and have one but he was already very late for his afternoon shift.

He glanced briefly in the window of a herb shop, at the display in ancient bottles that had not changed in many years, a sight that brought cries of 'Wow!' and 'Look at these 'erbs,' and 'This is IT man!' from newly arrived American hippies.

George took the padlock off the huge chain that held fast the doors of the bar and went into the gloomy interior. When he switched the electric light on, he saw that the door of the toilet had been unscrewed, and stood up against the whitewashed wall. He looked inside the toilet to see if the wall artist had struck again, and sure enough, there was one new piece of graffito alongside the reservoir pipe. It said:

A shipwreck at sea can ruin your whole day.
Aescypulus, 340 BC

Behind the bar were some used glasses in the sink and George was busy washing up there when there was a commotion in the doorway and a little man tripped on the step and came staggering into the interior, finally clutching the bar and gazing at George with curiosity. It was the man off the boat.

'Hey buddy, gimme a Bourbon will ya? On the rocks.'

George looked at him. Little had changed except now he wore a KISS ME QUICK hat, either bought or stolen from one of the little souvenir shops in the streets behind the harbour.

'I've told you before, sir, I can't serve a customer when he's had too much to drink. Now be a good chap and go back to the boat and have a kip. You'll feel a lot better for it.'

'Ya mean ya not goin' ta gimme a drink?'

'I can serve you a soft drink, sir, or I can recommend a Fernet Branca to settle your stomach and pull you round. It's an Italian drink made from various herbs.'

'Are you kiddin' me, buster? I doan want no goddam Wop fruit drink.

I wanna Bourbon. On the rocks. Do you understand English?'

'Look - piss off. I've told you before. The cops will close the bar if I serve a drunk.'

He turned quickly on his heel and made for the doorway, mumbling: 'Godammit I thought somebody said this was a good place to get a drink. What they got? Prohibition or somethin' in this place. Gotta get me a Bourbon someplace...'

A few minutes after his departure the bar owner arrived with a tool box and plonked it down on the bar with a sigh. 'Some day off for me,' he said, looking in the tool box. 'By the way, George, Mad Mike is barred. This time I mean it. I've got to come in here on my day off to fix that bloody door. I could have gone fishing today if it hadn't been for that headbanger.'

'Why, what did he do? Tear the door off the toilet or something?'

'No, he locked himself in there and couldn't get out. We kept hammering on the door but he must have fallen asleep. Everybody was bursting for a slash and they couldn't use Piss Alley as it was daylight, and the women can't anyway. So we had to unscrew the door.'

'I'll miss the graffiti. I'm sure it's him. There's a new one in there.'

'Yeah, very funny. A visit by Mad Mike can ruin your whole day. It's not him. I think it's Steve Primero.'

'Could be. He says he's been writing all his life for nothing. Maybe that's what he means.'

'A man of begging letters. Did you know he had a begging letter from Henry Miller when his first book came out in the States? Anyway, help me hold this door, George, before we get a discerning customer who likes privacy.'

'Jill the Pill's back,' said George as he held the door.

'Yes, and guess who's with her? Chelsea Elsie.'

'What? Randy Mandy's friend?'

'Right - and George, if they try smoking dope in here kick their arses right out. I down mind the heads sneaking in here for a *hierbas* - the hippies love that stuff, have you noticed? I reckon I could market it in New York - but *no way* am I going to get nicked for dope on these premises. *No way, Jose.* Chuck 'em right out. Much they'd care if I lost my livelihood. They're all on Cloud Nine: Wow, isn't life wonderful, you know? And I'd be back in England signing on at the Social Security office. Right, I'm off. See you tomorrow night. Anything you need?'

'No, got it all,' said George with a quick glance along the shelves and under the counter.

When he had gone George opened a bottle of San Miguel beer, taking the tin cap off with his teeth, to keep in practise. The price of beer was so exorbitant in Lola's late night music bar that George took his own, in his pocket, but had caused a row with Lola when he tried to borrow her bottle opener and she had called him England's answer to Nescafe Jack.

A young American came into the bar and gazed around. He wore the uniform of blue jeans, leather belt, shirt open to the waist, a colourful batik T-shirt under that, and a leather waistcoat.

He swung himself onto one of the straw topped bar stools and put his leather cowboy boots on the brass rail that ran along the bar just above floor level.

'Hi,' he said.

'Hi there,' said George.

'Ricard?'

George turned and looked along the three shelves of bottles. For once his practised eye had failed to notice that this particular bottle was missing.

'I'm very sorry, but we seem to be out of Ricard. Pity, that, I should have asked the boss to get me a bottle. He's just left.'

The young American's eye ranged over the bottles then lighted on a notice that said: SANDWICHES / BOCADILLOS: Bacon and Egg, Beans on Toast, Bacon and Tomato, Egg and Tomato, Bacon and Beans, Egg and Beans, Bacon, Egg and Beans, Bacon, Egg, Beans and Tomato. Egg on Toast.

'We've got a Marie Brizard, or I can give you a Spanish Anisette which is similar but much stronger.'

'Gimme a fried egg. Yeah. On toast.'

George sighed. He hated cooking in the bar. There was a small space partitioned off so that customers could not see the tiny kitchen space with a little gas cooker and a couple of pans to make basic snacks, and he did not like to fill the bar with the smell of cooking fat so early in the day. But the customer is always right, so he got the frying pan hot and dropped oil in then cracked a single egg into the pan.

The young American heard the sizzling and saw George's head poke around the partition. 'Would you like it sunny side up, sir? Or fucked up?'

Above:
Ibiza, the port and water-
front, after rain, and the
Domino bar. 1963.

Right:
The interior of the Domino
bar, the first 'foreign' bar
in Ibiza. 1963.

Right:
Terence Stamp dreams of
Hollywood in Nina and
Frederick's house in Ibiza.
1966.

Below:
An early 'hippie' - actor,
Terence Stamp. 1966.

© Frank Schwake

© Frank Schwake

Right:
Steve Seley,
b. Newark, New Jersey, 1915.
d. Ibiza, 1983.
He had affairs with over 200 women, and wrote pornography for Girodias and the Olympia Press in Paris in the '50s. Having been refused a passport by Senator Joe McCarthy, he called the American Ambassador 'Piddle-Puke' in a waterfront bar.
Author of *The Cradle Will Fall* and *Baxter Bernstein*, an early 'anti-hero' book.

© Frank Schwake

Below:
BOGGED DOWN IN COUNTY LYRIC. Steve Primero (Stephen Seley) and author Peter Kinsley, after comparing publishers' rejection slips.

© Frank Schwake

225

Left:
Ernesto Ehrenfeld,
b. Berlin, 1910.
d. Ibiza, 1978.
He hid in Italy and Nice
for two years, a German
Jew evading the Gestapo.
Caught twice, he escaped
death because his mother,
an opera singer, did not
have him circumcised.

© Frank Schwake

© Frank Schwake

Right:
Marty Healey,
Irish-American, shot by a
German soldier on the last
day of the war. Offered a
partnership in Playboy
magazine by Hugh Heffner
while they were at the
Chicago business training
school for veterans, he told
him: 'It won't work, Heff.'

 Steve Primero shows off his fireman's top-coat
outside the bar Estrella.

'Cherokee Frank': Capt. Frank Taylor, U.S. Marines (retd.). He went off to die like a true Red Indian on the Peninsular. After he had gone to the 'Happy Hunting Ground', the United States Air Force (as pre-arranged by Frank) flew his body back to the Arlington cemetery.

The author flies a Piper Cub from Avignon to Cannes after covering a factory explosion in 1961. This was the plane that the French pilot crashed on the Corsican mountain. He survived for ten days before dying in the wreckage that air-sea rescue had failed to find in the mist.

Right:
Tristan Jones: With both legs amputated, he taught limbless children how to sail. His books, *Ice, Saga of a Wayward Sailor, Yarns,* and *The Incredible Voyage* are sailing classics.

Below:
The author, with camera, aboard 'Barbara' with Tristan Jones at the helm, and Steve Llewhellyn on the cleat, in the summer of 1969.

© Chris Bligh

CHAPTER 16

London

A S THE British European Airways Trident took off from Palma, it burst two tyres, an undercarriage and the nose tyre.

The faces! McGinn looked around at them. Fear in every eye. The woman in the seat behind him started to cry, but she was the only one on the 'plane who showed signs of panic. The 129 true-blue British were going to show them!

The Captain announced he would circle for an hour to burn off fuel, that there were tyre marks on the Palma runway, and he would make an emergency landing in Barcelona. McGinn looked behind him again. One couple looked terrified, she a rather tarty type, he arrogant and bewiskered who looked to McGinn as if they had spent their time hacking their way through the commercial jungle, a publican or garage owner or somesuch, Jaguar-owning, camel hair coat wearing, gin-and-tonic drinking, diamond-wearing bourgeois Brits on holiday. But what was it all worth now? McGinn wondered if they would swap the Bentley or the Jag for two new tyres for this 'plane.

The stewardess let the weeping woman move closer to the door to be first down the rubber chute. And so... one hour to live, and people in their nervousness began talking to each other.

The stewardesses started the emergency landing drill: all hard objects out of pockets: pens, pipes, etc. Glasses off and rested on knees during actual landing. An hour to think about life and death. McGinn analysed himself. Was he afraid? At first, yes, a feeling of horror that the sun was shining out there and the few clouds looked lovely and the beautiful Mediterranean was lapping the beaches of the Costa Brava and he may never see any of it again. Not even the daffodils in Kenwood, an annual pilgrimage.

Now he sensed the fear of the passengers around him - venal people, most of them, scrambling for the first place in the queue, terrified of not getting served first, careful of their possessions (Many of them stood up and donned coats in case the 'plane caught fire after they had jumped and they would lose their coats.) Possessive to the end. But what would McGinn himself leave behind? A few novels, some diaries, some funny stories: not much, but better than most people leave behind when they depart ('It's a sad life, anyway. Not many of us will get out of it alive' as Luis Zukovsky said to Ezra Pound and to Steve Seley).

What now? A prayer? Perhaps a little insurance policy? But what is the point? The pilot announces he will fly past the Barcelona conning tower to check on the nose wheel.

They float down. The lovely brown mountains of Majorca are behind them now and ahead only the flat area of the airport. Little white *fincas* dot the landscape. Windmills turn slowly, like midget hairdryers in the distance. The buildings of the airport loom up: hangars and the green control tower. The pilot thrusts forward on all engines, and then says: 'They did not get a close enough look that time, ladies and gentlemen, so I'll come round once more.'

The passengers saw the control tower staff close up, Spaniards with binoculars trained on the wheels.

'We'll come in to land now,' says the calm voice of the pilot. But he does not mention the nose wheel.

As the plane lands all passengers crouch forward. McGinn then sits upright to observe. He looks at the four terrified round-eyed faces of the passengers with backward-facing seats. They are petrified. The 'plane is shuddering, trembling, the tyres squashed flat on the tarmac. Reverse engines, a surge of power from the great Rolls Royce engines and they are down, safe, and rolling unsteadily towards the danger area with fire engine and ambulances chasing along behind.

A round of applause for the pilot, with everyone British and Brave now. Nervous, high tension laughter. Everyone talking at once... STILL ALIVE. And everyone walked calmly off the 'plane and into the airport bus ('Mustn't let the Spaniards know we were nervous. Be British. Be Brave. Hearts of Oak, etc).

McGinn walked calmly into the bar and ordered two beers, one for the thirst and one for the celebration, but the bar is crowded with police, Guardia, Armada with their red cap bands, journalists and photographers with their Canons and Long Tom lenses.

McGinn shouted out loud: *'Y una bebida por los passajeros, por favor!'* and the barman speaks to the manager who calls that drinks are 'on the house' so the passengers start ordering large whiskies.

One hour later an announcement came that the 'plane was ready to take off for London, tyres and wheels changed and all ship-shape and Bristol fashion as the sailors say. But although every passenger went back aboard, they went to different seats to continue their conversations with their new-found pals from the bar. The stewardess walked down the aisle. She said to McGinn: 'The pilot wants a head-count, but some of them have changed their seats.'

'Of course they have,' McGinn replied: 'because NO ONE WANTS TO SIT IN THE WET SEATS.'

So to London, with a signed note of thanks and another round of applause for the ice-cool pilot, a Brit at his Best.

In Hampstead McGinn's sister in the downstairs flat (his own was sub-let) said: 'You can't stay here.'

'Where can I stay?'

'Get a bed-sit like everyone else.'

But he was allowed a camp bed next to the Labrador, Tiffany. She had the couch. McGinn stared at Tiffany, and she stared back. Tiffany clearly resented the presence of McGinn in her domain, and he resented her the couch which was more comfortable than the camp bed. McGinn continued to stare. Tiffany shuffled uncomfortably and eventually got off the couch, went and thudded on McGinn's sister's bedroom door upstairs and was allowed in for the night. The dog had not been born that could outstare McGinn.

Back with old friends in London McGinn took a bed-sit in Frognal but could not stand the landlady who put plastic bags inside the wastepaper baskets, watched the electric meter while hot water was being run off for a bath, and put a hot water bottle in McGinn's bed, the final straw, and reminding him of Ian Galbraith – who as a baby had been left on a doorstep in Australia – saying: 'Had one mother, don't want another.'

Jocelyn Kelsey, who shared with Ashcan at 57 High Street offered a couch temporarily, but stressed: 'I'm afraid there is an atmosphere of the country in the living room where you will sleep,' he said. 'Because I have recently taken delivery of a load of horse manure which has been liberally sprinkled on eight giant plant pots containing basil, rosemary, tarragon - remember you brought the *'racine d'estragon'* from France for me last year? - and a hand reared azalea which must at all costs not catch a chill, so I do urge you to keep the windows shut.'

McGinn moved in. This was 'la vie Boheme' with a vengeance, and the chambers certainly had the atmosphere of the racing stable about them. In the morning he shaved in a plastic bucket balanced on the lavatory seat. The pink and white Regency wallpaper in the living room had either been watered along with the herbs and azalea or used as a urinal to save walking down two flights of stairs, so that the wallpaper looked as if it had a bad case of trench foot.

The kitchen was indescribable, overflowing with old coffee cups and grounds, a lemon that had probably come from Valencia before the civil war and the floor like a mechanics workshop.

It was the Nur Hotel, Istanbul without the cockroaches.

McGinn was invited back to Kiedrych Rhys's flat (his back window looked into the kitchen of 57 High Street) with an actor called Hugh, Richard Burton's best friend from Wales, and acting in a film of 'Canterbury Tales' wherein all the British actors have grog-blossom noses like large loganberries, and faces like the marbling on a ledger. Tea, toast, scones, Double Gloucester cheese (Kiedrych loved his afternoon tea) and two bottles of *Macon Blanc*. Keidrych saying what a shit J.P. Donleavy is. When Gaynor Crist (on whom 'The Ginger Man' was based) suggested some small share of the enormous royalties from the book, Donleavy left an envelope for him. It contained a bar of soap. Crist had thoughts of helping Judith, his wife, who had been fined £1,200 and jailed in Madrid by Franco's government for going on a teachers' strike.

Jocelyn being quirky, refuses to read a newspaper which has been read by someone else, hence Ashcan and he buy separate sets of Sunday newspapers. McGinn, caught with Jocelyn's Sunday Times, made Jocelyn storm out for a new paper.

The S.T. had an item by Nicholas Tomalin referring to a character who could only be Derek (or 'Bill') Driscoll:

'A pair of pink eyes, familiar from many a liquid lunch in El Vino during my newspaper days, Frank Smollet had worked his way steadily through most newspapers, usually getting the sack for some act or drunkeness. I was always surprised to find him alive, let alone working.'

Tomalin adds: 'The physical attributes are actually those of our mutual friend B*** D*******.

McGinn rang Driscoll. 'I'm going to sue him' he said.

Driscoll may have been fired for irresponsibility or for his contemptuous attitude to journalism but never for drunkeness, and there lies the libel.

In the Flask with John Wilson Hare who has two plays running about the troubles in Belfast where Kiedrych turned up with Keith Burgess who had his hand bandaged because he had punched a modern sculpture at the top of Back Lane, shouted 'I can do better than that' and broke his hand. Kiedrych droning on about his job at the Ministry of Pensions and claims a clerk has been given the OBE for being subjected to repeated physical attack from destitute people trying to draw National Assistance.

McGinn's talk about selling his flat which was to be vacated in five weeks, interrupted by Robert MacDougall, crippled by Multiple Sclerosis while a student at Glasgow University. MacDougall had worked on the famous Ealing comedy scripts after the war and then gone to Hollywood. 'I had a house in Tanzer Road, Hampstead, another in the South of France and one in Bel Air. I'm 62 with no pension writing TV plays to scratch a living and I'd be half a bloody millionaire today if I hadn't sold those houses. My strongest advice, McGinn, is - as a writer, do not ever sell property.'

Later in the week McGinn met up with Frank Smyth who seems very interested in McGinn's plan to rent something near Pezenas, and he asked about shotgun licenses in France. He recounted a story about his brother in Yorkshire applying to the police for a black powder license to enable him to make his own cartridges. Two CID men visited him. He offered them tea; one of them asked him what he thought about Enoch Powell, and he replied that it was perfectly possible that Enoch's prophetic words about immigration causing a river of blood would come true some day. While refilling the tea cups in the kitchen, he heard one say to the other: 'I told you he was nothing to do with Black Power.'

Smyth then revealed that he had been having a love affair with the daughter of Admiral Sir Caspar John, 1st Lord of the Admiralty and son of Augustus the painter, and revealed that just for fun and to add variety to their sexual congress, he would occasionally don part of the admiral's uniform, jacket, cockade hat and sword, while on the job. Smyth then confessed that at a dinner party in Caspar's house, he had said to his host: 'I have a friend, Caspar, a scribbler, who also has an American scribbler friend, and they conclude that either you or Mountbatten was the fourth man...'

The Admiral had risen to his feet, furious, banged down his knife and fork and yelled: 'How dare you say such a thing? Get out of my house.' As Smyth reached the door, the Admiral yelled: 'And stop fucking my daughter.'

After parting company with Smyth McGinn adjourned to the Kismet Club near Leicester Square tube station and met Toby Tovey who was with Johnny Quarrel. Quarrel, who had had two plays running in the West End not long before, was off to New York to try his luck and write a novel. Quarrel was a handsome East Ender who had been a professional thief before his success in the theatre and told McGinn 'If the plays don't work I can always go back to 'oistin' (hoisting, or 'lifting' or shoplifting).

Tovey, owed £5 by Quarrel, went to his father's house in the East End, trying to trace the famous playwright with the two West End hits, and Quarrel's father said: 'I've no idea where 'e is, Tobes, me old fruit. I know one fing - 'e ain't workin.''

McGinn and Tovey ended the night at the Richard Steele pub where the usual gang had assembled: Burgess, Ronnie Frazer, Pip Perkins, Lucas Heller, Leon Griffiths, and Georgina Hylton, daughter of the bandleader Jack Hylton, whom McGinn had last met in Juan les Pins when the retired Hylton was living with a voluptuous and curvaceous Italian dancer nearly fifty years younger than himself.

After a long walk on Hampstead Heath, McGinn rang Marty Feldman to ask for an option on his first novel. Loretta answered and said he could do nothing on it for six months but she'd hold on to it for when he was free. One of McGinn's drinking pals was Carl Sullivan, who had had some of his fingers chopped off in an industrial accident when a lad, and had a small pension. Loretta Feldman was his sister, and they came from an Irish Catholic family, their father a successful pork butcher. The press reported trouble over their marriage because Marty's Jewish parents did not want him to marry a Catholic. One night, in the Flask, McGinn asked Marty about it and he said: 'That wasn't the reason. The real reason was that my parents were vegetarians and her father was a pork butcher.'

Carl Sullivan had pointed out to McGinn that there was £40,000 worth of teeth at the Flask bar, all crowns by Frank Sinatra's dentist who flew to England twice a year to do the stars. There was Marty Feldman, Loretta, Patrick Wymark and Marie-Lise Goetz, John Hurt's common law wife. From each gleamed a £10,000 smile. Later, however, when Loretta took Marty to Keats restaurant, he inadvertently bit into a French bread roll which was on a side plate, and his new crowns fell onto the tablecloth. The roll was for display purposes and rock hard. After that Marty took to eating salads in the back of his Rolls Royce with Loretta as waitress.

Toby Tovey gave a party the next week, but there were too many egos in one room. Virginia Dignam, wife of Mark the Shakespearean actor, produced a bottle of scotch from her knickers when drinks ran low. Virginia, film critic for the communist paper The Morning Star had performed the greatest piece of name-dropping McGinn had heard when he drank with her in the Railway Tavern and had asked her if she knew the words to the song 'Lord Rothschild said to me...' She started to sing it and the Governor rushed up and said: 'Stop that. I don't have a music licence here you know.' Virginia glared at him and said: 'Listen, darling, as I said to La Pasionara yesterday, when I was drinking with her in Moscow: 'When the Revolution starts in England the first ones against the wall will be the Hampstead pub Governors.' The Governor flinched. It was true. She had been drinking with La Pasionara in Moscow the day before.

Gordon Williams, author of the book that became 'Straw Dogs' as a film was claiming the way to tell if Guinness was bottled in Ireland or London was that the Dublin bottle had a label on the bottom saying: 'Open at the other end.' Williams had recounted to Frank Smyth how he had recently awoken chained to a bed frame in Glasgow, face down, and a woman wielding a whip had entered in the morning and asked:

'Would you like another couple of strokes, Commander?' Dressing hastily and hurtling out of the premises he came upon heavy oak doors leading to a counter and asked plaintively: 'Could ye gie us a half and half?', which, translated into English meant a half pint of beer and a single shot of whisky. A prim voice from behind the counter said: 'Excuse me, sir, but you're in the Royal Bank of Scotland.'

Gordon MacRae Williams had been telephoned by Christina Foyle and asked if he would present the literary prize to Cristy Brown, the disabled Irishman who had typed with his left foot a book called 'Down All the Days'. Williams said: 'Oh, no, Mrs. Foyle, Ah couldnae do that.' 'Why not, Mr. Williams?' she asked. 'Well, I might inadvertently take a step backwards and *ruin his literary career.*'

Frank Smyth was in good form, saying that he had sent Paul 'The Mouth' (the title of his book) Ableman to the wrong address as his deliberate mistake of the evening. McGinn, Clark and Burgess snorted some mescaline through a pound note in the kitchen to little effect, but later Clark crashed his girlfriend's Volvo in the back of an MG and was arrested. In jail he met Too Much Tommy, with a big black eye. Tommy Cholmondeley had just had his 200th conviction for being drunk in Soho. Once, he had fought and knocked out four policemen and they had had it in for him ever since. To celebrate the 200th conviction McGinn had typed a letter for him to Norris McWhirter asking if he now deserved entry in the Guinness Book of Records, to which McWhirter replied: 'Dear Mr. Cholmondeley, unfortunately your record has been superceded by a Yorkshire farmer who has 600 convictions for being drunk.'

A few days later McGinn received a postcard from Tristan Jones in Grenada, British West Indies, asking if he wanted to do a four months' trip up the Amazon. McGinn replied: 'Yes.' Later he met Frank Smyth and Judy Froshaug and John Hurt and went to the Kismet club, then the French pub for Guinness, then to Islington, to Frank's local. It was also Cyril Cusack's local. Cusack had the honour, with Ashcan, of being banned for life from the English stage for drunkenness three times in a row. When Cusack came in with his daughter, Sinead (known as 'Sinbad') they took one look at the Hampstead visiting team and fled.

Sally, the beautiful blonde nurse McGinn had met in Ibiza and taken to bed a couple of times, rang him to say she was going to marry a

British Army Lieutenant who was being sent to Northern Ireland.

McGinn, peeved and slightly jealous, said: 'Well, good luck to you Sally. At least you will be compatible: he goes around shooting Irishmen and you follow stitching them up.'

McGinn and Clark borrowed John Hurt's car for a trip, because John couldn't drive anyway (he was learning, for he had to drive in certain film scenes) and he did not have a licence. Trying to arrange insurance McGinn went to a West End office and glimpsed the face of an old acquaintance from Riviera days: it was Bill Powell of the Powell and Pressburger team who had made 'The Red Shoes' and other classics. They reminisced about the hotel Bill owned with R.A. Butler's family, the Voile d'Or in Cap Ferrat when it was full of stars like Jack Hawkins, David Niven, Kurt Jurgens, Eddie Constantine and Alec Guinness and when the beautiful Frankie Powell held sway in the little British enclave on the Cote d'Azure, while Hawkins and Powell took their kids camping in the hills. Sadly, it was only after he was dead that Hollywood recognised Powell's genius as a filmmaker who had influenced their own great directors.

CHAPTER 17

Istanbul

SPRING was in the air and another trip was essential, so they left London in John's little white open Triumph and got to Brussels and then to Antwerp, the quickest route onto the Autobahn, and drove through Germany all night, reaching Salzburg at eleven on Sunday morning. Excellent *Wiener Schnitzel* in Gasthof and slept until seven pm then drove on through Austria via Graz to Jugoslavia. Spring in Northern Jugoslavia and the farms looking wonderful with the blossom out in the orchards. Near Belgrade they broke the shaft which holds the back wheel and thought the trip was over, but a garage repaired it in three hours, and they reached Belgrade at four pm and ate whitebait and drank white wine in the Dalmatia restaurant where they had eaten before. On again through the night and stopped at Nis in a motel.

Next day Bulgaria looked as depressing as usual and they nearly had a head-on collision with a military jeep while Clark was trying to overtake three lorries, and worried in case the military reported the incident, but crossed the frontier into Turkey without trouble. They stopped in Edirne and drank with the Turks, all boozy types, the bar owner paying for their beers.

They checked in at an hotel opposite the entrance to the bazaar in Istanbul, and went to meet Ismet. In the bazaar a Turkish leather shop owner said he knew of an Englishman - 'dressed like Diplomat man' - who smuggles hashish from Lebanon to Istanbul and leather coats and furs to Genoa where they go by yacht to England. The Turk saw him open the wing of his Landrover and it was packed with money.

They had dinner with Ismet at broken Fork.

Reason: all the forks in the cafes have one prong missing so that shellfish can be hooked out with the separated prong. The owner, Sabri Baba, served yoghurt with aubergines, shish kebab, olives, cheese, salad, fruit and plenty of Raki. Raki is the stuff which Ismet complained was giving him the DT's. Then on to Beolu to a whore house run by Okti or Azis as he now calls himself. His minder has a Colt .45 to shoot customers who try to run down the stairs without paying. One of the girls is particularly beautiful with large breasts and petite figure, trapped, at eighteen, by Okti who pays nothing and buys only clothes for her so that she cannot run away. Okti was very worried the cops will close down his new 'business' with four girls. He looks a typical brothel keeper, curly black hair double-breasted gangster-type suit and running to fat.

At the British Consulate McGinn and Clark apply for a permit to visit fourteen year old Timothy Davey in Sagmacilar prison. The British Press had screamed about his savage sentence. His mother had let him take the rap. Davey said they had spent four days choosing the hashish in Afghanistan and his mother had paid for it. The American Drugs Enforcement Agency man in Istanbul had set up his capture and he faced at least twenty years in a Turkish jail.

McGinn dictated a story to the Sunday Times to the effect that he was well and girls had written to him from all over England and he was in good spirits and hoping for remission.

Clark and McGinn drove all night and stopped one hundred kilometres north of Nis. They slept in the car in thick fog then drove on through Belgrade to Graz. In the Gasthof elderly men wore Iron Crosses on the lapels of their Tyrolean jackets and in the enormous bierkeller nearby talked of what 'der Fuhrer' had done and said in the old days.

In Vienna next day they visited St Stephan's cathedral and it was crumbling into a ruin. McGinn bought a copy of his second novel in German for twenty-two schillings in a bookstore.

It was a thrill to see his book on display in another language, but German publishers had paid peanuts for it, and later, having the German translation thoroughly checked out, McGinn discovered that, against new laws (since the end of the war) in Germany they had censored the book. To the Germans there was no such thing as a good communist.

Vienna was full of rich old ladies eating cream cakes or shopping for expensive clothes. The city made McGinn feel uncomfortable. From boyhood he had flinched at harsh, guttural Germanic voices, no doubt brainwashed by war films, and he had reconciled himself to a lifelong fear and hatred of Nazis for what they had done in the war. Although his best friends in Ibiza were German, they were the kind of Germans who had escaped, who had been Humanitarians or 'freethinkers' under Hitler when they were young, and sought the kind of freedom in Ibiza provided for poverty stricken artists.

But Vienna - McGinn felt a little sick in his stomach. It was here that they had made elderly Jews scrub the streets, climb trees in the public park and sing like birds, and where Hitler had written 'Mein Kampf'. It was here that they had given the ash remains of murdered Jews to their grieving relatives, labeled, numbered and in a cigar or matchbox.

'Let's get out of here,' McGinn said.

'Don't you like the froth-blowing Bavarian fuck-pigs, then?'

'It's a beautiful city, but it gives me the creeps.'

They drove to Linz and stayed in a Gasthof, then on an autobahn crowded with hundreds of enormous trucks on the way to Hasselt in Belgium. The scene outside Frankfurt airport was like a Twentieth century nightmare, with lorries thundering by, hundreds of cars in the airport car parks, and a Jumbo Jet circling to land while a stratocruiser was taking off, and further along the road two German Starfighters buzzing the autobahn. McGinn longed for peace, anywhere, away from this Hell on Wheels.

On the boat from Boulogne, McGinn reflected on their trip. It had been worthwhile because they had got the story of the fourteen year old Timothy Davey into the Sunday Times and McGinn knew it would be milked by the Turkish newspapers and would be considered by the judge when the appeal comes up. McGinn was confident they would get him three or four years off his sentence.

'I keep thinking about the little whore we had in Istanbul,' he said to Clark 'she was very nice, really, and not like a whore at all - no stopwatch stuff but clinging and loving just like a very young virgin.'

'She's only eighteen. The torpedo with the .45 told me.'

'Yes, there's a lot of love in that little bird and it's a pity she's tied up with that shit Okti.'

'Did you give her money?'

'Yes.'

'So did I, but not enough for her train fare to Paris. Or even to Edirna, come to think of it.'

'That bastard Okti makes sure they can't do a runner. The torpedo collects the dough from the punters. We could go back and rescue her...'

'Next trip.'

'You're on. She can get a ticket to Ankara. She won't have a passport anyway.'

CHAPTER 18

Israel

WHEN Ted Francis paid McGinn the £250 option money on his adventure novel, the one Stanley Baker was supposed to film, it was decided that Israel would be a cheap trip because they would be on a kibbutz. It was the middle of August. All free flights had been booked by students. McGinn bought £5 worth of Red Leb. and made up some chocolate fudge for the trip: a quarter ounce of hashish; cocoa powder; almonds; peanuts; coriander; black pepper; brown sugar; nutmeg; cinnamon; butter; milk. It was based on the Alice B. Toklas cookbook recipe, and it was not only a marvelous turn-on but a high-powered aphrodisiac.

Next day they were in Calais at 6 p.m. but after several *pastis* and two bottles of Beaujolais they awoke feeling like death, in Belgium, with a dead battery. A push-start in second gear and off to Limburg and Ypps, near Vienna. McGinn took more 'fudge' in the car and was turned on all day. Next day, in Budapest they could not get an hotel. The Hungarians were tough at the border and wanted photographs plus £4 for a visa. They bashed on to Romania and stopped for a drink in a village after the border. The bar was filling up with iron-ore miners dressed in rags and clogs, some with 'toe-rags' instead of socks. To express life under the Communist State system they simply put their wrists together.

Razor blades were unobtainable. The bar owner offered the equivalent of £1 for 5 blades. One miner had his 2 year old daughter on his shoulder. McGinn gave the little girl an English pound note. The miners gathered round to look, and asked: 'Who is the woman on the note?' They were surprised to be told that England still had a queen. Clark and McGinn got drunk with the miners and later in the middle of nowhere crashed the car into a ditch and were lifted out and set right by ten Romanian students.

Out of petrol, they flagged down two Czechoslovakian cars. The Czechs were friendly, shaking hands on seeing a British number plate, but Clark's shifty eyes noted a little Volkswagen stop behind them and the driver watch the whole operation in case McGinn and Clark were spies passing information or documents.

In Bucharest, having slept in the car which now had a very wobbly back wheel they checked into the Hotel Union and sold 60 pairs of women's silk tights and stockings (bought at Woolworth's) for 800 lie (38 = £1), with very little profit but a means of getting Romanian currency without being ripped of at the border exchange bureau. With 800 lie they bought silver bracelets, cufflinks and medallions all with a fish design, as a means of getting currency in Turkey. Packing to leave next day, McGinn noted that his copy of 'The Godfather' had been stolen from the room (a banned book in Romania) and Clark's little transistor had been pulled to pieces in case it was a receiver.

Through the towns and Villages of Romania, with poor peasants in rags everywhere. The queues at the 'Carne' (meat) shops on Sunday morning reminded McGinn of wartime Britain.

'So where does all the food go from this agricultural country?' McGinn asked.

'Russia?'

'And the West for hard currency to pay for the military. The only well-fed people here are Army officers and the police. Fat cops and soldiers and skinny ragged miners - what kind of equality is that?'

At the Bulgarian frontier they tore the car apart, looking for smuggled goods. The solemn, dull, humourless Bulgars charged £3.10s for a visa and they refused to change an English £5 note because it had a number (a bank clerk's tally number) on it (the unrelenting face of official stupidity).

At the Turkish frontier a student called Mehemet asked for a lift to Edirne ('When I saw your car, I knew you were OK. Not businessmen') and he booked them into a 100 room hotel called Caravaserai which had been restored from a merchant's stopover in the days of the caravan trail to Northern Europe with carpets and silks and gems (each room had a space where a wall-safe had been).

Istanbul felt like home, and the news from Ismet in the bazaar was good: there was no need to 'rescue' the little whore from Okti's brothel, for she had done a clever runner herself. Having persuaded Okti that she needed a holiday and a suntan, she borrowed a tent, placed it on the beach, and made enough money in a week from clients, to be able to disappear from Istanbul. After a night on the *raki* at Sabri Baba's restaurant, McGinn tried to cure his hangover on the Galetta bridge in the Turkish wrestlers' tea shop, but the smoke from the *narghiles* drove him out and into the Yeni mosque, a peaceful haven from the bustling world, then to the Pudding shop, where the flower children gathered to plan their trips to Afghanistan and India. Where the notes on the board said: 'Jack - meet you in Kabul midday 20th - Susan' or 'Guys - got a lift. C.U. Calcutta. Leave message Amex.'

Ditching a car in Turkey proved difficult: ten signatures were required on one piece of paper, then swap for another piece and leave the car in a pound on the Galetta bridge dock.

Smoking a 'devil's piece' with Feret the photographer in the evening, then on to various bars, stoned where Clark talked for half an hour to a deaf mute, explaining their route across Europe by car, while McGinn talked French to a Turkish actor and the P.R.O. for the Ministry of Economics.

Next day, looking forward to drying out in a kibbutz, McGinn took the Dolmuss to the Naval Museum and the War Museum which had great statues of all the Sultans in their garb with pistols, swords and the most vicious weapons imaginable: pistols with knife blades, terrible steel hammers, then photos of Turkish officers with German officers, 1914-18, with American officers, 1943-45, and British officers in Korea in the '50s.

In Sabri Baba's with Feret, Ismet came in with Okti or Aziz. The brothel keeper says little Helga, his prize girl, told him she was 'keeping the campers happy' on the beach and then disappeared. He then said to Clark: 'Ismet says you are going to Israel. Bring me back one Philistine woman.' He then borrowed 20 lire from the restaurant and left it on McGinn and Clark's bill. Ismet then made a tearful farewell, smashing his glass on his forehead (no blood) to prove his companionship, and saying to McGinn: 'You are like a little boy - young here (pointing to his heart) and young here (pointing to his forehead)' McGinn said: 'Ismet, the secret of eternal youth is to laugh at the world - if you don't laugh, you'll cry.'

At 5 am, the bus left Istanbul, full of holidaying Lebanese, who had been in Bulgaria, and off they went to Beirut, fare £7. A good drive through the Turkish countryside with a view of the Dardanelles. They stopped at night in the Taurus mountains, where a bride in a full white wedding dress sat tearing into hunks of meat. Her headgear looked like plastic, like something off a grave at Highgate cemetery, perpetual flowers. The bus driver carved from the carcass of a dead sheep and after the meat was weighed, it was grilled by a fierce small boy who demanded cigarettes and flapped smoke in everyone's eyes. A hotel specialising in giant cockroaches in Adana that night and *sut* (warm milk) for breakfast.

At the Syrian border a passenger who owned a Casino bribed the customs officers with silk. A map of the middle east on the office wall did not show Israel as existing. More presents to customs at the Lebanese frontier post. Finally they booked into the hotel Bosphore at the bus station, where the cockroaches were marginally bigger and quicker than those in Adana.

'Must write a book about that trip someday,' said McGinn.

'Who'd believe it?' said Clark.

'The bus driver drinking sheep's blood and raki? The drivers fighting over the hot liver? The drivers switching seats at 60 miles an hour down that mountain while smoking joints like White Owl cigars? And who knows what they were smuggling?'

The next day, Sunday, they went to Hambra for coffee and croissants with the bourgeoisie, then to the Med for the first swim of the year. At a cafe, a baby Bustard strutted under the tables. McGinn gave it a peanut but it sidled off disdainfully, no doubt used to better fare.

Drinking in the red-light district, with whores, and hashish near the bus station, McGinn discovered there was no toilet in the bar and had to go (warned by barman) up a side alley which was a meeting place for queers.

One of them followed McGinn back to the bar, sat down, and asked: 'Are you a merchant seaman?' 'No' 'What you do here, buy drugs?' 'No, holiday' 'Where you from?' 'England' 'Where in England?'

'London' 'Where in London?' 'Hampstead' 'Do you know the William the Fourth?'

'Who'd believe it?' says McGinn to Clark's laughter.

Next day, in Cyprus, McGinn's old bank manager from London, Lt. Col (Artillery) Geoffrey Brierly, let them stay aboard his yacht 'Merianda' (later blown up when the Turks invaded Kyrenia).

The Greek police at Nicosia airport had a pink card on Clark (suspected communist sympathiser) and would only allow him seven days in Cyprus. His arrest in Athens and friendship with Elli Theodorakis had been circulated as far as Cyprus: Geoffrey Brierly who had a wounded leg from action in the desert with the 8th army, said his wife had decided he could not sail them to Haifa.

The food on the island was abominable, influenced by the British NAAFI, no doubt, with ketchup on everything. McGinn believed that Carl Sullivan's 'Famagusta Wimpy Training School' might really exist. A sail over to Snake Island was the limit for Geoffrey. In the harbour the after cabin had a temperature of 100 degrees.

Next day Clark, feeling guilty about his drunkenness and shouting about Greek Cypriots, walked the 16 miles from Kyrenia to Nicosia in the heat of the day 10 am - 2 pm, refusing all offered lifts.

In the duty free shop, about to board from Limassol to Haifa, McGinn met the new love of his life, Ann, with her little sister Belinda, from Wiltshire. Clark was drunk again and tried four times to jump off the tender to the Appolonia, restrained by the crew, one of whom knocked him for six and he slept in the salon. Meanwhile, at the deck rail, soon after sailing, McGinn was in a clinch with the beautiful Ann that lasted throughout the night, as they cruised on this marvelous romantic crossing beneath a million stars, just below the Seven Sisters, sailing due south, and watching the flash of phosphorus on the water. Ann, a very passionate and loving 21 year old, said she wanted to teach, and that she had only had one brief broken affair in Gloucestershire. She wanted to join McGinn on the Eilat venture, but she did not want to part with her 18 year old sister on her holiday. She promised to write and return to Israel later.

The atmosphere in Israel was heavy. Eleven of their athletes had been murdered in Munich, and the security forces were on full alert. Everyone was warned not to open a suitcase in the departure area, in case they contained bombs or guns. For some strange reason, McGinn's green suitcase looked much smaller that the one he had brought from England, and he thought it might not be his. He looked around. The only way to tell was a swift look. He opened one lock and felt a pistol pressing on his temple. He squinted up into the clear blue eyes of a young, slim, blond Israeli security officer, who said: 'You were told not to open your case.'

'I'm not sure that it's mine. The only way is to check.'

'Do it slowly.'

McGinn opened the other lock, had a swift glance inside, and said: 'Yes, it's mine. It looked smaller, maybe because I saw it from a height.'

In Tel Aviv, Project 67 allotted places to McGinn and Clark in the danger zone: Hagosharim, on the Lebanese border where, in Kiriat Shmone the schoolchildren had been murdered recently by infiltrating Arab terrorists from Lebanon and Syria, and they were warned not to go to the Kibbutz after dark. As they checked into an hotel, Israeli Mystere and Mirage jets swung over the hills, on border patrol.

Next day they checked into dilapidated huts where the inmates were mainly English, jolly hockey-sticks and team spirit Charlies, and one nymphomaniac called Glynis who was being stoked by an Italian called Marco. The other girls were clearly nonstarters. The other occupant of McGinn's hut was an RAF University entrant, a rah-rah-team 'hooray', whom McGinn christened 'Flying Officer Kite'.

Poor food, hard straw mattresses, but a wonderful swim in the National Park adjoining the Kibbutz built by the JNF of Great Britain and Ireland.

A 4 am start the next morning, working in the apple orchards, breakfast at 8, with the 600 on the kibbutz, all looking forward to knocking off work at 10 am because it is the Jewish New Year's Eve. They were given a cup of wine (a big deal here, McGinn was assured). After the evening 'party' when no one was allowed to eat or drink until all the poems, songs and speeches in Hebrew were over (about an hour and a half of boredom) Clark and McGinn took two bottles of wine back to the hut and drank them.

McGinn was told he would be working in the kitchen, Clark on the apple picking machines. Most of the resident Kibbutzniks are the peasant type, central European peasant stock, very hairy and stocky, broad and husky, except for one, who is thin, ginger-haired, very white and freckled, and has his Auschwitz number tattooed on his forearm.

At the 'Guest House' which makes money from tourism for the kibbutz coffers, the sad barman looks at McGinn and Clark as if they are depraved when they order a second and even third beer.

As McGinn swelters in the kitchen, washing the enormous pans, rather snobbish young Israeli girls, very supercilious, prance around as if they own the world. They never stop eating or nibbling, and McGinn knows their backsides will spread by the time they are 30. He knows why *plongeurs* hate everyone. The 'Yiddisher Momma' ladies in the kitchen try to force coffee on him, whose job it is to wash dishes, knives, forks, plates etc, separately, as they are exclusively used by orthodox Jews and must not be washed in the same water as McGinn's plates and dishes, gets the message and calls to the storeman, who, with a nod and a wink through a bleary eye, indicated to McGinn to follow him to the storeroom where he produced a hidden bottle of brandy and gave McGinn (bless his alcoholic heart) a quick slug, then back to the drudgery. The Israelis seem to think McGinn is one of the Great Train Robbers on the run.

The life was so restricting on the Kibbutz, McGinn wanted to get away as soon as possible, but he was awaiting a £10,000 film contract from Ted Francis in London, paid by Stanley Baker, and mail from publishers and agents, and so was trapped. He tried to imagine the life of a permanent *plongeur* but it does not bear thinking about. George Orwell did it in Paris to write his 'Down and Out in Paris and London' except that Orwell, or Eric Blair, was never really down and out and never experienced despair through poverty. He was only playing at it, and could have borrowed £50 from any of his Eton friends at the time. And Modigliani did it in Paris, then put his coat on and went back to paint. McGinn was working only five hours each day, but had to wash more than 100 dishes 4ft across, and buckets and pans 4ft by 1ft, all to be cleaned with wire wool. By 3pm he was ready to lash out at the snooty young girls who pranced around, nibbling.

Marco ('The Duke of Genova') the medical student keeping, or trying to keep, Glynis happy, is drinking in the Guest House. Marco, in his Italian way, orders a Campari, and in his Italian way Glynnis pays for it, an expensive drink at 5 Israeli pounds for a thimbleful. Later Clark got drunk on some Israeli boys' wine and tried to get into the bed of Liz, next door, McGinn being awakened at 1.30am by her friend Miranda (jealous?) asking him to intervene, after which Clark snored all night.

For one of the very few times in his life McGinn had thought of marriage with the lovely Ann, and 'settling down' and starting some serious writing instead of always breaking off to travel, to booze etc.

Switched into the apple-packing factory, McGinn was as bored with this mindless work as he was dish washing, and wondered again at how the army of low-paid and downtrodden workers stand it all their lives. He was speaking five languages in the little packing factory, as these Israelis come from all over the world: a smattering of German to 'Israel', the old man i/c machines; French to the overseer, who was fluent; Spanish to 'Mr. Horse' (Senor Caballo) from Barcelona; English to the Danish student, Gustav; Italian to the hairy foreman who asked McGinn if he was Italian.

On September the 16th the Israelis entered Lebanon to knock out more Arab terrorist villages. McGinn heard the tanks going up the road at midnight, reached for the Uzi they had issued him when they heard he had trained as a soldier, then realised it was Israeli tank carriers, used to deliver the tanks onto solid earth so as not to churn up the roads. In the morning French Mirage jets patrolled the frontier below the Golan Heights, flown by pilots in their 20s. Clark was not given a weapon but they respected him as he had a tree planted in his name - one of the foreigners who had stayed behind to help when the Six Day War was fought.

Next day was Yom Kippur and they closed the Guest House, the worst bar in the world. McGinn drank wine with Clark, however, enough to give him a hangover which was unwise, for next day he started work in the cotton fields. With four tough Israelis, he drove the 5 miles to the cotton valley, and natural cauldron and sun trap. An Israeli ex-commando, Adiss, 21, and McGinn climbed 20ft up a ladder and into the wire mesh cage that contains the cotton, while two men operate the American machine.

'Just like in a swimming pool' said Adiss, but it was not a good comparison; the heat of the fresh cotton, and the overhead sun made it almost impossible to breathe as they stamped it down, Adiss in commando boots and McGinn, 16 years older than him, in Hush Puppies, one of which went missing in the cotton. It took ten minutes to find the shoe, then Adiss drove the tractor with the big orange container which was then moved alongside the wire mesh cage and a hydraulic lift cascaded it into the cage. Gasping for breath, McGinn then picked up over spill from a ditch, climbed the ladder which was so hot at 11.30am he could not touch the sides. The temperature was now 40 in the shade McGinn crawled under the cage and vomited the water he had drunk, feeling sad that he would never again be as fit as he had been at 21, after years of smoking and drinking.

From potato picking in Beamish, aged seven, during the war, for £1 to cotton pressing in Israel aged 37, unpaid - that was some 30 year span!

At the infirmary he was given an injection by a French speaking nurse who told him: 'No work tomorrow, and you must drink 3-4 litres of water plus fruit juice every day in this heat.'

It was time to leave the Kibbutz for Jerusalem anyway, at the end of the week, mail or no mail, for he also wanted to see the Holy Land, and the places his father had been in 1915 in the war against the Turks, led by T.E. Lawrence. There were still lots of tourists in September in the Jaffa Road, in the Via Dolorosa, the Holy Sepulchre, David's Tower and at the Damascus Gate when McGinn and Clark checked into an hotel, where they demanded money in advance, even before they had seen their rooms.

The next morning, at 7am McGinn caught the No 22 bus from the Damascus Gate to Bethlehem, price 50 agra, or the price of a box of matches in England. A marvelous bus-ride in the sunshine, then through sunny streets to the Church of the Nativity, the whole place in awful taste with dusty bronze and silver and tin icons on the walls; then down into the bowels of the earth to the Site of the Star of David and the crib in the crypt. An immediate feeling of warmth, of well-being came over McGinn as he entered, not from the dozen lighted candles in front of the altar but a genuine spiritual experience that lasted four to five seconds. McGinn sat down and waited for it to return, but there was nothing. He watched an old man enter and reverently place a small carpet before the altar and when he left McGinn saw the carafe of wine on the right of the covered chalice, and thought of Seley in Seville cathedral taking a sip of wine there, pronouncing it 'rather shy' and for a few seconds McGinn was tempted to have a sip (was it consecrated? Had transubstantiation taken place?). He never found out for the little man returned and McGinn crept out of the crypt and up into the Palace hotel for breakfast and a wonderful view of the valley below the terrace which leads to the Shepherds' field, two kilometers away.

He walked around the tourist town, with its olive-wood carvings and hideous mother-of-pearl bric-a-brac in the souvenir shops. The local people were pleasant and polite. He looked at the children playing in the modern school-yard, and thought: What a wonderful line to have in a passport: Place of birth - Bethlehem, just so that the nasty little customs officers would do a double-take. Even better would be an address: The Stable, Bethlehem; and his train of thought ran on to a girl reporter on his old newspaper who had lived at 1 Lambeth Walk, and a woman who visited Ibiza who lived at 1000 Sunset Boulevard, and an English couple who rented 69 Calle de la Virgen in Ibiza town.

It was so hot by 10.30am he postponed a visit to Gethsemane and because shorts were forbidden (except long Bermudas) at every place of visitation, he was sweltering back in Jerusalem, and wishing he could meet that wonderful old water seller who sold the best crystal-clear mountain water McGinn had ever tasted, in a street in Istanbul. Thirsty, he visited the chapel of Veronica, where Pope Paul had prayed on his visit. The Faithful at the West Well sounded like a bunch of Red Indians giving war whoops.

McGinn was up at 7am next day, but he wore shorts, and had thought only of the 'Garden', so was forbidden entrance to a 'Church of Silence', classified as a 'most Holy place' by a huffy monk, which made him wonder if J.C. would have been shocked by the sight of a man's legs as this awful supercilious monk was. He thought that the way in which sour old men had perverted the teachings of Christ to their own ends throughout two thousand years was shameful and pitiful. THEY were the ones who cover up the human body as though it is a thing to be ashamed of. THEY, are the ones who say that sex is sinful and dirty. Their perverted minds have destroyed the Faith.

And so he left Gethsemane for the Agony of the walk back to Jerusalem with gout, and the sun hot on his head.

The walk was enlivened when two Arabs hailed a brand new Mercedes taxi, pushed a sheep into the boot, and drove off.

Clark turned up at the Damascus gate to celebrate his twenty-eighth birthday, drinking with an Arab gangster called George, who had a chisel stuck down his belt.

Next day, hung over, on the bus to Eilat, a tourist trap with sky-high prices, and the temperature over 40 degrees in the shade. McGinn hated the heat: when Keats longed for a 'beaker of the warm South' he meant a mild Provencal day. This heat was hell on earth and he dodged into air-conditioned shops all the way down the main street to get out of it. Six Geordie coal-miners were earning £60 a week in the Timna copper mines, wielding what they called 'a windy pick' and with a 'welly full of sweat'. Even in King Solomon's mines you're sure to find a Geordie, and one of them asked the Newcastle United score. Another, Malcolm, said: 'Aah had to ask the Timna pay office for a sub. on me wages and he give us a letter, aal in Hebrew. Aah thowt he wanted us to put his dog doon.' A Geordie 'hippie' they met said he thought the people in Eilat the rudest and most arrogant he had ever met and was working at Timna for £3 a day to save £100 to get to India.

McGinn decided to cut his losses, unable to bear the thought of living in Eilat (where Richard Llewellyn, author of 'How Green Was My Valley' was living) and bought two tickets from Haifa to Marseilles for £150. At their farewell drink in 'The Hut', the miners 'local' the Israeli owner threw the German miners out for their rudeness, saying that all his family had died in Auschwitz, adding that the English he knew were nice, kind people, but the Germans were still the same bullying bastards.

In Haifa they took a cheap room with five beds in it. At 11.30pm one of the inmates arrived and they realised he was a deaf mute and was blind as well, with one eye completely closed. He growled at their presence then went possessively to his cupboard near his bed and tested the two strong locks on the door. McGinn told Clark to offer him a cigarette, and he brusquely refused and showed his own packet of TIME cigarettes, which indicated to McGinn immediately that he was partially sighted, for blind men rarely smoke. The mute stripped down to swimming trunks, put his clothes and wallet in the cupboard and locked up, then went for a shower.

At 11pm they were shattered from half-sleep by his snores, so they dressed and walked up to the smart part of Haifa, like Hambra in Beirut, a little phoney Paris with expensive cafes, ice cream parlours, coffee shops, pinball table arcades and what passes for life for the *jeunesse d'oree* of Haifa and Beirut.

At sea, aboard the S.S. Nili, they saw Stromboli, and McGinn remembered his father saying he had seen Stomboli on the way to Gallipolli, on a troop ship in 1915. A boring, uneventful trip, and then through France and back to London to the Autumnal feeling of Hampstead and, later, a date with the beautiful Ann which lasted two nights in a Bayswater hotel but they decided they were not meant for each other after all. She wore all the silver bracelets, and necklace he had bought in Romania, and looked as lovely as she had that night on deck, in the moonlight with the phosphorus on the water...

CHAPTER 19

London

IN THE Kismet Club, McGinn met Francis Bacon who was with John Neville. The first act Richard Burton had made when he became rich was to lend the money to Neville for a car. Bacon had drunk two bodyguards to death, he drinking champagne and they, stupidly on a gravy train of large 'Mahatmas'.

All three moved to the Salisbury, then to Gerry's bar in Shaftesbury Avenue, where Bacon bought bottles of champagne, was annoyed when McGinn made himself a 'Black Velvet' by mixing it with bottled Guinness, and Bacon kept on pouring until the carpet was wet, all of this watched by a silent John Hurt in the corner with an artist called Liz, a cynical Geordie who had said on a beach: 'Aah can't stand blokes whose tits are bigger than mine.' McGinn and Bacon got into a furious argument when McGinn said Joyce had 'knocked' Shakespeare for not writing a subjective work. Bacon kept burbling on about Racine, and saying Shakespeare had a greater understanding of humanity than Joyce, and McGinn quoted Thoreau, requiring all writers to give an account of their own lives. McGinn said parts of the subjective childhood memoirs of Joyce were filched directly from Melville, and so they rambled on, drunk, until McGinn crashed out and into a taxi for the Press Club where he was refused a drink for not wearing a tie and later, much later, fell off a bus in Dalston Garage.

Driscoll was stirring up trouble. Some months earlier he had asked McGinn to 'ghost' the memoirs of Sean MacStiophan, the chief of the Provisionals, who had started all the killing, because before him the IRA had tarred and feathered collaborators and knee-capped informers but did not kill. McGinn had sent a message through Driscoll: 'Why don't you write your own fucking book - it's harder work than murdering women and children.' He then tried a journalist on the Observer who talked to MacStiophan in Belfast but instead of 'ghosting' the memoirs for money, wrote an 'interview' in his paper, upon which MacStiophan sent a message via Driscoll: 'It is just as easy for me to have a man shot dead on the streets on London as in Belfast.'

Panic reigned when Olwen Hughes, a literary agent and Ted Hughes' sister, rang Driscoll to complain McGinn had told a woman in the Flask that she was handling IRA books and 'didn't want mad Protestants bombing her flat.' Driscoll was told: 'Just don't ring me again - ever. It was you who got Olwen to ring New York for an advance on the book, and it's you they'll be looking for: the 'one with the red eyes' as the IRA call you, according to Dick West,' McGinn said.

For once Driscoll was speechless.

McGinn was hearing a familiar call, far off. It was the White Goddess again, but he feared the scene there with Seley suffering from nephritis, a liver complaint, and George with cirrhosis, and knowing that his own heavy drinking was now damaging his health. He knew that his drinking had frightened off Ann, whose father was an alcoholic. He also knew the danger of the White Island, where his friends were dying of drink. Everywhere he went in London there was a friend to drink with: to the Kismet where Toby was with Sandy Fawkes; to the Steele's where Leon Griffiths was with Ronnie Fraser or Lucas Heller or Pat Wymark; the French pub where Keith Burgess was with Fergus ('This will run and run') Cashin and Bernard MacElwaine. The Flask or the Capricorn club with Smyth, Robin Hall (who sang with Jimmy MacGregor). Toby Tovey who has named his black kitten 'Shasti' after Shasti Brata the Indian writer (When he used the title 'My God Died Young' meaning his mother, on his memoirs of India, Nabokov sued him and got one hundred dollars for stealing the line from one of his poems). Shasti always adopts a high-handed 'Indian colonial' manner with waiters and managers and tries to verbally destroy every painter and writer he meets. In Hampstead, he is still known as 'Rat Vindaloo'.

McGinn has realised that he is, at 37, afraid of dying, perhaps as a result of the experience at Palma airport, and is totally unsettled, in turmoil, with sleepless nights; thoughts constantly chasing one another, but of course he also realised that 22 years of hard drinking had taken its toll.

He met Clark who said his sister Ruth, a music critic for the Sunday Times and harpsichordist, has turned Lesbian and was necking with a girlfriend, and Ruth's husband, Ron ('The Badger'). Hall was livid.

'The Badger' was snuffling and gutting some poor author's book for serialisation in the Sunday Times on the terrace of the Roebuck pub, and complaining to McGinn about income tax. McGinn frowned at the Badger's blue pencil, slashing away, and said: 'I have found a way of beating the Income Tax.'

'Oh, really?' said the Badger, 'Do tell.'

'I have no income,' said McGinn.

The Badger did not have much sense of humour, and confessed he was also worried because he had to find a suitable subject for 'A week in the Life of...'

'An easy one to do would be Derek Driscoll,' said McGinn.

'Driscoll?'

'All you have to do is print the television programme.'

But things were not going too well for McGinn's Hampstead cronies, except that Leon Griffiths' 'Minder' was a winner. It seemed the TV 'talking heads' were the new elite, and McGinn recalled Seley in Ibiza asking: 'Who is David Frost?'

'He's a television presenter and interviewer,' McGinn replied.

'But what has he done? Has he written a book or made a movie or written a symphony?'

'Not that I know of...'

'Then why has someone written a book about him?' said the puzzled American who had been on the island for many years.

The only book selling was Mr. MacDougall's book on Multiple Sclerosis, the disease which had struck him down at Glasgow University. He claimed that flour, grain, oats, etc were bad, but potatoes chipped, boiled or sautéed, were good.

John Hurt was out of work and about to sign on as an apprentice carpenter with a cabinet maker he had met in the Salisbury bar, and not amused when Michael Caine told him: 'John, you know why the birds all go for me? It's me 'ooded, cobra-eyed look.'

Smyth was rarely out of trouble: coming out of a Bayswater pub he heard a shout: 'Frank, how are you?' It was Julie Christie who added: 'Come and have a drink.' They went back to her house, to a basement kitchen where what appeared to be a dwarf with a black beard and sunglasses sat at the bottom end of the kitchen table, saying nothing. Julie poured Frank a glass of champagne, and he said: 'Well, cheers, Julie, all the best. By the way, what happened to that little twerp Warren Beatty you were knocking it off with?'

'I think you'd better go, Frank' she said, as the 'dwarf' made little noises, and the situation dawned on Smyth.

Toby and Keith, the 'deep sea diver' and 'the shepherd' had been allowed to sign on again.

The Irish doctor, Dr. Slattery, died, and the new doctor was Ian Peek, M.O. with the Gloucesters when they were almost wiped out in Korea. Having perused the files, and realised that most of his patients were alcoholics and there was a long list of Hampstead suicides (Hampstead second only to Burnley, Lancs. in the suicide stakes in England), and when McGinn saw him for the first time to order gout tablets the good doctor confided:

'I appear to have inherited a rather *liquid* practise...'

CHAPTER 20

Ibiza

THE White Island and its Goddess, Tanit, had called out again.
Had anything changed over the years? The soldiers who had goose-
stepped in the Semana Santa parade of Easter 1970 no longer goose-
stepped. Not much had changed, except the prices, and the British tourists
who had paid £32 for two weeks in the Mare Nostrum, including flight,
ate strawberries and cream between hotel meals and were still
complaining about the hotel breakfast. Each time they complained, the
hotel added to the breakfast fare, so that the choice was: cornflakes,
porridge, other cereals, orange juice, and other fruit juices, tea, milk
coffee, chocolate, bacon, eggs, sausages (made to order, British style -
15% meat, 5% flavouring and 80% fat), baked beans, mushrooms, grilled
tomatoes, brown and white bread and buns and croissants. George had
asked McGinn: 'What's the Spanish for whingeing Poms?'

'The Spanish have another saying,' McGinn replied: 'You come to
my country and play. We go to your country to work.'

Steve Seley had been seen dodging the husband and wife painters.
He could spot them in the distance because they always wore orange
capes, like two gas-butano bottles, on the horizon, and Seley had been
seen running through the vegetable market with his straw *cesta* over his
head, leaving the marketeers pondering on the eccentricity of foreigners.

Over their first drinks, outside the bar Estrella on the waterfront,
Seley asked: 'So what have you been reading?'

'Baudelaire, Rimbaud and Verlaine,' said McGinn, 'and the writer
of the foreword cannot understand why Rimbaud gave up literature at
nineteen.'

'I can,' said Seley.

'So can I.'

'He couldn't stand the pain of the creative act,' said Seley.

'No. He was a nature mystic who preferred to be amongst Nature, or in a boat, travelling, seeing new landscape rather than spending his life in a little room, writing to make publishers rich after his death.'

'That's what I'm supposed to do. I sleep on a mattress on the floor of a little whitewashed room with a cold water tap trying to write just a few lines that will sing down the centuries. Just one good poem, and I'd be happy, but I'm bogged down here, bogged down and broke and living in a dump.'

'But just think of it, Steve. All those cockroaches are yours...'

'Don't joke. You're bogged down too.'

'You've written poems...'

'Yeah, I know:

'I want to lie down on the floor
My love, I find, was once a whore.
Instead, I eat an orange for my health,
And dream of wealth.'

McGinn said 'I mean the Aga Khan one. It's not so personal...'

'Ah, yes:

'The Aga Khan had mangoes sent
To where he went on pleasure bent
To Biarritz and Baden-Baden,
To St. Moritz and Berchtesgaden
To Saragossa and Berlin
To Shizuoka and Pekin
The Aga Khan had mangoes sent
To where he went on pleasure bent...'

'You sent it to him?'

'Yeah, and the miserable old sack of shit didn't send me a dime. Every year he had his weight in gold and jewels, but do you think he'd give a dollar to a poet?'

'To Zanzibar and Tasmania.'
To Madagascar and Rumania,
To Moscow, Kharkov, Vladivostok
To Singapore, Turin and Bangkok
The Aga Khan had mangoes sent
To where he went on pleasure bent...'

'Yeah, for all the good it did me, I might as well have written it on a lavatory wall...'

'I speak of quotations from Horace and Livey
And scrawl on the wall of any old Privy...

and so on and so forth, and maybe this is the last century for poetry. The literature of America is the funnies page... and all that's left for poets is suicide'

''By the time that I, began to cry (I was born in 1915)
'The rights of man (o, man!)
Were in the Kaiser's frying pan
The old fat cat, 'twas on fire,
Miss Lucy's baby was for hire
Franz Joseph licked his muttonchops
The Czar was tete de veau Cheops
By czarevitch comrade V. Lenin
As Woodrow Wilson stroked his chin
And Asquith with Sir Edward Grey
French letters sent to Poincarre
I HATE WAR like Franklin Delano, but a poet has everything to lose but his chains...
'Now who am I to say all this?
Who am I to criticise:
Who am I to place a kiss
Of death on 'noble' enterprise?
''Well, first of all I have no power to place...
A kiss of death on any such collective face
I have no power, I am unknown,

I'm not the Pope, I have no throne,
But I've got Rhythm as well as he
(Mine own Dispensation of Authority)
For I am a man who cannot see
Much more than human frailty...'

'Keep going, Steve, 'you'll soon have enough for the collected works...' said McGinn.

'Yeah and it can join the collected rejection slips. The only way is to bring out a braille edition - for those who cannot see. Cannot see? Why p-o-e-t-r-y, you readers of L'il Abner. You are not bogged down in County Lyric. When your heads rest on the pillow at night, you go to sleep, you do not writhe in turmoil.'

'Steve, Steve,' said McGinn, 'take it easy, man. You did your best. You did what you wanted to do. You chose freedom.'

'Freedom? I thought we had freedom in America, until that son of a bitch Joe McCarthy and his slimy gumshoes drove me out. They persecuted men who fought on the Republican side in the civil war here, and called them Reds when they returned home. But they sheltered Nazi war criminals and scientists as long as they were of use. I was 15 when I joined the Party - a kid. All we wanted to do was help the poor...'

'And you were blacklisted for life.'

'Yeah. I was naive. I couldn't understand why I couldn't get a job except humping refrigerators and pianos up four flights of stairs in Brooklyn.

'I'll go back to America when they have a black woman president.'

'The American hippies here say they'll go back when there's a junkie president.'

'That isn't as far off as they think.'

'Well, a lot of ex servicemen from Nam are junkies, and some join the police force and some go into politics. They start by accident; on patrol they shoot up morphine to stop crapping in their pants when the shooting starts, and get hooked. All junkies are constipated. Soldiers shoot up to 'keep a tight asshole', and 'lose' the medical box on every patrol. Maybe you should have gone in the Army and written a war book like Mailer or Irwin Shaw or James Jones who wrote The Great American Novel, 'From Here to Eternity'...'

'Yeah, - I remember the boxer who refused to box and was beaten up by his platoon? And remember in Irwin Shaw's 'The Young Lions' where a Jewish soldier was a relative of Irwin Shaw and made the mistake of showing it to Shaw who stole it for 'The Young Lions'. The relative threatened to sue so Shaw paid him 500 bucks to keep his trap shut. I saw the letter. You want me to be like them?'

'No, Steve, I don't. And if ever I put you in a book I'll call you Aaron Scruple. Didn't you say your brother Jason was arriving in Ibiza soon?'

'Yeah, he's in Germany right now. He's Head of the Arts faculty at Cornell now. Did you tell me it's your birthday soon?'

'Yes, December 17th. I'll be 37.'

'Dinner's on me. Jason sent me some money.'

They ate in San Telmo, salade a la creme, steak tartare, apple pie and cream. Seley presented McGinn with a copy of 'The Ordeal of the Rod', the book Maurice Girodias gave to young would-be American pornographers in Paris, saying of Seley: 'He is the master. This is the best ever pornographic book ever written...'

Seley signed it : 'Happy Birthday from R.B. Burns' (Seley's nom-de-plume with Olympia Press). 'The only autographed copy in existence.' 17th December 1971. He made McGinn promise not to show it to anyone on the island, because the truth was, he was a bit ashamed of it, having batted it out in an hotel room in Paris for Girodias for $1,000, at the time Girodias was publishing Jean Genet, Terry Southern ('Candy') and J.P. Donleavy ('The Ginger Man') all banned in England and America by censors as 'obscene'.

At the next table in the restaurant sat Elmyr de Hory.

He looked worried, as if his life had been threatened again by Fernand Legros.

Seley told Elmyr that Clifford Irving had told him a year ago that he was ghosting Howard Hughes' autobiography and Elmyr looked as if he could smell money, but he had other worries on his mind: apart from the French police wanting to extradite him, he had received a death threat from Fernand, who had put a plastic bomb, a flick knife and a revolver on the Montesol cafe table and asked Elmyr: 'Which one do you want?'

Next day McGinn awoke in bright sunshine and looked at the red bougainvillea growing over his terrace and the view of the Mediterranean 500 metres away, feeling it was always worthwhile to be in Ibiza in winter, in the brilliant sunshine, far from grey England.

In town he met two friends from Hampstead, Pip Perkins, photographer, and Lucas Heller, screenwriter ('The Dirty Dozen') who was driving Peter Sellers' car, a corvette Stingray. Every year Sellers bought expensive camera equipment and a new luxury car and sold it a year later as a tax loss. With McGinn in the Corvette, Lucas drove Perkins to catch his plane at the airport in seven minutes flat, from Ibiza harbour. Lucas Heller had arrived in England as a refugee and had been taunted at school in London that he was a Nazi, when in fact he was a German Jewish boy escaping the Nazis with his family. Lucas was German-Jewish. Peter Sellers was Welsh-Jewish and so was Leon Griffiths the last two known as 'The Taffia' in Hampstead. But whereas Lucas was accepted in America and became a top Hollywood screenwriter, Leon was barred from entry because he was a member of the Communist Party (he was barred from the Party, too, for waving a Hungarian flag around in the Daily Worker office, shouting about 'freedom'.)

Heller came to Lunch at Dora's next day, and when he was asked about screen credits by Seley, Seley told him: 'You're just writing warmed-up Tennessee Williams.'

Heller left in the corvette for Germany next day, chasing girls, for there was a terrible shortage of them in Ibiza in the winter months.

Jason Seley arrived with news that Nelson Rockefeller wanted to buy his statue of a horse and rider, made out of chrome car bumpers, modelled on the Italian statue, for $47,000 to put it in the Rockefeller Plaza in New York for strollers in summer and skaters in winter to admire.

In Sandy's bar in Santa Eulalia Steve, drunk, let loose with a stream of four-letter words to change the atmosphere from Bourgeois to Bawdyhouse. The British Colonials fled, but an American writer, Howard Sackler, author of boxing book 'The Great White Hope' and winner of the Pulitzer Prize (which Seley called the Bullshit Surprise) told the bar; 'The guy has brain damage' and told his wife: 'Take the children out of here - there's too much bad language.' Seley said 'You're in Spain now, No one's supposed to understand what I'm saying.'

Then Seley pinched Mrs. Sackler's very attractive bottom as she went by with the children, and she immediately told Howard, the Great White Hope, and he said: 'I'll take you outside and beat the shit out of you.'

Seley: 'You're sore.'

'No.'

'Have a drink.'

'No,' and with that Sackler clashed out of the bar.

Seley started to raise hell. Sandy, the owner, told him to shut up. Jason and McGinn beat a retreat to the Cellar to eat, followed by Steve who continued to raise hell, shouting about the New York Jewish art critics and saying that the New York Jews had ruined the theatre there and the accountants had ruined Hollywood.

McGinn heard an Englishwoman on the next table in the Cellar ask her husband: 'Do you think he's a Nazi?'

Seley had to smile...

Next day Jason had 'Ibiza 'flu' (hangover). McGinn told him: 'Your brother is the kind of man who gives megalomania a bad name.' Jason fled to New York.

When the Irving story broke, The Sunday Times wanted McGinn to do a story but he refused. They sent Magnus Linklater, a keen young man whose father was Eric Linklater.

'Did your father drink?' Seley asked him.

'Like a fish,' he said, and together they went to David Walsh's house in the old town. Walsh, a mediocre British painter, was supposed to have 'sketched' Hughes for Time Magazine. He claimed he had met Hughes who had a lined face! Walsh was being very cagey and shifty, clearly covering for Irving. McGinn thought he would sound him out, saying 'Anyone who can take an American publisher for money deserves all he can get. They've been living off writers for years, gnawing on their bones. The shoe is now on the other foot. If it is all a hoax, then good luck to Cliff.'

Walsh gave McGinn's shoulder a little squeeze as he left the room to get gin, and McGinn knew then that it was a hoax.

But the real story, which McGinn had no intention of pursuing, was that it all revolved around an English forger who was in great demand by Elmyr de Hory, Fernand Legros and Irving, because he could imitate handwriting to perfection and forge most documents, especially passports, and it was he who had forged the nine page Hughes letter and the certificates of authenticity by Paris experts which had been with the paintings sold by Elmyr and Legros, and it was not the paintings

(Elmyr could do a Modigliani in half an hour) but the *certificates* which convinced the buyers. Other paintings were done by students at the Ecole des Beaux Arts in Paris.

The forger, however, was known to make small mistakes so details had to be carefully checked against his work.

Back down in the town they met Marty Healey. Marty had a letter from his old Army pal Hugh Hefner asking for information on Irving. Marty did not know. however, that Irving's real name was Belsky and his *father* was the famous New Yorker cartoonist who did cartoons of cops, the reason being that his father (Cliff's grandfather) was a New York cop, a police Captain whose badge Cliff had retained for personal use in emergencies; kept in a safe place along with his ENTRADA and SALIDA stamps for his passport.

Seley continued to try and justify his action in signing a reference for Clifford Irving's good character, saying: 'Well, he's always helped me.' Later, he admitted: 'OK I'm doing it for money. I hope to get something out of it.'

McGinn said: 'That's better. It's better than trying to find moral justification for your action. I still advise you to keep your nose out of it. You are dragging in your father's name, because he was a member of the New York bar and Jason's because he is a sculptor and head of Arts at Cornell, without his permission.'

'You said you agree with Cliff screwing money out of publishers and now you've changed your opinion' Seley said.

McGinn said: 'No. I still agree. But he should not have conned you, as a friend, and Edith should not have got you to speak to Pressmen and say you thought the book on Howard Hughes was authentic. They both used you.'

'But he was kind to me. Offered me money.'

'All charity has an ulterior motive, as Huxley said: 'When we give pleasure to our lovers or bestow charity upon the needy, we do so not to gratify the effect of our benevolence, but only *ourselves*. We are kind for the same reason as we are cruel - to enhance the sense of our own *power*."

'Why do we know the name of Harriet Weaver?' McGinn asked.

'Only because she gave money to James Joyce.'

'Exactly - vicarious fame through charity. No doubt Cliff will feel good giving you money and everyone here will think he's one hell of a fine fellow, and he will glow accordingly.'

'Well, I believe in the old sayings, like: 'Never look a gift horse in the mouth."

'That's what the Trojans thought.'

Seley laughed. 'I wish I could go to Greece. I've never been there. I envy you your travelling...'

'It's the Sagittarian impulse, Steve, but when I'm here, I want to be somewhere else, like Arnold Bennett who wanted to live by the sea, in Fontainbleau, in Holland and on the south coast of England all at once...'

'And Gide wanted to live in Normandy when he was in Algiers and in Algiers when he was in Paris. But you'll settle down later. Age is the decisive factor,' said Seley.

'Do you fear old age?'

'No. Infirmity. I fear infirmity. Anyway, 'There's still plenty left' as a friend used to call out to me in Paris. And you'll be back in London next week. Walking over Hampstead to visit Karl Marx's grave. You don't know how romantic that sounds to an American.'

'My friend Driscoll told me he was there when they moved the body into the new grave and put the monument over it, and he said the grave diggers allowed him to take a cutting of the beard where the side of the coffin had caved in.'

'And what happened to it?'

'I believe he gave it to his brother as a birthday present. His brother used to keep a square foot of snow covered with plastic to see how long it would take to melt on the Heath, and kept a record each year.'

'Nuts.'

'Aren't we all?'

Soon afterwards, the news broke that Clifford Irving and Edith had been arrested, and everyone wondered how they had been caught so soon. They had covered their tracks well, the publishers loved the 'manuscript', Edith had laundered the money into another bank, the photograph on her fake passport was excellent, with the big glasses and the beautifully made Swiss passport.

Expertly made, but with that one little fault the forger was famous for: he put the number of her real passport on the fake, and they were trapped within hours.

CHAPTER 21

The Magnet

WHAT had brought McGinn to this beautiful island in the Mediterranean? It was a tiny dot on G. Mercator's Projection. Mercator had made his map of the Ancient World in 1595 and McGinn's Latin master had pointed out that this dot was in the very centre of the world. If anyone wanted to go to the centre of the world, they would head for the dot, which lay amongst the Balearic islands of Majorca, Minorca, Cabrera, Es Palmador and Formentera. There they would find the flat, oblong beds of static sea water which had supplied the salt for the whole of the Holy Roman Empire.

At London airport a stewardess said: 'Eye-bee-za? Where's that, then? Never 'eard of it.' Little did she know then how fame was heading its way.

The landing lights would fail at the little airstrip and the Aviaco plane would have to turn back to Palma, Majorca, or back to Barcelona and try again when they'd mended the fuse. It was primitive. Hot water, and even running water was virtually unknown, a flush toilet a luxury, a telephone a rarity, and cars were few. In the Fifties people still ran into the street when the plane flew over to see the magic bird in the sky; in the Sixties artists from Northern Europe and America discovered that food, drink and accommodation were cheap, but a luxury item such as mustard was unobtainable; in the Seventies peasants came from outlying villages to see the new traffic lights on the Vara de Rey; in the Eighties the tourists took over and a Spanish honeymoon couple were told in Barcelona that they would have to go to England to book a package tour as all hotel rooms were pre-booked by the agencies there;

269

and in the Nineties it was said to be the most expensive place in Spain.

To walk in and out of town from the countryside or D'en Bossa beach was always an interesting journey. A central point was the obelisk on the jetty, raised by public subscription to the memory of the Corsairs, the brave band of Ibicenco brothers who had repulsed pirates bent on stealing their goods and womenfolk. It was opposite the obelisk that the young Guardia Civil had fallen asleep on duty and the hippies had stolen his machine gun and thrown it in the sea on the other side of the island as a pacifist protest which led to the officer being court martialled and thrown out of the Guardia.

Along the harbour, on the left, was the bar that sold Green fairy, Spanish *absenta,* and where someone with problems could lose them for a few hours, drifting in mists of the *absinthe* and living in other worlds.

In the hotel Noray nearby Steve Primero would take his holidays, and do exactly that: live in Paris for a weekend. Armed with a bottle of *absinthe* and a copy of *l'Equipe* and *Figaro* and *France Soir*, he took a cheap room, closed the shutters against the harbour noise and sight of the ships, and sat in a chair, drinking and reading, and imagining he was back in Paris, the Paris beloved of American exiles.

Past the shop that sold seashells and the shop that specialised in yachting equipment, the Hotel Montesol sat on the corner of the Vara de Rey, and over on the other corner, opposite the old Falange meeting place, was Dirty Domingo's, not to be confused with Clean Domingo's which lay in one of the back streets on the way to the vegetable market. These were the meeting places in daytime, where people of a score of nationalities, dressed in fashions that startled the eye and became a morning passing parade, met to talk of last night's adventures and swap the gossip of the day. At night the scene would change to the harbour where the fishing nets lay stretched out to dry where great wooden crates contained the fisherman's gear, and the locals and residents bar-hopped from Toto's to Clive's to Merlin's then up to the Tavern or Pretty Pat's in d'Alt Villa, the old town where the Cathedral stood, then down again to the Calle Mayor to Wauna's or the George and Dragon.

They ate late in Spain and some residents of the Island did not finish dinner until close to midnight when they would come into town seeking excitement and music and drink and dope and conversation and sex. A New Yorker called Arlene had the Tierra bar and Lola had the late night club, and later it was possible to drink all night at the fisherman's bars where they served food to the returning night fishermen, and later drink wonderful fresh coffee as the early bars opened in the morning as the sun came up.

After the Vara de Rey with its string of taxis and host of banks, the Avenida Espana led out to the country and beaches which began at Figueretas, and the great, long D'en Bossa beach stretched away in the distance to the foothills of *El Corpus del Maria el Virgen*, the undulating hill that resembled the head, breasts and swollen belly of a woman in repose. From this beach the Ibicencos could foretell the weather: if Formentera in the distance was shrouded in a haze, it would be hot next day, but if the outline was sharp and clear, watch out for rain or a storm. If it did rain, the Ibicenco women would not clean their houses for four days after it stopped, to let the mud and clay dry first.

The almond orchards below the cemetery faced Rat Island, which lay in the Figueretas inlet like a sleeping rodent that gave it its name. Opposite Rat Island they built the first tourist hotels on the beach and the season started very early when the first batch of servants arrived from the Peninsular on 8 February to open up for seasonal cleaning. In this month the island was white with almond blossom and just after the middle of February the curious who had heard of the almond blossom full moon would arrive to see this amazing sight in the bright white valleys.

When the signs HAY HORCHATA DE CHUFA appeared on the bars and ice-cream shops, it was Easter, when they sold the drink made from chufa or tiger-nut milk, and hundreds of students arrived from Barcelona University to sample the exotic delights of the island. Then there was a six week gap until the real season started, when the date for the first swim was 20 May and the water would be warm enough for swimming until Guy Fawke's day, the day for the last swim of the year, unless a streak of masochism found in many Scandinavians, made winter swimming attractive.

When Steve Primero arrived on the island in the Fifties it was possible to look from the D'en Bossa beach to the Old Town and not see a single building. Later it looked as if a giant had dropped iced cakes on the hillside and alongside and along the seashore as development began. In the archaeological museum of the Old Town were many replicas of the Goddess Tanit, whose mystic power held sway over the island, the White

Goddess having centuries before cast her strange spell over the White Island. Phoenicians had come ashore here and brought with them their large greyhound-type dogs, the Podenca Ibicenca, and they ran wild until breeding them became a business in the Sixties. Romans, Saracens and Moors had occupied the island, leaving their traces and remains as the Phoenicians had left their catacomb on the hillside above the Via Punica, and their hunting dogs to live off rabbits on the main island and the Isla Conejero known as Rabbit Island or even Coney Island.

The Saracens left traces of their herringbone building style and the Moors left their houses, the low, flat roofs *fincas* built with thick stone and clay walls against the hot sun with roofs of *sabena* wood and slats and kelp and tile acting as watersheds for irrigation. These *fincas*, viewed in the distance from parts of the island would make a visitor think he was in Morocco instead of Spain.

There was no doubt that the island of Ibiza was a paradise long before it became a popular playground.

Out in the countryside, where the first flush of spring wheat made the fields look like English lawns from a distance, strange black dots could be seen tending goats or collecting hay from stacks. They looked like small, squat Guinness bottles, but turned out to be the peasant women of Ibiza, dressed in a fashion that startled women from the modern world. They wore a roll of cloth around the midriff to eliminate all suggestion that they had a woman's figure, and a head-shawl from which a pigtail peeped. The fashion dated from the days of pirates looking ashore and seeing what they would believe to be aged women in the fields, although some of them would be sixteen year old girls, their sensational hourglass figures hidden from lustful eyes.

On the end of the pigtail, each woman wore a coloured ribbon denoting her status: black for a widow, white for a virgin, blue for a married woman.

This fading fashion was captured in the primitive painting of Daft Tony, whose colourful depictions on plywood of palms and fincas and churches and the country folk of Ibiza sometimes adorned the walls of various bars in the port and the old town. As a baby he had fallen out of a window onto his head and had never been right afterwards. Spaniards in their tolerant way with people less fortunate than themselves said that Tony had been touched by the hand of God, and even though *'loco'* he had to be accepted in the community. If Tony did not have a painting to pay his bar bill, the Bishop sent someone down from the Cathedral once a month to pick up Tony's tab.

Buses radiated out from Ibiza town to the outlying villages of Balafi, Es Cubells, Cap Martinet, San Jorge, San Raphael, San Antonio, San Jose, San Carlos, Santa Gertrudis, Santa Ines (where the road sign said Sta. Ines, and British tourists called it Staines), and Santa Eulalia. This last was the town featured in Elliot Paul's book *'The Life and Death of a Spanish Town'*, about the outbreak of the Civil War in 1936 when local men defied the curfew and armed themselves against the Fascists which led later to more bloodshed than in any other part of Spain considering the size of the island. Santa Eulalia had truly died and it was jokingly called 'Four Streets in Search of a Town', with one popular bar, The Black Horse or *Caballo Negro*, or Sandy's bar, for it was owned by a ginger-haired Oxford-educated Dubliner by that name.

When the Republican army left for the Peninsular to fight at the front, they left hard anarchists from Andalusia in charge of prisoners in the cells of the old Castle, and when an Italian warship loomed on the horizon, a chance remark by a prisoner: 'Now it's our turn' led to the machine gunning of all in the cells. As a reprisal when Franco's army occupied the island, the same number of Republican prisoners were machine gunned in the same cells. Others were hanged or murdered by the *pistolero* assassination squads at night and the head and eldest son of every left wing family on the island was killed. To stop the slaughter, a Bishop had to be sent from the mainland.

This atmosphere from the Civil War hung over the island for many years after the war ended, and thirty years later the Ibicencos would not eat in a restaurant near the harbour owned by the hangman, and one of the *pistoleros* who owned a chemist's shop in the town, dared not go out at night.

There were other reasons McGinn had gone to Ibiza in the days before it was discovered as a tourist island. William Somerset Maugham had recommended it during a conversation he had with him in his home, the Villa Mauresque on Cap Ferrat near Nice, in 1965. McGinn was a foreign correspondent for the Observer newspaper in France at that time and had received a telephone call from Alan Searle, Maugham's secretary, asking him to visit them in the Maureseque. Maugham had news to announce: the sale of his paintings at Sotheby's to raise funds for young writers, having been influenced in this idea by seeing that John Braine was working as a critic for the Daily Express and believing that the author of 'Room at the Top' was wasting his talent in journalism. The story appeared on the front page of the Observer but later McGinn discovered it was all a ruse by Maugham and his poisonous secretary to divest his daughter, Lady John Hope at that time, of the paintings she rightfully owned, and which Maugham had given her.

'If you were starting out all over again,' McGinn had asked Maugham, 'where would you go?'

'Spain,' he said without a moment's hesitation. 'That is the country where you find the strangest stories.' Some of the stories he discovered in Spain were so shocking they were cut from his manuscripts, but he enjoyed the hours of research (hem hem) in the bars, a sort of Nescafe Jack society with American remittance men, London criminals, art forgers, Union Corse gangsters, millionaire gamblers, rich widows, retired Admirals, Air-Vice Marshals and Generals, wounded American and British war veterans, French collaborators, a Scandinavian who had blown up his own factory by mistake and was fleeing jail, tax dodgers, round-the-world yachtsmen, drug dealers, a German painter who had been tortured in Dachau, the Dutch consul who had been tortured in a Japanese prisoner of war camp, a former British soldier who had survived a German firing squad with seventeen bullets in his body, an Australian painter who had been left as a baby on a doorstep, master criminals and forgers of money, paintings and furniture, men who had cars stolen to order on the streets of New York and were driving them in Ibiza ten days later, a taxi driver who was wanted for murder in Cuba, pimps, prostitutes, painters, poets and would be's, a mainland Spaniard called Emilio who claimed he was the only sane person on the island and he had a certificate of discharge from Palma lunatic asylum to prove it! Then there was Ernesto.

Ernesto was almost a book himself. Born in Berlin of Jewish parents, his mother refused to have him circumcised as a baby. He escaped from the Nazis into Italy then into France where he hid in a room above a street in Nice and watched customers at a cafe for two years without daring to leave the room. His craving for a *cafe au lait* finally won and he crossed the street, entered the cafe and ordered one. Within minutes he was in the hands of the Gestapo who accused him of being *'salle juif'*. Ernesto protested that he was not Jewish and that they had made a mistake. All right, they said, get it out and prove it. His mother's decision saved his life - twice, for he was arrested again later and went through the same performance and escaped a second time. Now he slouched daily along the harbour, big artist's hat on his curly hair, long red scarf dangling, attractive to women and very successful with them, but failing to ever get his writing published.

Then there was Walking Marty. Marty had been shot by a German soldier on the day the war ended and received a Purple Heart and a full pension from the United States Army. At the Chicago Business School, filled with veterans from the war, his best friend drank beer with him every night and tried to persuade him to come into partnership on a idea he had to start a high-quality glossy magazine filled with pictures of beautiful naked girls. 'We'll make a fortune, Marty,' his friend insisted. 'Get lorst, Heff,' said Marty, night after night, 'who would buy a magazine like that?'

Marty never regretted his decision not to become a millionaire with Hugh Hefner of Playboy magazine. 'Why worry?' he'd say, 'the sun is shining and I go for a walk to Santa Eulalia and back.' For a month each year he took a stock of nuts and raisins and living in the wilds of Ibiza or Formentera, his head shaved, back to nature, a true hermit, eating frugally, swimming and contemplating the beauties of nature. His old pal Heff, on the other hand, scarcely ever came out in daylight.

The walk back from the Martello tower at the end of D'en Bossa was a walk through the lanes of brown and red earth fields and spring flowers and centuries old olive trees and the orange groves of San Jorge, producing one of the best tasting oranges in the Mediterranean, with the blue, blue sea over to the right and Formentera in the distance and a stop over at old Vincente Tur's bar Estrella Azul in the country lane, for McGinn's apartment was opposite, on the top of the Casa Anu, the villa Finnish Dora had built, now the Casa Dora, the climbing deep red roses and deep blue Morning Glory against the whitewashed arches of the terrace.

Vicente would sing the old Ibicenco songs which sounded, strangely enough, like a Red Indian chant around a camp fire.

His name, Tur, was a typical Ibiza name. Another country lane led past the old clay quarry for the terracotta artifacts and plates and cups made at the pottery opposite, its kiln fired by charcoal, and opposite the pottery all the names of Ibiza were on display on the headstones of the cemetry: Rieras, Escandells, Ribas, Ferrers, Roigs, Planells, Cardonas, Maris, Noguera, Torres, Castas, Verderas, Pugets, Boneds, Bonets, Serras, and amongst the few foreigners the imprints of a pair of bare feet on the gravestone of Sin Zapatos.

Into the Avenida Espana and down towards the old bullring near the harbour and the new post office and the centre of Ibiza town. It was there that Hannibal had recruited his army of slingers for the Ibicenco boys and men were reputed to be the most accurate slingshot men in the Mediterranean. When the first English dart-board was imported and the first darts were thrown by the foreign residents, McGinn watched the young Ibicencos regarding this game with a proprietorial air: this was something right up their street. They called it *'flechas'* to start with and then discovered there was a Spanish word *dardos* and within months the local men were beating champion English players at their own game. Here was an ancestral skill coming to the surface, an Ibicenco who had never seen a dart or dart board in his life throwing three double ones after a week's practice.

Someone hailed McGinn waving a letter, having come from the Calle Mayor. 'Can you give this to Tristan Jones? It's got an English stamp on it and was delivered to the George and Dragon. I don't have the time to go to his boat.'

At the *Cresswell*, Jones tore the envelope open and read the letter, on mauve notepaper.

'Saved by the bloody bell,' he said. 'I've got a charter. A week, just around the island and Formentera and Es Palmador. The Bishop of Chichester's sister.'

'The what?'

'That's who the lady is: the Bishop of Chichester's sister. Name of Peggy. Met her in London. Some character.'

'You'd better get the old yacht cleaned up then, a bit shipshape and Bristol fashion as you always say.'

'Not for Peggy mate. If she'd been in the black Hole of Calcutta she'd have made them whitewash it, but she can rough it with the boys. Tough as a mountaineer's boot and brave as a treefull of eagles.'

McGinn had a vision of her in Women's Voluntary Service hat, tweeds and thick woollen stockings serving cups of tea to strong men in moments of distress.

'Her doctor has ordered her to have a sea voyage,' said Jones, 'and she'll be with a lady friend. Come aboard and help me draw up a list of stores, mate, 'cos she'll be here next week.'

In the saloon of Tristan's boat was a medallion for jujitsu nailed to the woodwork, and the holster for a Walther PPK which means Pistol Politzei Kriminel, hanging on the porthole screw.

'I dropped the pistol overboard,' said Jones, craftily looking at the empty holster. 'I didn't trust myself with that aboard. You never know what you can do after a few bevvies.'

As he started to draw up his list of tinned goods and dried goods such as pasta, flour and rice, there came a rapping on the galley roof.

'Who the hell could this be?' asked Jones, going up the galley steps.

He popped his head out then looked back into the saloon. 'First tourists of the season, mate,' he said.

'Hello there,' said a small Englishman who had a fishing rod in his hand and his wife by his side. 'Are you English?'

'Er... well, Welsh, actually.'

'British, anyway. I knew you were because I saw your little packet of cornflakes in your little kitchen.'

'Oh.'

'And the flag, of course.'

'That's what they call the Red Duster, isn't it?' his wife said.

'That's right.'

'Did you sail this boat all the way from England, then?'

'No. I had it sent out by parcel post.'

Jones retreated down the companionway, firmly closing the hatch above his head. 'They'll be coming aboard for tea and drinks next,' he said, starting to put on a yellow PVC raincoat. 'And talking of drinks. When they've gone, let's have a wet ashore, mate. I've got nothing aboard: dry as a nun's... humour on this boat.'

'It's a bit warm for that coat, isn't it', McGinn asked.

'I wear the same clothes all winter, mate. I don't believe in all this washing and changing. Keep the body temperature constant throughout, that's what I say.'

'You're stitched in for winter, then?'

'That's about it. No colds or 'flu for me. Come on, let's go. The bucket and spade brigade have scarpered. Thanks for bringing that letter. I'll get my old boat ready for that charter, don't you worry. My pension's not due for another two weeks and that cornflake box is empty. Did our tourist friend but know it, I was about to eat the box.'

Tristan Jones was another ex-Serviceman on the island who lived off a small pension, but the British contingent was paid about a tenth of what the American veterans received. Like Walking Marty, Jones had been wounded: in a riot control operation in Japan, bayoneted in the stomach, and he was receiving twenty four pounds a month disability pension. He had been on the Russian convoys to Murmansk and his worst job had been to retrieve a body of a sailor after he had hit the water going overboard and the intestines burst with the shock of the icy water and stretched out and had to be hauled in with the body. In the shroud, the tradition in the Royal Navy was to put the last stitch through the nose, in case there was a flicker of life, but in those waters it was not necessary, for a man was dead within seconds of hitting the water.

'Now there's a pretty picture,' said Jones as they walked towards the Estrella bar on the harbour.

At a table were Steve Segundo, the big Swede who lived in Santa Eulalia, Harrison a former American marine who claimed the sun really had burnt a hole in his head because he had stood guard outside an American naval Base in Rota, for three years in the boiling sun, and Elki, whose name was Ilka, a good painter on a pension from the Finnish Arts Council and who everyone believed was drinking for Finland in the next Olympics.

'It looks like the gathering of the outpatients for a psychiatrists' convention,' said Jones.

'If we join them,' McGinn said, 'you can say good-bye to today.'

'Good-bye, day,' said Jones.

Steve Segundo, who had arrived on the island a few months after Steve Primero, hence the name, had been in the American Merchant Marine when his ship was blown up by a floating mine about twelve miles off Atlantic City, New Jersey, during a poker game. Ericcson had grabbed all the money, stuffed it in his underpants and jumped overboard with the rest of the crew, swimming towards the distant seaboard lights.

Two of his shipmates who were not strong swimmers tried to cling to Steve Segundo's neck, screaming for him to save them from drowning and dragging him down with them. He had killed them with a blow to the head and swam on to be met by a coast guard cutter who dragged him aboard and said they had seen the incident through binoculars and he was under arrest. He stood trial for murder in Atlantic City but was found not guilty and freed on a plea that 'it was me or them.' He had brought expensive drilling equipment from the States to Ibiza to drill for water for the farmers, but Spanish State control would not allow him to use it.

All of Elki's artist's grant went on drink. He had been arrested for throwing beer bottles at the bullfight and warned to stay off alcohol by the judge. Arrested on the Vara de Rey the day after, he told the police: 'But I have not had a drink today. This is yesterday's drunk.' In Ibiza he lived in an old abandoned car opposite the Banco Balear, frequently taking a taxi home to it from the harbour in the early hours. Although he had money, no hotel or *pension* would take him with his Bohemian ways, and to a visiting Finnish girl who had offered to send him a postcard home, he had given his address as The Old Ford, Vara de Rey, Ibiza. This accommodation, however, was much more comfortable than his usual place of abode in winter in Finland, where he wrapped himself in a carpet and slept in the park. Elki claimed that when the Russians had beaten the Finns before the Second World War started, the Finnish commander had gone to the Russian commander and said: 'OK, you have won. We have run out of ammunition. You can have my country,' and the Russian had said: 'We don't want your bloody country. We're going home.'

Harrison the ex-marine was houseproud and his tiny apartment looked like a highly polished, clean and shining recruit's accommodation in boot camp, with boxed blankets, clothing and footwear arrayed and everything ready for inspection. The look on his face could only be described as smug, and he wore a pair of beautiful calf-length boots which he proudly displayed by sticking his feet out full length so that passers by could see them.

'They finally got here,' Harrison called as Jones and McGinn approached. 'The boots, man, the boots. Look at those beauties. Made by General Franco's bootmaker on the Peninsular. Remember my

German chick from last summer? The one who promised to send me a present for services rendered? Well here they are. Arrived through the mails this morning. Aren't they something?'

'The hell with your boots,' said Steve Segundo with a very strong Swedish-American accent. 'Come on - let's open a keg of nails here. What are you fellers drinkin'?'

'Give me a San...' Elki began to say.

'Not you.' shouted Steve Segundo 'Them. You've had enough. You should get something to eat.'

'I ate last night,' said Elki. 'I dined with a Scottish man called Jock who lives in Jesus. We ate porridge.'

'Porridge?' cried Jones. 'I haven't had a good plate of porridge in years. I'd give my left tit for a plate of porridge.'

'Not this porridge,' said Elki, absentmindedly drinking Steve Segundo's beer, which was immediately snatched out of his hand.

'Why, what was wrong with it?' asked Jones, taking a seat. 'Did he put salt on it instead of sugar? That's what Jocks do, you know. Or did he put a large whisky over it - you wouldn't have objected to that. I was in the Hebrides once when this Jock opened the drawer of what they called a Press, a big wardrobe with drawers,, and *cut* a slice of porridge out of the drawer. That's what they do up there, pour the porridge in for the winter and cut a slice off when it's needed.'

'So what was wrong with the porridge, Elki?' asked Steve Segundo, signaling to Jaime the bar owner for service.

'The porridge was OK. It was the cooking facilities I did not like. We went back to his terrible old *finca* in Jesus and he poured some paraffin in the hole in the squat-bog and lit it, then put the pan of porridge on to cook.'

'Bloody hell, I've heard of rough living conditions.' said Jones.

'It was rough, yes,' said Elki. 'and Jock could see that I did not approve. 'What's wrong Elki?' he ask me. 'Don't you like porridge?' 'I like porridge, Jock, I assured him, but this is the worst bloody kitchen I have seen in my life.'

'Hey, what are you guys drinking? This is on me. I inherited a little dough from the States, a small tobacco farm my family owned. Let me get this.'

Harrison waved a one thousand peseta note and ordered the drinks in fluent Spanish, acquired, he once confessed, from the girls who chatted him up while on guard at the Rota Naval base, rounding off the lessons between the sheets when off duty.

'Isn't Russian George due in on the boat Saturday?' asked Steve Segundo.

'That's right,' said Jones, 'and I'll be glad when he gets here with that bloody Stilton cheese. Steve Primero has talked about nothing else all bloody winter. 'Do I make a hole and pour port into it? Do I drink the port with the Stilton? Do you let the port soak through the cheese and if so for how long? ' I'm fed up with him and his bloody Stilton.'

'Chelsea Elsie brought him one from England last year,' said Steve Segundo, 'and she started to walk all the way up the hill to his pad in the old town and started to get hungry and nibble at the cheese. By the time she got to his door she'd eaten practically the lot. There was about enough to put in a mousetrap.'

'Anna Banana did the same with some Roquefort cheese from France. When he goes on his weekends to Paris he says he dreams of Roquefort cheese. Anyway, it smelt so good on the boat coming over that she ate the lot before the boat docked.' said Harry, 'and he says it's the only thing that keeps him from suicide, the thought of Roquefort cheese. He gave Anna Banana hell for doing that, called her a greedy hog and all. She said: 'So go hang yourself,' and he said: 'I would but there's not an almond tree big enough or strong enough on this goddam island to hold me,' so he's still with us.'

'If that German supermarket owner had gotten hold of him he wouldn't have been with us - when he tried to steal the Roquefort with Hippie Henry' said Steve Segundo.

'You mean Deaf Henry?' said Houseproud Harry.

"No. Hippie Henry, the American, a professor of poetry from LA. He drove the getaway car. They say he's the only hippie in Ibiza who draws his old age pension in the States.'

'There's a German supermarket here?' asked Elki.

'Never mind that', said Jones, 'What about the Roquefort cheese and the getaway car?'

'Yes, Elki,' said Steve patiently, 'A German guy opened up what he laughingly calls a supermarket on the Jesus road, and there was a rumour that he had French cheese. When Steve Primero heard this he said to

Hippie Henry 'let's rob the son-of a-bitch.' Trouble is Henry panicked. I think he was ashamed, you know, two good Jewish boys like him and Steve robbing a poor struggling German businessman? Anyway, he had a few items secreted about his person and flew into a panic before he got to the cash desk and made a run for it. The little Ibicenco girl on the cash desk must have thought he had a sudden case of the trots because he dashed out and took off at a rate of knots up to the old town and Steve's apartment. He had a small jar of ersatz caviar, you know? Lumpfish roe, a slice of smoked salmon in plastic, one lemon and a flea collar for Fatty. 'So where's my Roquefort cheese?' Steve asked.

'I got caviar and smoked salmon, but I forgot the cheese,' Henry said.

'Yea, you got a flea collar for that fat dawg and no cheese for me. I want my Roquefort. Look at me. I'm shaking. All that bullshit for nothing.'

'I got a lemon for the smoked salmon' Henry said.

'A lemon?' Steve shouted, 'You risk jail for a lemon? The goddam island's full of lemons - and you the biggest. There are two Henrys on this island - Deaf Henry and Dumb Henry.'

'You know that little Polish guy, Axel?' Jones asked. 'He tried to rob a supermarket in Germany once when he was starving. He panicked too. There was a great mountain of pieces of butter wrapped in silver paper. He snatched one and ran for it, down three streets and stood panting down an alley craving to eat his bit of butter, and when he looked at it it said: Free sample.'

'No, you've got to be a bit of a professional for supermarkets,' said Harry, easing his feet in his big boots, ' like the Fat Man.'

'The guy who is supposed to be working with Cliff on his new book about the millionaire. He's a pro. He goes in with a tin opener and a spoon. Starts with the fish course, the caviar and salmon and stuff, and then goes on to the *pate de foie gras* then the corned beef. He leaves the tins on the bottom of the shelf.'

'Hey, that's pretty good,' said Elki. 'You get a good meal with a tin opener and a spoon.'

'But it's not a very healthy diet,' said Harry. 'He should eat more green stuff. Like Walking Marty got scurvy once, living on salt cod and chick peas all winter here when they didn't have many green vegetables on the island.'

'He could always graze on the new wheat between supermarkets,' said Steve Segundo.

'Or have a swift blast on a bottle of lime juice,' said Jones.

'Nah - he don't do it any more. He got caught. In Amsterdam.'

'What happened? Did he got to jail?' said Elki.

'No. They were very nice about it. They said: 'We've been watching you eating and hiding cans. This is not good for our business. You are eating all our profits.' And the Fat Man said: 'I'm sorry. But what do you want me to do, man? Vomit?' They said: 'We let you go this time, as you are an American visitor, but don't come back here or we call the cops next time."

'Don't you guys ever do any work?' came a shout from the corner, where Steve Primero stood with his *cesta* over his shoulder.

'Watch your language, you,' shouted Jones.

'What are you drinking?' asked Steve Segundo as he joined the group.

'I'm on the wagon. Until St. Patrick's Day. After Mardi Gras my liver is twitching.'

'I thought you said you had a spare?' said Jones.

'Yeah, right. Did I ever tell you that? ' he addressed the group around the table. 'My wife in New York said that. I had a twinge of pain in the heart and I said 'Ouch' and she said: 'What's wrong, dear?' and I said: 'I've got a pain in my heart and she said...'

"You haven't got a heart, you've got two livers." chorused Steve Segundo, Harrison and Tristan Jones.

'Oh, I've told you before...'

'Yes Steve,' said Steve Segundo. 'We've just been talking about shoplifting from supermarkets. Did you get 'Time' magazine?'

'No. He's on to me. Searched my bag this morning. Imagine that? A goddamned millionaire searching a guy's bag. Why aren't you in Santa Eulalia, anyway?'

'You mean Verdera himself searched your *cesta*?'

'Yeah, all he found was an empty bottle. What brings you here, anyway? What's wrong with Sandy's bar?'

'It's too clean, he barred me.'

'It's the only church in Spain that sells wine. I told him that and I told him to put his apron on. What did he bar you for, anyway?'

'I took a goat in last Sunday morning, and for a joke I stood the son-of-a-bitch on the bar. I thought it was funny till it shat on the bar, then Sandy threw me out. Me and the goat.'

'I'll lend you 'Time' magazine, Steve,' said Harrison.

'Of course - now you can afford to buy it. Thanks. You know I just used to roll one up at the stand outside then walk into the shop and ask if the British Sunday papers were in yet, then walk out waving the magazine. But he's on to me now. I went into Fortnum and Masons the other day - you know that's what we call that fancy shop next to the Alhambra, Elki, with the Worcestershire sauce and the English tinned goods - and my *cesta* was hanging off my shoulder. Somebody jostled me in the doorway and I fell against the shelves and twenty rolls of toilet paper fell off the top shelf into my bag. So I just hitched it on and took off. I had a year's supply of toilet paper.'

'But they didn't see you?' asked Jones. 'They watch me like hawks when I go to buy my cornflakes.'

'If they did they wouldn't dare say anything anyway,' said Steve. 'All because of that cheque I gave to Bud.'

'You mean Bud of Bud's bar? You gave *him* a cheque?'

'It was meant to be a joke. You know how when the 6th Fleet come in here he always puts a photograph of his son in the US Navy uniform in the bar to attract custom? Well, I was riding his ass about that and he said to me: 'Steve, you're a bum. You never had a job in your life.' I said: 'Wrong Bud, my old buddy-pal. I had one job that lasted four days and one job that lasted four minutes. The four-day job was with Lufthansa when they were employing Jews in New York trying to get friendly to open their airline all over he States. After four days of listening to their bullshit I threw the typewriter at them and walked out. 'So what was the four-minute job?' Bud asked. A cigar factory, I said. I discovered that they were selling at fifty dollars a box, and I was loading them for fifty dollars a week. So I put a box under each arm and walked out with two weeks wages.'

'But what about the cheque?' asked Steve Segundo.

'Yeah, Bud said: 'You'll never have any dough.' and I said: 'But you don't know my family in the States who are all millionaires. I keep my wealth quiet here, and I'll prove it to you.' So I wrote him a cheque for one million pesetas, as a joke, you know? He went into Fortnum's later and dropped the cheque by mistake. They picked it up and the manager read it. Wow! That old fart in the fireman's coat is the eccentric American millionaire. He must be if he can write a cheque for one million pesetas. They handed it reverently back to Bud, and ever since they've been bowing me in and out of the goddamned shop. Anyway, I've got to be going.'

He heaved the straw *cesta* onto his shoulder.

'That bag looks heavy, Steve. What's inside? A gas bottle?' asked Tristan Jones.

'No. I gave my gas fire to Luis at Toto's bar as collateral against drinks. I freeze my ass off to get some internal heat.'

'Yeah - he says you've drunk that gas fire ten times over. And I know what's in your *cesta*. Booze. Let's see.'

Harry stood up and peeped into the bag.

'Thought as much' he said. 'Some wagon.'

'Wine doesn't count,' wailed Steve Primero. 'Wine isn't booze. Vodka and gin are *booze*. You gotta have a little wine with your meals. Quit buggin' me. I'm leaving.'

He strode off in the direction of the Calle Mayor, closely followed by a favourite dog, Otto. Steve Primero was under the impression that dogs and his donkey loved him for himself and not for the sugar in his coat pocket

'Why is that dog always following him?' Harry asked.

'Maybe he owes it money,' said Jones.

Steve suddenly returned to the table. 'Hey, somebody catch hold of this dog. He follows me everywhere and hangs around outside my pad, howling, interrupting my work.'

'But Steve, he loves you,' said Harrison, sarcastically, grabbing Otto's collar.

'Yeah, and if anybody touches me, that dog would have his throat out. Wouldn't you Otto baby?'

'Let's see, shall we?' said Jones, taking a rolled up copy of the *Diario de Ibiza* and starting to slap Steve Primero around the head and shoulders with it.

'Seize him, Otto. Go on, boy, go for his throat. Attack, Otto. Attack. Hey, lay off, Jones will you? Get him Otto. Go for him boy.'

The dog looked curiously at Steve and Jones, but its real interest lay in the wrapped sugar lumps in a saucer on the table.

'That's not a guard dog, Steve,' said Jones, with a final hefty slap to his arm, 'its a watch dog. It watches while someone beats you up.'

'Why you no-good son of a b... you no good toe-rag, Otto. What about all that sugar I gave you? You ungrateful cur, you whelp, you flea bag. You're supposed to protect me. All right. No more sugar for you. You're *finished*. Got me?'

The dog managed to keep one curious eye on Steve Primero and the other on the sugar bowl. Steve snatched the saucer and pocketed the sugar lumps, saying: 'Hold him, Harrison. And don't let him go. I've had enough of unfaithful diabetic dogs. You hear me Otto? The affair is *over*.'

'So, he's gone on the wagon till St. Patrick's Day?' said Harrison when Steve had gone. 'I'll bet a bottle of Ricard he doesn't make it.'

'Done,' said Jones. 'I'll take that bet because I know he can do it. He'll fill himself with Miltowns and Dormadinas and Mogadons but he'll do it. He hasn't recovered from Mardi Gras when the waiter who serves him in *Es Quinques* arrived wearing a bridal gown, white elbow-length gloves, the lot, and plonked his nosegay of orange blossom on Steve's table just to annoy him.'

'Have you heard about this new bar that Doris Karloff is opening with Ewald? Everyone in drag, and men dancing together?' asked Steve Segundo.

'Yeah, he'd better just open one day a year - Mardi Gras - because that's the only day female impersonators can wear drag legally in Spain. Any other time they can throw you in jail' said Harrison.

'Isn't Florence of Arabia in partnership with them - you know, Youssef?' asked Jones.

'He's not a partner, he's just helping with the opening night. Wauna wants him out of that flat she's renting to him. He hasn't paid her any rent for four months.' said Harry. 'I wonder if it was Youssef who sent that porno parcel to Ewald.' he added.

'Doubt it,' said Jones. 'Youssef's from Morocco. He wouldn't know how to send a parcel from Sweden.'

'What's this all about?' asked Steve Segundo. 'I'm out of touch with all this gossip, living in Santa Eulalia.'

'The cops went to Ewald's house in Casas Baratas and arrested him because the Post Office opened a parcel that had been sent to him from

Stockholm to his *Apartado* number. There were twenty pornographic magazines, a mink glove and a woolen cock-warmer, knitted by hand, with a heart on it.'

'What did Ewald say?' Steve asked.

'Denied all knowledge of course. Said it must be a joke. But he was given a bad time and they confiscated the magazines. He asked if he could keep the mink glove and the cock-warmer, and they said yes, but he would have to pay duty on the fur as it was imported from Scandinavia, so he just kept the cock-warmer. He said he is going to give it to Wauna for a birthday present.'

'The Hamburg iron,' said Jones. 'What a sight. He looks like the Straw Man from the Wizard of Oz with that battered felt hat and tatty shorts.

'What's this 'iron' business?' asked Steve.

'Iron hoof - poof. Cockney rhyming slang,' said Jones. The Aintree iron, what the Beatles called their manager. The Hamburg iron - Ewald. I hear a farmer offered him a job as a scarecrow in San Jorge.'

'It's not a scarecrow those farmers want in San Jorge, it's a legal adviser. Haven't you heard about Fast Jack? The poker player?' said Harry.

'Is he still in San Jorge?' asked Jones.

'Not after today. No sir. That son of a bitch taught the Ibicenco farmers how to play poker and let them win thousands of pesetas from him. They thought they'd got a real American mug, then when he'd softened them up he took them to the cleaners. He won four farms. They'd have bet their wives and daughters in a game. They're crazy gamblers these people. The cops picked up Jack with the deeds of the farms in his pocket, and made him give them back and then kicked his ass out of the village with a threat of deportation out of Spain if he so much as looked at a deck of cards again. The cops are looking for another guy from there, a Limey called Gerry, who took a packet of dough from the local priest playing Chinos. I hear he bet the poor box and lost again. Gerry taught the English chicks in the girlie bars how to play Chinos and they supplement their wages with their winnings.'

'We call that game Spoof,' said Jones, 'guessing how many coins in a hand. What happened to Gerry, anway?'

'The cops are looking for him. Maybe the Vatican issued a warrant for him, who knows? They asked George the bartender what his surname was as they only knew him as Gerry. George said it was Atric, so they put a wanted man description all over Spain for a Limey called Gerry Atric.'

'Let's go see George. Is he still working the George and Dragon?' said Steve Segundo.

'No. That's Olly, a new guy. George is working three different bars now to save money for another trip. He does Wauna's in the morning, fills in at the Taverna at midday and does an evening shift in the Whisky-a Go-Go, which is where he probably is by now.'

'Ok,' said Elki, who had sat silent, staring into his beer. 'We have a drink in each bar on the way.'

In Wauna's bar Doreen sat in her usual corner in front of a gin and tonic and Fortune sat in the opposite corner, chatting to Wauna.

'Hi Steve, Hi Tris. Hi Ilka,' Fortune called as they entered 'Have a drink.'

'What happened to Harrison?' Steve asked, looking around.

'He mumbled something about the boots hurting his feet and he's gone home. He thinks they might be a bit too tight for him.' said Jones, accepting a San Miguel from Fortune and blowing her a kiss, before turning to inspect a group of four tourists who sat in the corner seats.

'I don't suppose any of you are looking for a day's sailing?' he asked them. 'I've got a sailing boat here and I do charters by the day to supplement my Royal Navy pension.'

'No thanks, old chap,' said one of the men. 'I think we'll wait till summer comes. We're thinking of buying a property here so we're on a sort of inspection trip. I think we prefer Majorca, actually. It's a bit tatty here, don't you think?'

'Oh, I don't know that I'd say that. It's different, that's for sure. It's more... bohemian... than Majorca, and I think more interesting, the people are more individualistic, if you know what I mean.'

'Oh yes. We've certainly seen some freaks and weirdos here, but I do admit it has a certain charm.'

Just as he said this there was a sound of dogs fighting on the street and the howls and shrieks of those that had been bitten by their opponents. As the noise of the fight disappeared around the corner and the dogs ran, nipping at each other's heels, a bedraggled rat limped into the bar.

'Oh, my Gawd,' said one of the lady visitors, 'look, it's a rat, it's been savaged by those horrible dogs on this island. Half of them should be put down.'

'That's what the Ibicencos say about the tourists here in the summer,' said Jones.

'Wauna - there's a rat in the bar for heaven's sake,' squeaked Fortune, hitching her beautiful legs higher on the bar stool.

'So who'd notice?' said Wauna, trying to peer over the bar. 'All right. Get me my broomstick. It's in the closet there, by the loo.'

'You don't need your broomstick, Wauna. They've got taxis here now,' said Jones with an evil grin.

'There's a harbour here, too, and you'll be in it if you don't button your lip, sailor.'

Suddenly Doreen got down from her bar stool, saying: 'Oh, look - poor little thing. It's hurt its leg.' She picked the rat up and the lady visitor let out a scream. Doreen examined the rat's hind leg and then put it up to her left shoulder, stroking its head. 'Did the nasty dogs hurt your leg, then?' She held the rat in her left hand and stroked it with her right, while the rat snuggled into the neckline of her dress. 'Look, it's trembling, poor little thing,' she said, while the group of visitors hastily gathered up their belongings and fled from the bar.

'Put the bloody thing out in the street, Doreen, will you - I'm losing customers like the New York Mets lose baseball games. When it's 'Be Kind to Rats Week' I'll let you know.' said Wauna, having tried, and failed, to squeeze through the gap in the bar counter where Fortune sat. 'And wash your hands afterwards.'

'And comb your hair,' said Steve Segundo.

'And brush your tooth,' said Jones.

'I thought we were going to see George?' said Elki, finishing his beer.

'Yes, come on,' said Steve, 'I haven't seen George in months.'I need some cheering up.'

At about this time, George was telling the American off the boat: 'How many times must I tell you – I'm not serving you. Why don't you go to the George and Dragon?'

'What's the point?' the little man slurred. *'You'll only be down there!'*

CHAPTER 22

Cops and Robbers

THE winter was short in Ibiza, with only two chilly months, January and February, but the low temperature was alleviated by the sight of spring flowers and trees in blossom, mimosa at Christmas time, the almond blossom in the first two months of the year, then cherry and peach blossom, set against the fiery red earth of the fields and emerald green wheat and grass, and the sea, always the blue Mediterranean in the distance. The days were magnificent - in some years the sun shone in a cloudless sky throughout the first two months - but the nights... well, the nights could be a strain when winter madness set in, and the bars were open all night and young men cruised in search of girls, the summer girls, who had gone home to England and France and Germany and Scandinavia. That was when the fights started, when the frustration led to fisticuffs and there was nothing to do but drink.

It was Dutch Katie who first noticed what a bad waiter Rapido was. He always forgot something, no matter what the order. It seemed that his mind was elsewhere when foreigners were ordering drinks, as if he were listening to the conversation on the next table, although everyone knew he didn't understand a word of English. She did not like bars much anyway, and she had divorced her husband, an English doctor, because of the British licensing laws which dictated his life, meaning she served lunch at 3.30 pm weekdays and at 2.30 pm on Sundays when the pubs shut.

Katie Pote was probably the only woman in Europe who could give her grounds for divorce as 'the British licensing laws'. She would rail at Rapido in fluent Spanish, but the young sixteen year old waiter simply looked blank and returned with whatever he had forgotten: the spoon, the sugar, the gin, or the ice or the fried air.

Even the name the foreigners had given the waiter, Rapido, made visitors laugh. Possibly because he had been a solicitor in England, or because of the large amount of money he owed the bar, Deaf Henry got marginally quicker service than Pot Peggy, Walking Marty, Too Much Tommy and Jill the Pill. Ignored by Rapido as a pariah, Nescafe Jack sat on the edge of the group, waiting for an invitation.

Katie Pote had been joined inside the bar by a Polish Merchant seaman off a salt boat moored off Salinas waiting to be loaded. Although she spoke seven European languages fluently, Polish was not one of them. They communicated in broken English as Katie watched Tristan Jones go by, wearing his yachting cap at a jaunty angle and carrying his British Seagull outboard motor over his left shoulder on the way to the repair shop. She waved to Steve Primero in his fireman's coat, suffering, full of tranquilisers, avoiding bars; at Elki, bent on another bender; at Chelsea Elsie with a heavy suitcase; at Crazy Hans, followed by Mr. Smith and Sir Edward, and, newly arrived from London, Hairy Pat, trying to catch up with the long-distance drinkers.

'I tink, yes, I haff enough to drink now,' the Pole was saying to Dutch Katie. 'Now I want some chicken.'

'Well, you're in luck here because Juanito at the Balear restaurant serves the best farmyard chicken I've ever tasted. Absolutely delicious. It's called *pollestra* here.

The Polish merchant seaman looked blank.

'How much is this chicken?' he asked.

'Well, it's more expensive than usual because it's much better, and bigger of course. I think it's forty-five pesetas.'

'Is that for short time or all night?' said the seaman.

Katie laughed: 'Oh, you mean *chicas* - girls. Not here, my friend, the whorehouse closed years ago. Why don't you go and play darts instead?' She stood up and waved goodbye to the confused seafaring man and followed Chelsea Elsie through the back streets. Outside the Bar Manana she had laid out a stall, and it looked like a scene from Petticoat Lane - where you buy a pair of pigeons and they fly right back again - with Elsie behind her stall, arms akimbo.

'Apples a pound pears, darling, get your lovely kippers 'ere,' she called to Dutch Katie who was amazed to find a display of British goodies that could have come from an old Army and Navy catalogue, the type of fare Colonials used to dream of in far outposts of the Empire. The pride of her display was twelve pairs of kippers laid out on the paper cover of her little stall. Below them lay packets and tins and bottles. There was HP sauce, Birds Custard Powder, Dettol, Fairy Liquid, Daddy's Sauce, Worcestershire Sauce, Heinz Baked Beans (some with sausage), Oxo, Alka Seltzer, Andrew Liver Salts, Sharwood's Curry Powder and Paste, Mango Chutney, Lime Pickle, Piccalilli, PG Tips tea bags and tins of Ovaltine.

'How did you manage to get that lot over to Ibiza?' Katie asked.

'I caused an airport strike, darling,' said Chelsea Elsie, hitching up the bra strap that supported her ample bosom.

'They weren't going to let me on the plane with this lot, so the passengers went on strike first, then the customs men went on strike. They thought I was joking when I said it was hand-baggage. I sang: 'Why Are We Waiting?' and the passengers joined in, then they offered to take a plastic bag each as hand-baggage, so they finally allowed the flight to take off. Course I gave them a cabaret on the way over. Did a strip in the aisle. They loved it. I sang 'I'm one of the ruins that Cromwell knocked about a bit,' and then took the hat round.'

'Got any cornflakes Elsie?' asked Tristan Jones from behind Katie and the small crowd that had gathered.

'Too bulky, darling. Anyway, Fortnum's sell them.'

'Yes, at ten times the price.' Jones picked up a bottle of HP Sauce. 'This is the sauce label that Marty Feldman sings isn't it? In French. Makes it sound sexy. It says its *tres bon avec potages at la viande*. Good with soup and meat, and made from oriental fruit and spices. Houses of Parliament Sauce. Just think about it Elsie. Three hundred years of British Empire with access to all the spices of the East and what are we left with? A bottle of HP Sauce.'

'Put the bugger down if you don't want to buy it.' shouted Elsie. 'If you don't want the whelks don't muck 'em abaht - and take your baby's fingers orf the slab.' she sang. 'Piss off, Jonesy - go and nick some beef. You can't afford my luxury goods. You haven't got a pot to piss in.'

'So you did a strip on the tourist plane did you?' said Jones. 'You should have had a shower first. You've got more tide marks than the North Sea.'

Chelsea Elsie picked up a kipper and threw it, catching Jones squarely in the face before he could duck.

He did a quick disappearing act into the Bar Manana out of Elsie's range of verbal abuse and ample supply of projectiles. Wiping bits of kipper and scales off his bristling beard he addressed Snowy the bar owner: 'Do you allow this sordid commerce outside your premises, Guvnor?' He suddenly stopped talking when he saw the small policeman in the uniform of the municipal police, navy blue with green piping, standing at the bar. 'Evening Captain, the usual?' Snowy called out. 'Yes, Elsie's doing it for charity - Oxfam you know.'

'Is that right?' said Jones, eyeing the policeman suspiciously, as Snowy winked at him. 'I always thought she worked for Oxglut - you have to stuff yourself with as much scran as possible in case there's any left for starving Indians.'

The little policeman swayed slightly on his feet.

'Dardos no bueno,' he slurred, taking a sip of his brandy. *'Pistola mejor'* he hiccuped and started to take the tiny pistol from its holster. Snowy ducked behind the bar and Jones ran into the toilet and locked the door.

'Senor... senor,' Snowy called plaintively from behind his protective cover as the policeman aimed at the dartboard.

'Uno, dos, tres, quatro...' the policeman chanted as he fired six shots into the board, getting one bullseye, one inner, three magpies and an outer. The policeman turned and staggered out of the bar, through the frightened crowd around the kippers who parted to let him through, then ran into the bar to see what had happened. Snowy's ashen face peeped up from behind the counter.

'He shot my dartboard,' he whispered. 'Ruined it. Look - bent all the wire. I mean - you don't expect the Old Bill to behave like that, do you?'

'They're trigger happy, Snowy. The Guardia have shot several passengers of cars with GB plates for going through a road barrier on the mainland without stopping. They shoot the passenger in the back of the head 'cos they think it's a left hand drive car, and can't understand it when the car keeps going,' said Chelsea Elsie.

'What's all the noise? I heard shots,' said George, pushing through the crowd.

'The old Bill just shot up my dartboard,' said Snowy.

'You're lucky he didn't shoot you, mate,' said Tristan Jones, 'for serving him that rot-gut *corriente* brandy.'

'He wouldn't have shot you out of hand just like that, Snowy,' said George. 'Not straight off. They always fire a warning shot into the heart.'

'Hasn't Chelsea Elsie got one for sale? There's a rumour she smuggled one through Spanish Customs in her knickers.' said Jones.

'That wasn't a dartboard,' said Snowy. 'It was a spare wheel for Wauna's car.'

'Not for Wauna's car,' said George, 'she's smuggled two spare wheels back already - inside her bra. That was a Morris Minor in her knickers.'

'Shut up, you lot.' cried Doreen from the crowd, 'there's more important things happening than a copper shooting up a poxy dartboard - the Dog Catcher's in town.'

'What? The Dog Catcher?' called George, 'you'd better watch out then, Doreen, and get yourself a collar and lead quick. Tell you what - I'll give you a quick Bob Martins and have you painlessly destroyed by the RSPCA.'

'It's not funny. You know what they do to dogs. They hang them. They wouldn't waste money on dogs. They can waste ammunition shooting at bloody dartboards. Come on - he's on the Vara de Rey.' said Doreen who held five dog collars in her hand, ready to put on any strays who might fall victim to the wire noose on a long pole, the tool of the Dog Catcher's trade.

'I've left my bar unattended, but go ahead and good luck. Throw the bastard in the harbour.' said George.

'He's already got Fatty and Tikki.'

'Come on,' shouted Chelsea Elsie, 'let's get the bastard. Snowy?'

'Yes Ma'am?'

'Keep an eye on my kippers.'

'Certainly, Ma'am,' said Snowy, a former Merchant Seaman with a dry sense of humour, as he pretended to take out a glass eye and place it on one of Elsie's kippers.

The crowd, about a dozen, trooped out of the Calle de la Virgen to

the Vara de Rey where they found the Dog catcher's van and opened
the back door, releasing Fatty and Tikki who scuttled off in the direction
of the harbour and the safety of the foreign bars. The Dog Catcher tried
to run when he saw the assorted foreign dog-lovers bearing down on
him, but Doreen grabbed him and put a half-Nelson on him while Chelsea
Elsie snapped his pole in half, shouting: 'It'll be your dick next time
you cruel bastard.'

'Piss off or we'll hang you,' shouted Doreen, as Chelsea Elsie took
the snapped off pole with the wire noose on it and put the noose around
the Dog Catcher's neck.

'Here - see how you like being strangled, you little rat-fink,' shouted
Elsie as she tightened the noose and caused the little man's eyes to
bulge from their sockets.

There was a sudden sound of police whistles in the distance and the
crowd scattered, leaving the Dog Catcher lying on the pavement with
his own noose around his neck, gasping for air.

'What the hell's going on?' Hairy Pat asked Steve Primero when
the dog lovers had fled.

'Situation normal in Ibiza,' said Steve. 'He picks up every dog
without a collar. Doreen puts collars on strays. He gets a hundred pesetas
for each dog, so he takes the easy way - picks up valuable poodles and
daschunds, so the owners go screaming to him and pay him to give the
dog back. A nice little racket.'

'I'm just looking for a room for tonight,' said Hairy Pat. 'Do you
know of anyone?'

'Sorry, Pat, but you can't stay with me.'

'No, I know that, Steve. You like privacy.'

'Here - try Galbraith. Here he comes now - the Aussie painter. He's
an expert on crash pads. He'll get you a flop.'

Hairy Pat called to Ian Galbraith who joined them and accepted a
beer and said: 'No problem, Pat. I'm staying in Santa Eulalia tonight,
so you can have my room at the Montesol.'

'You staying at the Montesol?' asked Steve.

'Only for three nights till I find a new apartment. They're weird,
though. I was lying in bed yesterday morning when two guys came and
unscrewed my bedroom door, and replaced it with a new door and a
new number. I mean - seven o'clock in the morning. I couldn't believe

my eyes. Anyway, it's One-Oh-Six now Pat, OK? Remember the number, One-Zero-Six because the key's in my car but the door's open. There are two beds. Use the one that doesn't have the blonde in it.'

'You're kidding.'

'Yes, unfortunately. Use the one that wasn't slept in.'

'Wasn't that Doreen I saw just now?' Hairy Pat asked. ' With the dog collars? She had more dog collars than the archbishop of Canterbury.'

'She's got a kind heart,' said Steve.

'The police pick her up twice a day because she hasn't got a passport,' said the Kangaroo Kid. 'She tells them her father was a policeman but they think that's some kind of slight on their profession.'

'She worked for a vet in London, you know,' said Steve. 'She loves animals. I can sympathise with people who prefer dogs and horses to people.'

'Yeah - a rat limped into Wauna's and she picked it up and started stroking it. She could have caught something.'

'Or it could have caught something from her,' Pat said.

'I saw a Spaniard kissing her last night,' said Steve.

'Brave man,' said Pat.

'But he had his fingers crossed,' said Steve.

'Hey - you two guys wanna eat with me? Es *Quinques?* He's got *potache* and *higado* - liver. But I don't recommend the *lengua,* the tongue, because although it's very good he gives you itty-bitty little portions. Come on, let's go. But I can't pay for you.'

'No, I'm off to Santa Eulalia.'

'I'll join you, Steve,' said Pat, 'now that my accommodation is fixed up - thanks to you, mate. Have a drink.'

'No, I'm off. I've got to paint a sign for a beach bar.'

'Saying what?' asked Steve.

'Chip butties, egg sandwich, sausage sandwich, omlette sandwich, egg and chips, sausage and chips, sausage egg and chips, omlette and chips, corned beef and chips, corned beef egg and chips, the permutations are endless.'

'I can feel my heart contracting already,' said Steve.

'They've started the package tours already,' said Hairy Pat. 'Chelsea Elsie came on one. She sells the return half of her ticket to anyone wanting to go to London. I saw two of them on the harbour just now. One woman said to the other: 'Is that the Mediterranean?' and her friend said: 'I don't know, we came by air.'

'I'm hungry,' said Steve. 'All this talk of food. Jeez - what I wouldn't give to be in Paris now. Just to taste some *pate de campagne* or some celery *remoulade*. They can't even slice a tomato properly here. I just saw three millionaires in Juanito's eating bits of liver and gloating over it. They've never had a decent meal in their miserable *lives*, those assholes. The height of culinary achievement - a bit of burnt liver in Juanito's.'

'You're stir crazy, Steve, you should get off the island. Take a trip.'

'Why don't you buy a car, Steve? You should have a boat, Steve, you should travel more, Steve. Don't you know what *broke* means? I'm bogged down here.'

'I know,' said the Australian. 'I didn't go to Art School in Italy for three years to write chip butties on a board.'

'We could go to Juanito's for *pollestra,*' said Hairy Pat.

'If I have any more chicken I'll grow feathers,' said Steve. 'Besides, Juanito isn't a chef, he's a butcher with a fire.'

'Besides which, you're barred, aren't you?' said the Australian.

'No. Not barred. Just not made very welcome, that's all. Did you hear about that incident in the summer, Pat? He served us the usual shit on toast, undercooked fish and practically raw chicken and soggy fries made in olive oil, so I just picked up the whole goddam table and threw it into an open sewer they were repairing on the harbour. A secret policeman jumped up and arrested me - stuck me against the wall with the barrel of his pistol up my left nostril, and told Juanito he would have to denounce me officially, but he refused, which was very nice of him. 'But he threw your table into the sewer' the cop said to Juanito. 'Oh, I don't mind that - it's the things he said about my cuisine I object to.' His *cuisine*? Come on, Pat, lets go to *Es Quinques*. It's cheap and it's easy, but don't order the tongue. He's mean with the portions.'

In *Es Quinques*, little Jaime greeted Steve Primero like a log-lost brother. *'Hey, Esteve, hay lengua.'*

'See that, Pat? He's trying to make up with me because I complained about the size of the portions he was giving. Just think if we were in France now we'd be ordering tongue with caper sauce, the meat melting in your mouth. OK. OK, Jaime,' Steve called to the *patron*. '*Lengua*. Pat?'

'*Higado*,' said Hairy Pat.

'You're sure you want liver, Pat?'

'Yes, the liver's good here.'

'But I might be jealous if the liver looks better than the tongue.'

'So order the liver and cancel the tongue.'

'No, it's ordered now. Let's just see what happens. I bet he tries to make me jealous with your liver - you watch.'

Steve suddenly let out a yell. 'Holy Cow! I can't eat that. Pat - look what he's trying to serve me.'

An enormous ox-tongue, the size of an outsize football boot, lay flopping over the sides of the little dinner plate, steaming gently, the vapours filling the small dining room of the cafe and drawing the eye of every customer within.

Hairy Pat could see the impish face of Pepita, the small and buxom wife of Jaime, peeping from behind the kitchen door and trying not to convulse with laughter, while the chef himself tried to keep a straight face and say: 'You complain of small portions, Esteve. No more complain, OK?'

'OK, Jaime. OK - you got me. But slice this up so I can eat it like a civilised human being and not a caveman.'

Jaime returned the whole tongue to the kitchen and came back with it sliced and in a neat circle around the serving dish with a sprig of parsley in the middle.

'Hey, that liver looks good,' said Steve when Hairy Pat was served, 'You want to swap? No, no, but it looks good. Let me just try a little, to see what it's like. Here - try some of this tongue. You know I like to order the same dish as the person I'm eating with in case I get jealous. Wasn't that a horrible sight - that tongue steaming away like that? Fancy giving that to me - a guy who couldn't even attempt to gut a chicken or a fish.'

'What's that noise?' asked Hairy Pat as a disturbance started in the street. Tristan Jones, who had been talking to an attractive Spanish girl, had had his yachting cap snatched from his head by the fisherman who had threatened him on the harbour, the *marinero de la tierra*, as Jones had called him, and a fight was about to start in the street. Jones had snatched the cap back from the fisherman and stuck it back on his tousled head, this time at an angle which was not so jaunty, and he glared with one furious eye at his protagonist whilst attempting to date the beautiful Spanish girl, an operation which was enraging the fisherman, for she was most likely the daughter of someone he knew. Trying to watch the cap snatcher and the girl was proving to be difficult for Jones.

'Look at that,' said Steve Primero to Hairy Pat. 'That fisherman is murderous with jealousy. This is some country. You can't eat their food and you can't screw their women.'

'Yes, but do you see who that boatie is trying to date? It's the daughter of the banker, Matutes. She's twenty-three and she wasn't let out without a chaperone all her life until she reached twenty one, and even now she has to be in by nine o'clock at night.'

'Yeah, they'll cut his nut off if he doesn't watch out. He's a bad ass, that Tristan Jones. He sits on the Vara de Rey on Sundays eyeing up the Spanish wives, these little dumpy things who haven't been looked at by a man in thirty years, surrounded by their kids with hubby doing his big macho act buying them ice cream and cokes, and there's Jones trying to pick the wife up - deliberately. It's a wind-up, as the English call it, of course. The wives can't believe it at first, then the husband catches on to the grins and grimaces and twitching eyebrows and bristling beard and he starts jumping up and down in a frenzy.'

'Watch it, here they go...' cried Hairy Pat as the fisherman snatched the cap again and stuck it on his own head.

Jones caught him with a right hook that sent the fisherman flying into the doorway of a souvenir shop.

The gorgeous Miss Matutes took the opportunity to use her discretion and hurry off, consulting the minuscule white gold wrist watch that her father had given her for staying a virgin, and wondering if she would dare to accept the little Welsh captain's invitation to - what had he called it? 'Tea and crumpet' - aboard his little yacht which he had promised her he was moving away from the slaughterhouse and over to the mole the following Saturday, and wondering if he really did have a golden rivet in the boat that he had promised to show her. Perhaps it would be better to refuse his invitation, as he was always getting into fights and trouble... although they were very interesting and exciting... these foreigners...

Jones had not been in the George and Dragon for more than five minutes after the departure of Miss Matutes when the street seemed to Steve Primero and Hairy Pat to be suddenly filled with Ibicenco fishermen, although their actual number, including the *marinero de la tierra*, was five.

'Brought reinforcements, have you mate?' called Jones from the open door of the bar, slowly taking off his waterproof coat and cap and carefully placing them on a bar stool.

'Come on then, me hearties. The more the merrier, as they say in the Royal Navy, 'If in doubt, ask the biggest bastard out'. I'll be right with you.'

He finished his San Miguel and wiped the froth from his beard and moustache, then strode out into the Calle Mayor with the gait of a fighting cock, choosing the biggest of the fishermen and knocked him out with a similar right hook.

The others were so startled at the speed, that Jones had knocked out two more of them, and then the one who had started all of the trouble, before they could recover from their surprise. The other two, smaller and younger than the rest, having seen the slaughter, turned and fled in the direction of the harbour. Jones returned to the bar and put on his coat and cap and ordered another beer.

'I buy this one for you, Captain,' said Crazy Hans at the bar, having seen the action from the bar and believing in taking out little insurance policies. 'So where is your next voyage?'

'My next voyage, mate? Down to South America, the River Plate. I'm going to drop my hook on the Graf Spee.'

'Ho, ho, very funny, Captain. You still don't like Shermans do you? For you the war is never over. But for me it is over. Come on, I invite you for a drink in Figueretas. We pick up some nice girls.'

'Have you got your car then?'

'Yes. I haff my car.'

'I thought the police took it off you earlier today. They seized it, didn't they?'

'Yes, that is true. They seized it and took it to their Headquarters. So I went there and took it back.'

'I'll take a rain check, Hans.'

'What's that?'

'An American expression. Meaning we'll have that drink some other time.'

'OK. OK, no problem. Look there goes Steve Primero. Did you hear about him with the Sherman tourist? 'Don't take the tin foil off'. Ho, ho, ho. 'Whatever you do, don't take the tin foil off'. That Steve Primero - he's too much.'

'No, that's Tommy. He's Too Much.'

'Where is Tommy? I haven't seen him today.'

'Divesting some rich lady of her savings, no doubt,' said Jones, 'and heading straight for the slammer if he stays on his usual form.'

'I saw him yesterday with poor Wolfgang.'

'Poor Wolfgang? Why poor? He hasn't handed over his travellers cheques and Deutschmarks to Tommy has he?'

'No, no, not that. He fell in love last year with Tourist Guide Tricia, the English blonde in Figueretas. He went back to Munich and it cost him a small fortune to divorce his wife; lawyers, alimony, the full legal rip-off. When he came back to Figueretas with the new gold band in his pocket he asked where Tourist Guide Tricia was and they said the hotel. He walked in and found a wedding reception going on. Tricia had married a mainland Spaniard who has a travel agency. When Wolfgang showed her the wedding ring he'd bought and said he'd divorced his wife, she said: 'Oh, sorry ,darling, I didn't think you were serious.'

'Well, the Spaniard is a lucky man to get Trish. She's a beauty. A beauty, boyo. She's what they call an English rose. Peaches and cream complexion, rosebud lips, blue eyes, blonde hair, and intelligent, too. I'd crawl on my belly through broken glass, from Samarkand to Tashkent, just to throw stones at her shit.'

'Ho, ho, ho. You sound as if you are in love with her, too, Captain.'

'No, not me, mate. Can you imagine her aboard my boat. She's nearly six feet tall. No, for years I've been looking for my ideal woman, but I haven't found her yet.'

'You should get a Sherman girlfriend.'

'Oh, I do. Whenever the boat needs cleaning up, I invite a German girl down for tea or drinks and as soon as she sees the mess she says: 'Ziss is like the inside of a Bulgarian Sewage Inspector's office,' and she gets to work with the soap and water, mate.'

'But this ideal woman? What is she to be like?'

'Well, she'd have to be very strong, with arms eight foot long so she could reach the gas stove from the bunk and cook, then she'd have to be about three foot tall with a flat head so I could stow her in my for'ard dodger.'

'You'd better not let Wauna hear you say that or she'll thump you again, Captain.'

'Yeah, if Wauna came aboard my boat the Mediterranean would rise by three inches.'

'I like her though.'

'Oh, I like her too. Offered to give her one once - on a bed of roses. That Bonnie Ronnie the bent barman said: 'They'd have to be big bloody roses,' and Wauna said 'I'm a lesbian and a bloody good one,' and that when Pat the Rat said there's many a slip twixt the...'

The siren on the Alicante boat hooted loudly, drowning momentarily Tristan Jones' words.

'...and the lip,' he finished, cocking an ear to the sound and looking at his watch. 'It's later than I thought,' he said. 'Emile went by just now, I should have known that time was marching on.'

'Emile?'

'The Danish painter. He only paints by night. In charcoal as well. Moonscapes, seascapes, all black as a guardsman's boot. For some reason he thinks the police are after him. I don't know whether it's here or in Copenhagen, but he never comes out until dark.'

'Nuts.'

'Yes, I suppose so. But aren't we all, Hans, aren't we all? All men who live on small boats are nuts. They end up ironing the dishcloth.' Jones signaled to the barman for two beers. 'That Ibbo fisherman who started the fight thinks I'm nuts. You know why? He and his mate asked me what the English do with all the almonds they buy from the island. They've seen the boats loading up for years, sack of almonds for England. I said they make a paste out of them and put it on top of cakes and sell them for Christmas. I saw them tapping their heads significantly as they walked. Thought I was round the twist - almonds made into paste and spread on cakes - who did I think I was kidding?'

'Here comes Wolfgang now.'

'The British tourists who come in here used to say to George when he was working here 'We know you're George, but where's the dragon?'

and he always said: 'She runs the bar next door called Wauna's.' said Jones.

Wolfgang and Hans spoke rapidly in German, with Hans commiserating with him over the loss of Tourist Guide Tricia, then Jones slapped Wolfgang on the back and said he was sorry to hear the bad news.

'Crazy Wolfgang, they call me now,' he said. 'Here we are together - Crazy Hans and Crazy Wolfgang. So we drink instead. Come on, everybody have a drink on Crazy Wolfgang.'

'I don't know about that,' said Jones. 'At least you're not doing night shifts in a factory on the Ruhr.'

Crazy Hans stood on the wooden support of one of the bar stools and stretched up so that he could blow a blast on the long brass and copper hunting horn that was nailed to the ancient beam. 'Now, then, Hans, none of that,' called Olly the barman. 'We don't have a music license in this bar.'

'OK, fill the glass one for Wolfgang. Go on.' called Hans, pointing to the yard of ale surrounded by horse brasses, a standard piece of equipment in English country pubs.

'What is that, exactly?' asked Wolfgang.

'It's a joke, mate. Don't fall for it. They fill the bulb at the bottom with beer and when you drink it it splashes in your face.' said Jones.

'Isn't that a glass replica of a hunting horn?' asked a little Englishman in a blazer and a college tie.

'Don't be daft,' said Jones. *'That's* a hunting horn,' he pointed to a copper instrument on the beam, 'and *that's* a yard of ale.'

'You're all wrong, I'm afraid,' said Olly, leaning over the bar and polishing a glass, 'what that is, in fact, is a British military artifact and it's used for shooting sheep-shit over lighthouses.'

'Ho, ho, ho,' laughed Hans, 'and where do we get the sheep-shit?'

'The place they make the beer, mate,' said Jones, looking at the draft beer he had been served from a tap that had a fake Watneys English beer label on it. 'You can get done for that, you know,' he said to Olly, 'selling this gnat's piss under an English name like that.'

'It fools the tourists, seeing that sign,' said Olly. 'Pete the Parrot put it on the pump, but it's his brother who takes things a bit too far. 'Pint of English bitter, sir?' he says to them, 'why change your habits for a fortnight?'

'I saw Pete the Parrot limping into the Post Office recently. Did he fall off one of those bicycles he hires out to tourists?' asked Jones.

'He probably dropped his wallet on his foot,' said Olly.

'You're a bit disloyal to the chap who employs you, aren't you?' asked the Englishman with the striped tie.

'Who are you when you're at home then, short arse?' Doreen asked him, glaring in his direction from her stool in the corner.

'Just a visitor. I'm waiting for a golfer chappie called Real Estate Roger by the locals here. He's got a very nice house and pool on his books that my sister is interested in buying as she's just inherited a tidy sum from an aunt. The house belongs to that film star - that girl in the James Bond films -.' he said to the curious listeners.

'And Real Estate Roger is selling her house, is he?' asked Jones.

'Oh yes.'

'Does she know?' Doreen asked.

The little man spluttered into his gin and tonic, 'I jolly well hope so,' he said. 'You don't really think... ah, here's Samantha now. Hello, darling...' he greeted a strapping English woman in tweeds and brogue shoes who bounced into the bar, calling: 'I finally made it. My God, what an awful flight. London Airport was sheer hell, darling. And I had a hell of a job getting there from Surrey. I'm gasping for a drink.. G and T darling.'

She breezily chatted to the bar in general as she elbowed Tristan Jones aside and squeezed up to the bar where her brother stood. Jones tried to hold his ground, but all he could do was see a broad tweed-covered back and a broad beam covered by a tweed skirt. 'Couldn't get the Rolls as Henry was using it for golf, and Jack had the Bentley, so I was lumbered, as usual, with the bloody Daimler and you know how I hate driving that in traffic and I had things to pick up in the West End and then of course the usual bloody bottleneck at the flyover and road works... police patrol car... breakdown... hold up'. She paused only to take swift sips from the gin and tonic Olly had poured for her. '... and then to cap it all... car park full... flight late as per usual...'

The voice of Doreen, a sort of grating, from which the faint Irish brogue had been removed after years in London, cut through the flow of sentences emanating from Samantha's lips.

'Oh, bloody 'ell,' said Doreen, 'that's the kind of accent I came all the way here to get away from.'

Without so much as a glance in the direction of Doreen, the stream of information about her journey continued. If Samantha had heard, she gave no indication, simply making a half glance over her shoulder to where Tristan Jones was steadfastly trying to maintain his former position at the bar and then shuffling backwards with her ample bottom so that the wiry little seafarer was moved further up the counter.

Jones had clearly had enough. He opened the yellow Sou'Wester jacket that was usually kept shut to insulate him in his worn seaman's jersey against inclement weather, then started to unzip his trousers. He began to nudge Samantha in the ribs, harder and harder.

For a full minute she ignored the poking in her ribs, with Jones feeling like a mosquito attacking an armoured car, then suddenly she turned with a growl: 'Yes, yes? What is it?' she said furiously to Jones.

Jones, with his left hand, slowly opened the yellow jacket and Samantha looked down and saw that Jones was holding in his right had what looked to her like a miniturised, varicosed shillelagh in the gloom of the bar.

'What would you do with *that*, girl?' Jones asked her.

Scarcely pausing to interrupt the half finished sentence on her lips, she turned her head away haughtily and said: 'I think I'd *wash* it for a start...' and turned her broad back on Jones '... and of course, *furious* when the damned Spanish customs wanted me to open the parcel...'

Jones, crestfallen, decided it was time to cast off, and moved, slowly and carefully away from the bar and the tweed costume and the voice that went on and on...

'George,' he called in the Calle Mayor, spotting him hurrying towards the harbour. 'You're finished early, mate.'

'Yes, the cops came in again. They want more whitewash on the walls and the toilet fixing. I've just had three large cognacs and I'm going to have another. Coming?'

'Not half. I've just had my bloody ear bent in there by the kind of woman who lost the British Empire, mate. Look out - here's your dog.. Hello there, Bullshit' he called as a large black-haired griffon ran up to the hurrying figure of George and tried to jump up and give him a kiss.

'Down Bullshit, down. What are you doing in town, anyway? Come for a drink, have you? Wauna will shoot you if she sees you, Bully. She's doing her nut.'

'Why? What's all that about?' Jones asked.

'You know how she loves dogs?'

'What? You mean she still loves dogs after what happened with Joey, her Mum?'

'What was that ?'

'Well, you know she's on five hundred dollars a month from the Actors Union in California and Wauna was very pleased to see her when she arrived, but she had a new set of false teeth she'd paid a fortune for in LA before she retired. Her welcoming supper consisted of slices of York ham. Unfortunately, she put the teeth by her bed and there were bits of ham still in them and the bull terriers ate the teeth. Now she's got to send to LA for a new set. But you say Wauna still loves dogs?'

'Oh yes. Hey - that Joey, you know if I was casting a war film I'd have her play Winston Churchill in drag. No, it's just that Wauna puts out a plastic bowl with water for the dogs at the entrance of the bar. Bully comes into town, picks up the bowl bangs it on the deck, asking for a refill. He picks it up and bangs it down three times and if no one fills it he runs off with it - don't you, Bullshit, you little tea-leaf, you little thief you, you old toe-rag. Come on mate, let's have that cognac. Bully will shoot off as soon as he smells it. He hates the smell of booze. If he gets a whiff of my breath he'll be off to the hills. Oh yes, poor Wauna had to buy three new bowls.'

They sat on the narrow terrace. There was a group of American hippies at the next table, all in their early twenties. George took a piece of string out of his pocket and attached it to Bullshit's collar and the dog obediently lay by his feet, under the table as they gave their order.

'Hey, man, there's a movie on in town tonight at the *Cine Serra.* You wanna go to a movie, Joe? Betty?' one said.

'Bullshit!' George called down as the dog began to agitate and the smell of the cognac drifted below the table.

The American hippies looked sharply at George, who took a sip and said 'Cheers' to Tristan Jones before they drank.

'What kind of movie is it, Bernie? I mean, like, is it something we'll dig, you know?'

'Bullshit!' George shouted, tugging at the string with the restless griffon straining at the end.

The hippies looked at George and at Tristan Jones. Jones certainly looked like a rough customer in his oilskin and with his bristling sailor's beard, an earring through one lobe and a tattoo on the other.

'Man, I dunno, Joe. Like, I think it's one of these *avant garde* movies. You wanna go see it?'

'Man, I dunno. What do you think, Betty? You wanna see this movie?'

'What's *avant garde* mean?' Betty asked.

'I'm not sure,' said Bernie, 'I think it's French for bullshit.'

'Bullshit!' Shouted George, and started to lean down to reach beneath the table..

'Hey, man, if you've got something to say say it directly to us man,' Joe called to George who was endeavouring to untie the dog straining at the string. Suddenly released from captivity, Bullshit shot off along the terrace, fleeing from the torture of drink and lighted dog-ends burning his paws.

'Bullshit - come back here, you toe-rag,' shouted George.

'It's no good, mate. He's gone now,' said Jones.

'Gee,' said Betty, that's the name of his dawg...'

'Here he comes... *grab* him,' George called as the little dog that made occasional appearances on the Vara de Rey came trotting along the pavement heading for the fisherman's houses and the Mole. Jones was quick, he reached down and his hands grasped a furry back which twisted suddenly and the little dog shot away out of reach of George's outstretched hands. The little mongrel scampered, on short legs with a fearful glance over its right shoulder and in seconds was gone, into the back streets.

'The little bugger's done it again,' said George. He has a collar with a brass nameplate on it, so he belongs to somebody. He's probably got a name like... I dunno, but he's a foreigners dog, not a Spaniard's.' I think he must have had an early traumatic experience with the dogcatcher.'

'Or he just hates humans,' said Jones.

'I'll get him one of these days,' said George, 'just to see what his name is. I don't suppose you want to do a shift at Wauna's bar next week do you?'

'Not me, mate. I know my place in a bar - on the customer's side of it. Why?'

'Wauna's taking some time off. She's not feeling too well. She went to the doctor and had a full checkup - heart, lungs, liver, kidneys, blood pressure, the guntz.'

'So what's wrong with her?'

'I dunno. The Doctor said: 'If you don't stop eating and drinking so much, one day soon in your bar you will burst. SPLAT! Just like that,' so she's on a diet.'

'Yeah - I've heard about her diet. Her mother asked what was for breakfast and she said 'All I've got is eggs, darling,' and serves her a large Avocat with ice. Look - here comes that little dog again.'

'No, he's seen us, look at him go.' They watched the mongrel give them a wide berth, keeping out a sharp weather-eye as it made a large semicircle around the cafe where they sat and shoot away between the wooden crates of goods that had been unloaded on the harbour.

'Talking of dogs, do you remember Dog Meat Douglas the Jock?'

'Oh yeah, he was a millionaire, wasn't he, all made out of putting old kangaroo into new tin cans. Wasn't Jeremy skippering for him?'

'For a while, but Jeremy was a good sailor, and he didn't much like that floating plastic soap-dish anyway. He certainly was the night we took that bloody sausage dog aboard. You wouldn't believe how ugly this dog was, George. It had the body of a dachshund, the legs of a corgi, the head of a cairn terrier and it smelt as foul as a basket of whelks on a wet windy night in Whitstable. So we took it aboard.'

'What - aboard the soap-dish?'

'That's right - aboard Dog Meat Dougie's pride and joy. We gave it a bath in his luxury bathroom suite, using his Paris shampoo and talc, then put it on the silk cushions of the master bedroom suite where it lolled around in paradise like a sultan waiting for the dancing girls to come on, and we fed it on the best minced steak from the fridge. I tell you, George, if dogs smoked we'd have given it a Cuban cigar. That bloody hound had the best day of its life. If Dog Meat Dougie had found out it would have been the tin-tack for the crew and a rope for Jeremy off the yardarm. Anyway, I'm off back aboard, mate. I've done enough drinking and fighting and not enough of the other for one day. How about you?'

'Well I had thought of having a quiet night, but I can't stand the strain. The strain of looking at that log fire and wondering what's happening in the bars down town.'

'Nothing is happening in the bars down town.'

'I know. But don't we always go in the hope that there is? I tried to have a night in last week. Finnish Dora had an idea to do some smoked sausages in the chimney and hung them in a string bag, the kind you buy oranges in. Trouble is Beethoven the cat smelt the sausages and reached down into the chimney to try and claw up the bangers when it fell, plop, down the bloody chimney and right into the fire. My nerves! It let out a yell that must have been heard in Majorca, paws and legs outstretched like a cartoon cat and screeching blue murder. Luckily the door was open or it would have gone through the plate glass window. It didn't stop running until it got to Salinas.'

'Here comes Hairy Pat if you want a drinking pal. He looks four sheets to the wind already. See you, mate,' said Jones, standing up and hurrying off before Hairy Pat could persuade him to take another drink.

'I don't believe this island,' said Hairy Pat, joining George on the terrace. 'I just left the taverna where there's a Spaniard dancing with a rubber doll, life-size, in a back room.'

'Oh yes, I've seen him with his dancing partner, but he usually only comes out when it's a full moon. It's not a full moon tonight is it?'

'It's full moon every bloody night here, matey. Snowy has just been told he has to get a dart board licence because of the noise. The noise was made when the cop shot up the board, incidentally. And Dennis is in jail'

'Dennis the Menace? That's my mate. What happened?'

'He went into a barber's shop near the church, grabbed a cut-throat razor and started to sing 'It's a Long Way to Tipperary'. The barber called the cops. They couldn't understand him anyway, pissed as a rat, gabbling away, trying to tell them he'd got the wrong barber's shop. They thought he was an escaped lunatic trying to assassinate the barber, little Manola.'

'Manola's? Bloody 'ell, he got the wrong barber's shop. He must have thought he was in Tipperary's and wanted a sing-song.'

'The cops went to the Montesol and asked his wife to bail him out, and she said no, keep him in for a month at least - while I have a holiday, she said. By the way - have you heard about Charlie One-Oh-Three in Majorca? About the prize?'

'No. How is Charlie?'

'Not very well. The greatest Landlord of them all called 'Time ' for him last week. That's the story.'

'I'm very sorry to hear that. Poor old Charlie - ex-American serviceman, wasn't he? Army?'

'That's right, retired in Terrano, Palma. A photographer spotted him looking great with his sun tan and silver hair and large 103 cognac in his hand and sold the snap to an advertising agency who won first prize for the advert of the year. The agency decided to award a prize to Charlie as well for the wonderful photograph, but when they got to Terrano...'

'He was brown bread.'

'Right.'

'Poor old Charlie One-Oh-Three. Here's to him.'

The solemnly raised their glasses.

'Go easy on this stuff, it's very dangerous,' said George.

'Is that right that Doris Karloff and Ewald the Hamburg Iron are opening a dancing bar for men in the old town? I just saw Youssef on his way home to make a shirt for himself for the opening night.'

'In Spain? Are they nuts? If they can do that, my prick's a bloater. I suppose they're going to sell joints on the door as well? I should cocoa.'

'Why do you say this brandy's dangerous stuff? Seems OK to me.'

'I'm only basing on what happened to Tristan Jones in Palma, but I'm talking about bottles of it, not sips. I mean really hitting it. Jones wound up in Palma lunatic asylum with the darbies and the leg irons on him to restrain him. When the Old Bill picked up a gibbering foreigner they can't understand they sling him in a funny farm rather than the nick in case he does himself injury. So there he was in Palma and the door opened and in came this head banger who was Hungarian and produced a Benson and Hedges cigarette tin, painted black, with wires in it, and told Jones he would be rescued by partisans from the mountains that night. While he was strumming the little makeshift receiver there was another head-banger goose-stepping up and down in the corridor outside, back and forth, back and forth. Jones made enquiries about the jack-boot Jerry as he called him and it turned out he was a German tourist who, for a one thousand peseta bet, had gone down to the bottom of the hotel swimming pool, lay flat, and drank a bottle of Fundador under water.'

'Crikey,' said Hairy Pat. 'That deserves an Iron Cross.'

'Or a wooden cross,' said George. 'He thinks he's on the Paris victory parade with the Fuhrer dancing on the Arc de Triomphe. When they let Jones out he had to see the shrink first. The shrink pulled a bottle of cognac out of his desk drawer and pushed a glass over to Jones who had the sense to say : 'No thanks, doc. Never again,' and the shrink said 'If you'd taken that, we'd have kept you in.' Then the *Madre Superiora* had to give him back his pesetas and the watch they'd taken when they'd felt his collar, and she was in the middle of a prayer session. Jones said it went something like this, but in Spanish: 'Our Father, one hundred, who art in heaven, two hundred, hallowed be thy name, three hundred, thy kingdom come, three hundred and fifty, thy will be done, three hundred and seventy five, on earth, three hundred and eighty, as it is in heaven, three hundred and eighty one, give us this day our daily bread, three hundred and eighty two, and forgive us our trespasses as we forgive those who trespass against us, three hundred and eighty three and your watch *senor, vaya con Dios,'* and he was free.'

'*Jaime*?' Hairy Pat called to the patron of the bar, '*San Miguel, por favor.*'

'But don't let me put you off,' said George.

'Jeez, George, pass the stomach pump. You've put me off for life. I reckon you'd make an agnostic out of a praying mantis, George.'

'Cheer up, Pat, after all here you are in Ibiza, another shitty day in paradise, mate. Come on, let's paint the town red. I must say I like it on the customers' side of the bar, as Jones says.'

Later, much later, as dawn crept over the Mole, and Hairy Pat staggered off to find the Australian painter's hotel room, George awoke in a rowing boat which had been dragged into the dock for caulking.

His flip-flops had fallen from his feet, and George was giggling and chortling in his slumbering position because seven dogs were licking his feet. There was Tikki from the harbour, Otto from Santa Eulalia, Fatty also known as Hardcastle, evicted from the George and Dragon by Madrilas who had gone there to paint the bar at 3 am with two cronies, and Tyke, Whisky, Don Blanco and Tita. George suddenly leapt up and looked at his watch. He remembered being asked by the owner of the

Taverna to close up for him and pushing various drunks out of the door. He remembered going back to the fisherman's bar which was open now and filled with men who had finished their night's work and were drinking beer and eating tortillas. George managed to get his little green van that he had left on the dockside and almost fell into the driver's seat. As he took off, along the quay, he looked in his rear view mirror and saw half a dozen fishermen running behind him, screaming at him to stop, and trying to catch the half million pesetas' worth of brand new blue nylon fishing net that George had managed to catch in the van's axle.

George stopped and had to reverse so the fishermen could unwind the net from beneath the van, with George - or Jordi as they called him in Ibicenco - promising free cognac all round for the whole fishing fleet by way of compensation.

The seven dogs continued to follow the green van as George finally drove off along the harbour, but he lost them before the customs post. Not far from the customs post, from the tightly closed door of the George and Dragon, there came a sound of laughter, and corks popping and glasses chinking and paint being splashed around...

CHAPTER 23

Men Dancing With Men

DAWN in Ibiza, with stragglers from the all night restaurant, C'an Xic, near the bullring, wending their way homewards; late night bartenders, taxi drivers, policemen and night owls of several different nationalities, and Emile the Dane who painted only by night, with two charcoal drawings of the harbour by moonlight under his arm.

In the Calle de la Virgen, trapped by the sleeve of his jacket, caught at the elbow, was a fisherman, snoring softly, the cloth of his coat secured by the hinge of the door when George had tried to eject him in the early hours. Inside, on one of the barstools, sat a rubber doll, the late dancing partner of the snoozing fisherman. By the barstool, in an alcove, slept Randy Mandy, locked in by George, who had failed to see her sleeping form in the gloom of the bar.

A group of foreigners, half a dozen strong, harangued two taxi drivers on the Vara de Rey for refusing to take Bullshit in their cabs, under the 'no dogs, no fleas' rule they operated. 'Right, we'll all walk, if they won't take Bully. Come on, boy,' called a young American, and the party set off to walk to Figueretas a mile away, with Bullshit trotting happily alongside them.

In an hotel room not far away, Hairy Pat awoke and wondered where he was and how he had got there.

In the next bed to him lay a small Spanish businessman from the Peninsular, noticeable always by the dark clothing and the inevitable briefcase full of plans to convert Ibiza into a new Monte Carlo. He watched Hairy Pat cautiously, wondering what this mass of hair and beard was doing in his room. Pat climbed out of bed and went to the wash basin, watching the business man watching him in the mirror. The little man lay stiffly at attention, like a guardsman sleeping, wary in case he was suddenly attacked by this madman in his bedroom.

Hairy Pat brushed his teeth, using the toothbrush and toothpaste he found by the mirror, watched all the time by two wary black eyes, then splashed his face with soap and water, having sniffed the Pink Camay that lay in the soap dish. Still watching each other in the mirror, Hairy Pat quickly pulled on his trousers and shirt and slipped on his shoes and shot out of the door, glancing briefly behind to ascertain that the number of the door bore no relation to that given him by his Australian benefactor.

Over in Santa Eulalia a former Grenadier Guards officer almost seven feet tall and known as Tiny Tim, found himself lying in a ditch with a bicycle on the side of the road and tried to remember the circumstances of his headlong flight by bicycle from a party at the top of the hill. He had been wearing a Harris tweed sports coat and immaculate grey flannels and a pair of Lobb shoes made of crocodile skin with gold buckles, given to him by his wife before she left him for less entertaining company but a more stable relationship. He remembered falling off the bicycle, his money scattering and deciding to sleep the rest of the night away and recover the heap of scattered pesetas at first light. The money was there on the tarmacadam road.

So was the bicycle.

The shoes were missing...

Leaving the hole in the wall that served as her tiny apartment, Little Mimi, famous for having battered Brendan Behan over the head with a frying pan in days of yore, set out on her big adventure - to return from Beirut with two suitcases of hashish and earn enough to buy a shop and retire, at the age of seventy, from the hectic life of an old hippie. All was arranged. The Lebanon was expecting her. The two special suitcases would be ready for her to take to the airport on the first leg of 'the biggie' that they all dreamed about. Unknown to her the suitcases were of a special make recognisable to police, customs and drug enforcement officers at the airport, who would nudge each other and say: 'Here comes another one.' On the Vara de Rey little Mimi checked her handbag before getting into the taxi: British passport, old age pension book, photographs of her children, long deceased, and a lipstick she had not used in many years. Her silver hair glinted in the sun now rising over the Banco Balear and she waved one hand in farewell, saying softly: 'Bye bye Ibiza. See you again soon...'

On the harbour Walking Marty was stopped by a blonde haired, muscular night club bouncer who asked him: 'Hey, Marty - do you speak French?'

'Not much. Why?' Marty asked.

'A French broad gave me a note at the door of the club last night and I can't understand it. Look here.' He produced a scrap of paper which said: *'Je voudrais coucher avec toi.'*

'It said she wants to fuck you,' said Marty.

'Gee, I wish I'd known that,' said the bouncer.

In his splendid villa with a magnificent view of the Mediterranean, Elmyr, having had a sleepless night, was trying to write a letter to his old friend, lover and partner in crime. 'Dear Fernand,' he wrote and tore another sheet off the pad. 'Dear Doublecrosser,' he wrote and tore that sheet off. Far below the hill on which the villa sat, a beachcomber padded slowly along the length of the Playa D'en Bossa, ever hopeful of finding something valuable, but the only thing that had come ashore was Whisky, a part Alsatian, part something else dog that had been thrown overboard from a passing ship and adopted by Finnish Dora.

Elmyr decided he could not write a letter. Instead in red ink he underlined all the passages concerning cruelty in Jean Genet's 'The Thief's Journal' and parceled it ready to post Fernand Legros. Unknown to Elmyr, however, the 'Little Egyptian' was already in the cells at the police station in Geneva, where he had been hiding from the Law. Fernand had spent a week in full drag, having shaved his legs for the sheer silk stocking he wore, showing under the long silk dress, and he sported a black straw cartwheel hat and full makeup of lipstick and mascara and a long jade cigarette holder, frequenting the most expensive hotel bars in Switzerland's most expensive town. That very morning the page boy had called out: 'Telephone for Monsieur Fernand Legros,' and Fernand had heard a voice say: 'Hold on one moment, sir, there's an international call for you.' Four minutes later the squad car arrived and Fernand lost one false eyelash and broke one stiletto heel as he was assisted into the rear seat between two detectives.

The beachcomber, now a dot in the distance, drew level with the

Mare Nostrum hotel, known to the British package tourist fraternity as the Hairy Nostril, and searched briefly the dustbin without result. Not far away, by the bar Azul, in Finnish Dora's empty swimming pool, George slept fitfully, for a little dog called Stroppy or Strop-bollocks was serenading him with a song George had taught him to sing, on a high note, its little snout raised to heaven, sounding for all the world and Dora's neighbours to hear, like a speak-your-weight machine singing 'Ave Maria.'

George awoke with a start, pushed away Stroppy with one bare foot, realised in an instant that his flip flops had been stolen, no doubt by someone in greater need than him, and saw that he had been locked out, for all the *persianas* were tightly shut and bolted from the inside. George leaped out of the pool and took a small comb from his shirt pocket and combed what was left of his once blonde locks. Immediately Bullshit, who was guarding the house began to leap up and down with excitement. George combing his hair meant George was going out or into town or for 'walkies.' The faithful dog followed him through the garden to Vicente's bar where he waited hopefully until George was served a good stiff vodka as a phlegm cutter, then disappeared, realising there would be no 'walkies' that day.

The bar Azul being a favourite hiding place for taxi drivers seeking relaxation from their work, George soon persuaded a driver to take him back into town where he had to open and prepare two bars.

At the Taverna he gently released the trapped fisherman who rolled over and continued to sleep against the step of the house adjoining the bar, but the reception he got when he unchained and unlocked the stout wooden doors was different.

Randy Mandy came at him like a fireball, arms flailing, fists flying, with George managing to ward off some of the blows but suffering a cut cheek in the melee as Randy Mandy let loose a stream of verbal abuse which made George glad he had had that phlegm cutter at Vicente's bar before facing the rigours of bar life in town.

When she had gone, having kicked the prostrate fisherman in the backside muttering about him having kept her awake half the night by knocking on the bar door trying to get in, George began to tidy up and await the delivery of beer and soft drinks.

The harbour dog Tikki paused briefly to mark his territory by urinating swiftly on a line of blue jeans put out by a boutique owner in the Calle de la Virgen, but on receiving a loud shout of *'FUERA!'* from George as he was about to enter the bar, and hazarding a guess that he was not welcome in the morning gloom of the Taverna, he scampered quickly down Piss Alley and onto the Calle Mayor hoping for a better welcome in the George and Dragon.

Some primeval instinct or built-in canine susceptibility to bad vibes made Tikki pause on the threshold and check the expressions on the faces of Olly the barman and Pete the Parrot who stood within. Their expressions could only be described as stunned, for the interior of the olde worlde British bar had changed beyond all recognition. It looked as if Steve Primero's old drinking pal Jackson Pollock had drip-painted his version of a hundred and one dalmatians dancing on piano keyboards. The black beams had been painted white. The white toilet seat had been painted black. The bottles were black and white alternately, all of them empty. The refrigerator had black stripes down it, as had the till.

The once highly polished horse brasses - Pete the Parrot retained the used slices of lemon in drinks for this task whereas Wauna economically retained them for re-use in fresh drinks - had been done in white gloss, whereas the yard-of-ale had been carefully done in black gloss, and the copper and brass hunting horn from the Portobello Road, London, was done in black and white dots, as if Madrilas and his cronies had not quite assimilated a lesson in *pointillism*.

Like the bottles on the shelves, the bar stools had also been painted black and white alternately, but the zebra effect had been carried to its extreme when Olly brought the attention of Pete the Parrot to a deceased cockroach that lay on the bar counter. It had clearly been overcome by paint fumes while making a dash for freedom from the plastic covered sandwich display case and had been trapped in flight by the Madrilas gang, one of whose members may have been a miniaturist, for the tiny body had been carefully done in black and white dots, with all the care of a man engraving the Lord's Prayer on the head of a pin.

'Back to the drawing board,' said Pete the Parrot. 'I'll kill the bastard. Look at that - he's even painted the hard-boiled eggs.'

'Ready for Easter,' said Olly.

'I'll murder him. Where's the key? He hasn't taken it with him, has he?'

'No, luckily he left it where I told him, under the stone outside. Here it is,' said Olly, handing the key over.

Pete the Parrot looked at the ancient iron key. It had been carefully painted in black and white stripes, a final departing touch from Madrilas and his merry men.

Back in the Calle de la Virgen the proprietor of the Taverna regarded George's face, now displaying bits of sticking plaster he had found in the first aid kit to cover up Randy Mandy's scratch marks. 'Thanks for coming in early, George,' he said. 'Cut yourself shaving?'

'No, I haven't shaved yet,' said George.

'You can shoot off now, but listen - before you go...'

'Yes?'

'It's St. Patrick's Day coming up soon.'

'March 17th.'

'Right. And I want no trouble in here. Doreen's barred no matter who's on duty, and so is that loud-mouthed Irish scribbler...'

'What my mate? But he's a good singer. Sings all the Paddy songs.'

'Never mind that. He's barred. He was rude about my bar. Said I had a meter on the salt. And I don't want any recurrence of last year's fiasco when he talked you into putting *creme de menthe* in the beer and there were so many technicolour yawns in the Khasi my cleaning lady resigned. He's at the top of my shit-list, after Doreen. What's that rubber doll doing in the back room?'

'Oh, some fisherman brought it in last night. He was dancing with it. Pretty, isn't she?'

'Another two hundred pounds of air in her and she'd look like Wauna.'

'Do you want me to get rid of it?'

'No. I know the fisherman you mean. Enrico. He's in the book for two hundred and fifty pesetas. I'll hold his girlfriend hostage until he divvies up.'

Far from the shaded, narrow streets of the old town, over the hill where the bones of Phoenician warriors lay at rest, the tall and lovely Fortune Ford left her apartment in sun-drenched Figueretas, glancing fondly at the geraniums in the window boxes and the clinging bougainvillea on the walls as she descended the hill to the taxi rank. Her red Balmain dress was cut low at the bosom, showing off her suntan, and her silk coat was slung casually across her shoulders. She briefly opened a crocodile skin handbag with gold clasps, by Asprey of Bond Street, London, the type that the Palace recommended as presents for her Majesty the Queen by emergent African nations before they went bankrupt, and took out her purse to check that she had the taxi fare to town. In the purse was a pawn ticket, representing the family silver, pledged in London.

At the taxi rank a lone driver was slumped at his wheel, smoking a cigar.

'Are you free-o?' Fortune asked with a winning smile.

'Senora?' said he driver, adjusting his beer belly.

'Are you free-o?'

'No, no frio, Senora. Caliente. Mucho caliente - 'ot.' He waved the soggy cigar butt at the blazing sun.

'I mean,' said Fortune, carefully enunciating the words to try and compensate for her inability to learn a foreign tongue, 'are you free-o to take me to the town-o?' She pointed at the taxi meter.

The driver suddenly gave a smile of understanding, flicked up the metal flag with the word *'LIBRE'* on it, indicating that he was free for hire, and said: *'Libre. Libre senora.'*

'Look - I want a taxi, not a fucking library book,' said Fortune.

The driver jumped out of his seat and leapt to open the door for Fortune, saluting her as she settled back. In town, she over-tipped him and walked sedately from the vegetable market towards the Calle Mayor. From the corner of her eye, she saw Steve Primero's fireman's overcoat at the top of the market place, but there was a huge straw *cesta* over the place where his head should have been. In Wauna's she ordered a gin from George and drank it neat, noticing George's look of chagrin as she tossed it back.

Fortune confided to George that she was looking forward to a weekend in Barcelona with Jaime, her boyfriend who was a milkman and had not been off the island for several years. Just then, Steve Primero passed the open door and Fortune called out to him: 'Steve - drinkie, darling?' and he came in and said sadly: "I'm still on this goddamn wagon, Fortune. I'm determined to stay on it till St. Pat's.'

'Didn't I see you in the vegetable market just now, with that straw bag over your head?' Fortune asked.

Steve laughed. 'Yes. I was hiding. I just got to the market and I saw these two figures like two orange gas butano bottles in the distance - it was soothsayer Cyril and his ever present better 'alf, as he calls her. He's been stopping me from going for my mail with that goddamn ivory ball. I'm expecting a letter from my daughter about her visit.'

Suddenly he raised his voice: 'Goddamnit, she'd better write to me soon. The younger generation. Ungrateful, no manners. I sent her some money...'

'What do you think she'll do with the peseta, Steve?' George asked. 'Have it made into a medallion?'

Steve laughed. 'You're just about right, there, George. No goddamnit, she should write. I am her father, after all. I hope she's not getting into too much dope over there in the States. It's dangerous there for college kids. Damn it. I mean it. If she doesn't write to me soon I'll cut her off with a dollar.'

'But where will you get the dollar?' said a voice in the corner of the bar. It was Mad Mike, awakened by the sound of Steve Primero's shouting.

'Not from you, that's for sure,' said Steve, rounding on the slumped figure in the corner. 'Goddamn serviceman. You get enough dollars from the United States Government to make the Greek geek look like a pauper. But you had to have your ass blown off to get it - you asshole.'

'What did you do in the war, Daddy?' growled Mike.

'Steve was in the Long Range Deserters Group,' said George.

'Anyone who puts a uniform on deserves all he gets, that's all I say,' said Steve. 'The war we should have fought in and didn't was the Spanish Civil War and that led to the rise of...'

'Calm down, darling, calm down,' said Fortune. 'You'd better have a drink. Give him a vodka, George.'

'No, I'm off. I'm staying on that wagon if it kills me.'

'And everyone else,' said Mad Mike.

'You know, you should have a pace-maker in your brain, not your heart,' said Steve. 'You're the kind of man who gives alcoholism a bad name.'

'Talking about pace-makers, darling, Canadian Link is back from Barcelona. He had a pace-maker put in in the hospital there. And he's pushing eighty you know. Amazing stamina.' said Fortune.

'And did you hear what Gordon the Flute said to Link about that?' said George. 'Link was saying how well he was feeling and Gordon asked him how much the whole operation for the pace-maker had cost. Link gave him a figure of well over a hundred thousand pesetas and do you know what Gordon said? 'A waste of money,' he said.

'Yeah, well you'd better watch out on Sunday. He's playing in the town band and you know what that means. I'm staying away if that fruitcake's in town.' said Steve, making for the door.

In the Calle Mayor he met Jill the Pill.

Hey - Jill. Wait a minute, will you? Maybe you can help me...'

'Sure, Steve, what's the problem,?' said Jill.

'Well, I'm off the sauce till St. Patrick's Day, and I'm on Miltowns. I can't take these Dormadinas or Mogodons or Nocturnas because they stay with me right through the next day. The way I sit nodding in these bars these guys think I'm on smack.'

'I can give you half a dozen strong tranqs to see you through,' said Jill the Pill taking a silver snuff box from her *cesta* and searching amongst the contents. 'But you should drop some acid - that would get you through.'

'Are you kidding? Last and only time I tried that stuff the whole old town of Ibiza picked itself up, soared into the air, dived into the sea, came out again and righted itself. And in town all the people had horns growing out of their heads.'

'It depends on your frame of mind, Steve. That's how your subconscious sees people.'

'Depends on your frame of acid you mean. Doctor Frank N. Stein must have made the stuff I took. I thought I was going nuts. The booze is enough of a problem for me.'

'I don't drink.'

'You know what Schnozzle Durante said about people who don't drink? When they get up in the morning, that's as good as they're going to feel for the rest of the day.'

'Not if you snort a line of coke.'

'Be quiet out there,' came a call from Mad Mike in Wauna's bar. 'I can't sleep.'

'Juice head,' Jill the Pill shouted.

'Pot head,' called Mike.

'Meat head,' shouted Steve Primero through the open door.

'Shut up, you. You're the kind of man who gives megalomania a bad name,' shouted Mad Mike.

'Let's move away from here,' said Steve Primero. 'He makes my liver start to twitch.'

'I can tell you how to cure your liver, Steve,' said Jill the Pill as they walked down the Calle Mayor. 'Next time somebody shoots up you should take the needle. If you shoot smack eventually you get hepatitis. With hepatitis you can't touch alcohol for two years. In two years your liver pulls round. You're cured.'

'Gee, thanks for the medical advice, Jill. You want me turned into a goddamn junkie to cure my liver. That's real island philosophy. What I really want is a little - no a lot of money. It's *the only* material thing that interests me.'

'Sell the Jackson Pollock you have in your pad, Steve.'

'There's no Jackson Pollock in my apartment.'

'I'm sure Elmyr could find one. Get it?'

'Oh no. I'm not getting involved in any of that criminal bullshit.'

'But you were great friends. They'd believe it if you suddenly found one. It'd would be worth half a million dollars. He lived in your pad in the village when you went to Mexico, right?'

'Yeah, and he never did pay the rent. Five bucks a week. Jackson couldn't afford a White Castle hamburger. I arranged dinner at Bob and Betty Davis's apartment, the rich Jewish art buyers, and he asked for a hundred dollars for five canvases and all they repeated was: 'But Jackson, we've spent our quota for this year.' He offered them at five dollars each, and still they said no...'

'OK. OK sorry I spoke. You don't like Elmyr anyway, do you? And he probably couldn't do a Pollock. Did you hear what Robin Maugham said? Somebody asked him if he believed Elmyr had done the fakes and Robin said: 'I doubt it. He can't even paint his face.' Which reminds me - are you going to the opening of Doris Karloff's bar tonight?'

'Tonight? I thought it was next week.'

'They don't want it to clash with St. Patrick's Day and with Far Our Phyllis's party, so they've brought it forward. Everybody's dressing up. There's a run on ostrich feathers. Pacha's night club isn't even bothering to open. Everyone will be there, and they're serving *absinthe frappe*, your favourite drink. The Green Fairy. The one you take into the Hotel Noray when you go to Paris for the weekend.'

'Stop. Stop. You're making me want to drink. The Green Fairy, eh? The drink that saw off Oscar Wilde, Verlaine, Rimbaud, Lautrec. *Absenta* makes the heart grow fonder, and home is where the hard-on is...'

'So you'll be there?'

'No. A wagon is a wagon. I'm going home.' he said, hitching the *cesta,* containing five litres of wine, onto his shoulder.

In his tiny apartment, Steve Primero locked the vodka bottle in the cupboard and took out some of his early journals to read. Jill the Pill's reference to Jackson Pollock made him look up those days when the bar owners of the Village would give him five bucks to go to another bar to shout against McCarthy and they'd take Pollock out and jump on his face on the sidewalk to shut him up. Here was the reference to Ditzel's Brooklyn Bakery and to James the Seley family's black chauffeur driving the limousine towards the lights of old Broadway, and Beefsteak Charlie's, and Dinty Moore's, the Winter Garden and the Astor, and Peacock Alley in the Waldorf, The Palm Court at the Ritz, and Sherry's where he had eaten lobster Newburg and Nesselrode Pie, and to Joe's for the bluepoint oysters. Brushing away a furtive but manly tear, Steve Primero's reverie was interrupted by the sound of loud music coming from a new boutique that had opened opposite his apartment.

He tried to read on. Here was a reference to the attempt at matchmaking by the rich Jewish family in the mansion opposite when he had gone with the daughter to the house and looked into the ballroom where a hundred men sat at tables covered in paper. 'What are these men doing?' he had asked her. 'They come every year to count Daddy's money.' Steve Primero looked around the cold water dump with the mattress on the floor, his ear drums shattered by the pop music blaring out in the street below and thought he could have been a millionaire if he'd married... but the damned thing called integrity had stopped this... He jumped up and flung open the window and looked down on a Go-Go boy bobbing and swaying to the rhythm of the blaring music outside his boutique.

'You asshole,' he shouted, and took a large red apple, a present from Fortune - 'for your health, darling' - which had lain there for a week and threw it: a direct hit, on the forehead of the Go-Go boy who collapsed in the street.

'Next time it'll be a hand-grenade, clam head,' shouted Steve Primero. 'Have some respect for other people.'

But the music continued and later more music started further down the street where they were opening up the only bar in Spain where men could dance with men.

As darkness fell they came like butterflies out of the night, dressed in silks and sequins, satin and lace, feathers, frills and furs, and fabrics from India and Japan, and woollen shawls and leather boots and stone-washed jeans and satin shorts and leather sandals from Greece and beads from Morocco and jade and pearls and gold bangles from Tibet and hash pipes from Afghanistan and diamonds from Cartiers and army shirts and navy bell bottoms and espadrilles from Andalucia and shoes from Saks, Fifth Avenue, and handmade batik blouses in peacock colours and leopard skin and patent leather dancing shoes and mascara on false eyelashes and beauty spots on rouged cheeks...

At the door, Doris Karloff clanked as he greeted the guests with chain-mailed gauntlet.

Ewald came as a Green Fairy, to the titters of the assembled throng.

'He's misunderstood again,' someone said. 'It's the name of the drink they're serving - that mind-blowing stuff that tastes like licorice.'

'No,' said Youssef, 'Doris wants to call the bar The Green Fairy. His English is not very good.'

'He made a good job of it anyway,' someone else said.

With his lanky frame and spindle shanks, Ewald looked like a praying mantis trapped in the gossamer of a spider's web, with a skirt of the flimsiest gauze and shirt of *broderie anglaise,* all of the ensemble in pale green and topped off by a pair of fairy wings, glistening and transparent, and, held delicately in his fingers, a green wand with a star on it.

'Abracadabra, darling,' someone said, 'get a load of *her,*' as Doris Karloff crushed Ewald's artist's fingers in a studded leather gauntlet, and Ewald let out a small squeak of pain. 'If she casts a spell on you, dear, you'll change into a green frog.'

'He's not as green as he looks,' said Pot Peggy, overhearing the remarks, smiling as the gangling, viridescent apparition glided into the packed bar where the music blared out and the words were: 'Even the Bad Times were Good,' and then changed suddenly to the romantic theme: 'Love is in the Air...' and sure enough men were dancing with men just as Doris Karloff had predicted, and there was Youssef in a new shirt of brilliant colours, hand sewn that same day, doing some kind of rumba with Gordon the Flute wearing one of Fortune's Balmain dresses, and, sitting shyly in the corner like two young lovers, was the island's gerontophile Jeweler with a 90 year old whom he kept in luxury and was only unfaithful when American bishops crossed the Atlantic to visit him with his worldwide reputation for preferring men with one foot in the grave...

Doris Karloff finished greeting guests and joined the throng at the bar where the famous green fairy *absenta* was being served and the French contingent dripped it from a height with still mountain water.

'Zeez ees 'ow we do eet in zee good ol' days,' said Jean-Jacques, dripping the water from a tiny glass jug held high above the glass and letting the drops fall slowly onto the powerful liquid turning it milky. "Eet is made from zee vurmvood...'

'You mean wormwood.' said Peggy.

'Zat's what I said, vurmvood, wiz zee flavour of fennel.'

'Flannel?'

'No, fennel, zee 'erb...'

The conversation eddied and flowed, snatches of gossip and comment heard between gaps in the blaring music...

'Doris Karloff used to be a model before she came here, you know.' 'Oh yes? What did she model? The Indian head nickel?' 'No, she did the S.S. cap badge.'

'He looks so *butch,* but he'd give his right arm to be ambidextrous...'

'That Cockney barman, George... I asked him for a shandy and he said 'Do you want it in a straight glass or a gay glass', the cheeky sod.'

'She said they'd charged her fifteen times what the real bar bill should have been, but she couldn't remember ordering the drinks anyway so she couldn't argue with them...'

'That's what comes of drinking with an empty head...'

'My God, she looked like Whistler's mother...'

'Then he said: 'Girls are all right, but it's not like the *real thing...*'

'He'd screw a frog - if it would stop jumping...'

The bitchiness and gossip stopped for an instant when Elmyr arrived. Elmyr had no need of ostrich feathers or fancy dress. He wore a smoking jacket the colour of port wine, a black bow tie, a silk shirt from Athens, black trousers and Italian shoes. There were slaps on the back and kisses on the cheek for the King of fake paintings, and Elmyr glad-handed and kissed his way to the bar where he refused a Green Fairy and was offered several island drinks: *hierbas, frigola,* or *mij y mij* which was an invention from the Taverna, consisting of *Fernet Branca* and *creme de menthe*, and the choice of Tequila Sunrise, Cuba Libre or a chocolate and brandy drink called Lumumba which had been invented around the time of the world's first hijack, of Patrice Lumumba, staged in Ibiza. Elmyr settled for a glass of champagne.

In one corner, with Sandy Fawkes, Lionel Bart was proclaiming to all who would listen: 'I admit it, I'm a male chauvinist poof.'

In white fur, Sandy from Santa Eulalia arrived and was welcomed by the throng. He was closely followed by Robin Maugham and Ursula Andress and Diana Rigg and Terry Thomas and Leslie Philips and Lulu and Susie and Denholm Elliot, the stars with homes on the island who made brief appearances at the opening of art galleries or restaurants or bars, then went back into hiding.

Wauna made a brief appearance to test the strength of the opposition, and by her side was Princess Indira, her companion of many years, a Brahmin cut off from her family fortune when an English newspaper revealed that she was working as a dancing girl in a night club in London. Indi, distressed and broke, was forced to join the BBC.

'That's funny, darling,' Wauna said to her. 'That shirt Youssef's wearing. I'm sure I've seen that material somewhere before.'

'You have darling. We bought it in Cortes Ingles in Barcelona, don't you remember? I warned you the Arab wouldn't be a good tenant. When next you enter the flat, you'll undoubtedly find two big holes in the curtains, for that's the material we made them with.'

'I'll kill the little bastard,' Wauna snarled, bunching her fist ready to wade in, across the dance floor, and knock Youssef into the middle of next week.

'Slowly, slowly, darling,' said Indi, 'don't spoil the party. We'll settle his hash later.'

'Hash? You got hash?' said the hippie who was being held up by

Steve Segundo to stop him collapsing, stoned, on the dance floor.

'Shut up, shit brain,' snapped Wauna and elbowed her way through to the bar where Far Out Phyllis had joined the stars to drink champagne.

Two municipal policemen, in their navy blue uniforms with the green piping, stopped suddenly at the packed throng in the entrance to the new bar where men could dance with men. They pushed their way through until they could see what was going on inside and their faces turned the colour of the whitewash on the bar walls. Breaking, unusually, into a trot, they hastened towards Headquarters with the news that either the foreigners had gone mad or there had been an invasion from Mars. They had seen Ewald dancing with Gordon the Flute, Doris Karloff doing the rumba with Youssef wearing Wauna's curtains as a shirt, and the waiter from Es Quinques in full bridal dress with a bouquet of fake orange blossom trying to get in to ask Doris Karloff for a dance.

Some sixth sense or some signal to the antennae that the famous wear told them that all was not well. Perhaps someone had seen the two policemen almost running down the street to report this new, outrageous 'happening' in Ibiza, and had put the whisper around the bar, for suddenly the stars began to drift away, having paid a duty call and wished good luck to the proprietors.

Luckily for Doris Karloff and Ewald and Youssef, the drinks had run out and very few people were left by the time the real police arrived, having delayed their raid on the new bar where men danced with men until after their supper and card game in C'an Xic, so they simply told the new proprietors of the Green Fairy to report to HQ next morning to receive the formal notice of closure and to pay one hundred pesetas for the plank that would be nailed across the door for the rest of the season, announcing the end of the Green Fairy and their premature belief that men could dance with men in Spain.

With St. Patrick's Day looming up, several of the heavy drinkers slowed down in order to conserve their energy and strength for that monumental binge. There was, however, one exception: Gordon the Flute was playing in the town band on the Sunday before the feast day. The Sunday dawned bright and clear, with a cloudless blue sky and the sun hot in the Vara de Rey with the linnets chirruping in the plane trees as Gordon and the town band made their way, in their newly brushed smart uniforms and peaked caps, into the square in front of the Hotel

Parque and took up position opposite the Bodega on the corner.

'Do the band get paid today?' asked Steve Primero as he stood with Steve Segundo listening to the lilting air by Mozart. 'Yes. Last Sunday of the month.'

'I'm locking my door tonight. That bastard Gordon will be on the rampage again. How much do they get paid?'

'Nothing. A tiny sum. But enough to get slaughtered on if you drink cognac in the bandsmen's bar.'

They drifted away towards the hotel Montesol where the Sunday morning throng had gathered to sit in the sun and gossip and watch the fashions go by. The *apertif* session lasted late in Spain and no one thought of going for lunch until two or even three in the afternoon, to Sa Punta in Santa Eulalia or to Portinatx. The Figueretas experiment had failed miserably due to sabotage: the English family in Winston's had the idea to do a 'Happy Hour' with half price drinks to promote their excellent roast beef and lamb and pork, the traditional British Sunday lunch, and the bar was packed from 11 am until midday. Unfortunately the Dutch owner of the bar opposite, Herman, decided to thwart this competition for his roast chicken and *apfelstrudel* and *apelbollen* by advertising: Happy Hour 12-1pm to which Winston's customers adjourned at midday. Unhappily for the British and Dutch, Pepe the Paella heard about their dastardly schemes to win clients and advertised: Happy Hour, 1 - 2 pm. His bar-restaurant specialising in *Gambas, Calamares, Pinchitos, Buttifarra, Sobresada* and Paella was packed to capacity and by 2.30 pm the streets of Figueretas were filled with reeling drunks having sustained three solid hours of half price drinks. The following day the dustmen noticed an excess of foreign food in the bins, for no one had managed to eat before passing out at siesta time.

George, taking a well-earned morning off from his duties in three bars, was joined at the Alhambra by Harrison, his new boots glistening in the morning sunshine. He ordered a *cafe con leche* and stirred one lump of sugar very slowly, gazing into space.

'You're very quiet this morning, Harry,' said George.

'Yeah.'

'Is there something wrong?'

'Yeah. Like I got a problem, George.'

'What's the problem, Harry?'

'You know like this German chick sent me these boots, made by General Franco's bootmaker on the mainland? We had a great summer together. And... like, I mean, man, what a present to get, handmade tooled leather custom built boots by the *Jefe's* own man...'

'So what's the problem?'

'The problem is, George, I can't get the fuckin' boots *off*.'

'Shit.'

'Right. Ten goddamn days sleeping in the mothers, and I can't for the life of me get the fuckin' things off.'

'Have you tried putting a little oil in them to ease the leather?'

'No. I can't do that.'

'You know what the mountaineers do, Harry? They piss in 'em to soften the leather up, make 'em stretch.'

'George. I'm not pissing in my boots and I am not, repeat not putting any goddamn oil down them, for a very special reason, George.'

'What's that?'

'You know I was going on a trip to England? So I took my dough out of Credito Balear in American dollars, easy to change in Paris or London, you know? Two thousand greenbacks, George. And you know where I hid them?'

'In the boots.'

'Right.'

'That's why you can't get them off.'

'No, it's all in big bills, but I ain't pouring no goddamn oil on those greenbacks, no sir.'

'You should walk to Santa Eulalia and back with Walking Marty, that should sweat them off.'

'You reckon? Hey - there goes Marty now. Thanks, George. I may just do that.' Harrison left his half-finished coffee and hurried off in the wake of Walking Marty, striding towards Pen and Ink corner and the road to Santa Eulalia.

The two Steves had made their way to Jaime's bar, the Estrella, on the harbour, to watch the arrival of the midday boat. As they sipped coffee the customs and police officers lined up a dozen flower children and hippies from the boat and marched them in the direction of the headquarters. As they walked there came the plop-plop of little bundles of hashish and pills being flicked into the still waters of the harbour.

'We should have been under there in a rowing boat, and we could have got the lot,' said Steve Segundo.

'No. I'll stick with the gin.'

'We're getting old, Steve.'

'Yeah, dammit. Don't I know it. Old and bogged down. I remember sitting here and all you could see in the distance was fields. The barber used to come out and shave me for a *duro*. One day an American tourist gave him a dollar tip and he showed me.

'I said to him: 'Tipperary - yes, it was little Tipperary before he lost his shaving license - you will live to regret the day that happened. Once the rich arrive, the goddamn prices go up and then the artists have to leave because they can't afford to stay.'

'You words are coming true. So you are leaving?'

'Feet first.'

'Not to the States? Never again? McCarthy drove you out, right?'

'I'll go back when there's a black woman president.'

'I remember the day I got here I left a transistor, a camera, a pair of binoculars and my clothes in two suitcases on the harbour here and went on a bender that lasted a week with Raymond de Trafford, Jack Beeching, Bernie Bishop and John West. When I came to, all the stuff was still there, untouched. Now they have to chain the garbage cans to the tree.'

By siesta time the whole harbour area had gone quiet, and a few old men, with berets pulled low over their eyes against the setting sun, fished off the Mole. In the evening the crowds came out, families together, strolling in the *paseo,* around the Vara de Rey then down in the Calle Mayor, past Sam's Hamburger and Juanito's and Toto's and Clive's and Merlin's to the Mole to watch the boats, all very harmonious and peaceful, with the young girls eyeing the boys and young wives wheeling babies in prams and parents and grandparents strolling together...

Then Gordon the Flute appeared.

He had torn his English sports coat in two halves, and was waving them and shouting outside Sam's Hamburger, yelling insults at the passing parade who took one look at the fiery red face and the glaring eyes and hastened on.

Hurling one half of his coat into the air, he proceeded to play the bullfighter, taunting young Spaniards, shaking the other half of the coat at them and yelling: '*Toro... toro...*' But, failing to provoke a fight, he picked up a folding chair from outside the hamburger stall and waved it in the air yelling: 'Come on, then, if you want a fight. I'll take the lot of you on.'

By now half the town were stretched along the Mole and the quayside ready to return to the Vara de Rey, while the other half were just starting out on the Sunday evening stroll. Gordon the Flute had the street blocked. As a group of a dozen or so made a move towards the hamburger stall, Gordon rounded on then with a yell and they hastened back around the corner of Juanito's restaurant. Then Gordon turned on the other group, trying to get past him to the harbour and with a shriek, sent them scurrying back to the Calle mayor. It resembled the scene from the Charlie Chaplin film where he is a policeman holding back the mob creeping up on him from the houses on each side of the street.

'Hey - *tranquilo,*' a Spaniard called out to him.

'You what?'

'*Tranquilo. Tranquilo, hombre.*'

Gordon let out a battle cry and charged towards the offender waving his chair, screaming: '*Tranquilo?* I'll give you bloody *tranquilo* matey,' and the man fled back into the Calle Mayor.

For three quarters of an hour Gordon the Flute held the whole town to ransom, and then someone went for Tristan Jones aboard his yacht and asked him to have a word with Gordon to calm him down.

'Come on, Gordon, mate, time to go home,' said Jones, walking straight up to the gesticulating figure in the street.

'Hello there, Jones, my old shipmate. May the skin of your arse never cover a banjo. Get your dukes up.'

'Come on, now Gordon, let these good people have their Sunday evening stroll. Let's go before the *Armada* come down and clap you in irons.'

'Them and who's army? Petty Officer, were you?'

'Oh, up and down, Gordon, up and down, you know.'

'I eat Petty Officers for breakfast. I was aboard H.M.S. Ironside when you were in nappies, mate. Here, cop some of that...' he swung at Jones who ducked under the swing and came up with a swift right hook to Gordon's chin and he fell, unconscious, into Jones' arms.

George appeared from behind the crowd and went to the unconscious figure now lying in the road. 'Come on, George, give me a hand with him. He can sleep it off in the bar. He'll have a bit of a headache when he wakes up, that's all.' They put a hand under each armpit and hauled Gordon the Flute to his feet and dragged him away through the crowd who proceeded on their evening *paseo*.

One Spanish fisherman was heard to say: '*Capitano del barco. Mucho hombre.*' remembering Jones' right hook from a previous occasion.

'I think the Goddess Tanit is the goddess of destructive orgies, mate,' said Jones to George as they laid Gordon the Flute to rest on the cushions in Wauna's bar, putting the two halves of his smart sports coat under his head as a pillow. 'Gordon the Flute isn't the only one on this island who's a bit doolalley. It's not full moon tonight is it?'

'I daren't look in the diary,' said George. 'If I did I'd never come into town that night.'

'I hear Too Much Tommy's in the slammer.'

'Yeah. Vagabondage, as they call it. No visible means of support.'

'But he had at least five hundred quid on him when he arrived.'

'Booze, girls, cards, clubs, taxis, it soon goes. They're deporting him. For four years if he gets an air ticket out, but seven years if he goes the pauper's trail: Palma nick, Gerona nick, French frontier etcetera, and that takes two or three months, before he gets to the Paris consulate. The consul here can't do anything because he's on a temporary passport only.

'When the consul was in the nick she heard a Dutchman call out: 'Do you want sugar in your yoghurt, Hans?' He's been in a year over his time. Won't come out. Prefers the nick to the town. Fewer problems in there, so he's interpreter and general factotum for the warders.'

'Do you know that's an appalling indictment of society when a man prefers prison to freedom.'

'Oh, I don't know,' said George. 'Probably the hash is cheaper in there than it is out here.'

'I hear you've been winding up the tourists, George, when your dogs followed you into the Hairy Nostril.'

'Oh, yeah, Bully, Tyke and Whisky came into the cafeteria, and these English tourists said: 'You're English, aren't you?' and I said: 'Welsh, actually,' and they said: 'How do you get your dogs here? With the quarantine laws and all?' I said: Oh, they come on the Thompson package tour for dogs. It's a plane with kennels, a special quarantine plane for dogs, so they come on holiday with the owners. 'Ooh, isn't that lovely. We can bring our dogs next year.' They'd believe anything.'

Tristan Jones laughed and slapped George on the back. 'I've got a better one than that, mate. You know that sexy blonde Caryl in the Piccadilly Bar in Figgies, the one with the big Bristols? She's great at the wind-up. Some tourists came in and ordered English breakfasts and a pot of tea. 'Milk in the tea?' she asked them and they said: 'Oh, you're English. Do you live here?' and she said 'No. We commute from Henley on Thames. We get the early morning plane here and fly back in the evening. I'll be watching Coronation Street on the telly at home tonight.' 'Ooh, it must work out expensive,' they said. 'Well it is,' said Caryl, 'but we make so much out of English breakfasts it's worth it.'

'I heard a good one from the airport bar,' said George. 'Four beers,' a woman said to the Spanish barman. '*Frio*?' he asked. 'No. Four-o,' she said, holding up her four fingers.'

'It's a funny old island, this, George.'

'Aye. We should swap it for Gib.'

'Then I could get work with Gordon the Flute and Dutch Dick, going round all the British fincas painting houses and mending roofs.

'Don't mention roofs to Gordon and Dick. It's a very sore point with them - and with Joe the Blow.'

'Why? What's happened?'

'They'd been commissioned to put a new roof on the gaff while Joe the Blow is doing his porridge in Strangeways, and as it was an ancient roof of kelp and rotten slats and split *sabena,* they torched it to burn it off quickly and get started on the new one.'

'How can he afford it when he's in the nick and his boat's been smashed up in that storm?'

'Well he had - or thought he had - a little nest egg for the future.'

'Not the insurance? The insurance had run out on the boat. He'll get nothing for that.'

'Not the boat. He had ten kilos of Red Leb stashed here and Jill the Pill went to visit him in chokey and she was the only person who knew where the dope was hidden. Not even his mother knew. He kept dead schtum about it, but when his Mum told him she was getting Gordon and Dick to put a new roof on the *finca* he had to tell Jill where it was hidden, so she could get there first. But when she got to Casas Baratas she almost had a heart attack. 'Where's the roof?' she screamed.'

'No.'

'Yes. 'You pair of bloody drongoes - you've just burnt up a load of Red Leb worth the price of a new yacht for Joe. He'll kill you when he gets back.' she shouted.'

'And what did Gordon the Flute say to that?'

'Not a lot. He just said: 'Ee - I thought it had a funny smell."

CHAPTER 24

The Wearing of the Green

A TIME to fish and a time to mend the nets: in Winter the Ibicencos returned to doing the things they liked to do most: working in their gardens, planting early peas and the popular broad beans that were eaten young and green, in omelettes at Easter, or stored for the potache, the vegetable soup, and the Scottish seed potato that grew so well in the island soil, fishing for pleasure with rod and line; going to football matches or dinghy sailing on Sundays with the evening paseo of courtship and family meetings.

As tourism advanced (they no longer said: 'Eye-bee-za? - Where's that?') at Heathrow airport. A roller-skating rink was built for the teenagers, and Glory Park, a race track for horses and greyhounds, and archery and skeet-shooting, new ways for the locals to spend their new-found wealth, and then they built a Casino for gambling, banned during Franco's time.

One noticeable facet of the prosperity was that the children grew taller than their parents and their grandparents, who were tiny, due to the interbreeding of the basic sixteen families on the island, and also to the better diet after the lean years in Spain following the Civil War - when the diet was salt cod (bacalao) and chick peas and fruit in season.

Even the foreigners who led the hectic bar life would occasionally take a country walk to recover, breathing the pure air and walking through orange orchards and olive groves and fields of almond and fig and carob, full of dwarf irises and marigolds and poppies, admiring the skilful dry-stone walling they thought existed only in the English countryside. For the Isla Blanca. the White Island, was a paradise for country lovers, where field mushrooms grew just off the sea shore and giant mushrooms the size of dinner plates grew by the dirt track that led to the top of Atalaya, the highest mountain on the island and there was fresh watercress in the only river in the Balearic islands: at Santa Eulalia del Rio.

There were many festivals and feast days in the Spanish calendar, San Juan and San Jose being the two favourites as many of the boys on the island were named after these saints... but in the early part of the year the first was Three Kings,* when the children received their Christmas presents, on January the 6th, Epiphany, followed by Mardi Gras the last Tuesday of February, heralding the six weeks of Lent, then Semana Santa, or Holy Week, just before Easter. when only classical music was allowed to be played in all the bars, a law enforced rigidly by the municipal police.

Amongst all of this was St. Patrick's day, celebrated by everyone claiming to have Irish blood in their veins, along with certain Red Indians, black boxers and Russian-Jewish writers, like Captain Frank Taylor (U. S. Marines, rtd.), Nick the former champion boxer of the Sixth Fleet, and Steve Primero from Newark, New Jersey, who were seen strolling down the Calle Major wearing green sashes and bunches of drooping clover leaves in their lapels. the nearest Ibiza could get to shamrock, and they had heard a radio report that there were one hundred and twenty seven bands swinging their way down the green line painted the length of Fifth Avenue, New York.

They were joined by Doreen, wearing a green felt hat and green two-piece costume and a red-bearded Irishman from County Mayo who had managed to get some real shamrock through the mails from a friend, and as they met up, the Americans were singing a song they had heard so often on St. Patrick's day back in the United States:

'Oh. we'll have a Standing Army of the hundred thousand men...
Led by a General, whose name is Finnegan,
All the ships will be painted green,
Maggie Murphy will be Queen,
When Ireland gets Home Rule...'

*There was no racism in Ibiza. Each year one of the Three Kings was black, and threw sweets to all the children who associated a black King with kindness and love.

The Wearing of the Green

In Wauna's bar George wore a green tie and Mad Mike had donned a green baseball cap and bottle green trousers; Jill the Pill wore green lipstick and green nail varnish and Fortune wore a green velvet two-piece costume by Christian Dior, and emeralds.

Mike looked at Frank, Nick and Steve and said to George: 'Get a load of these guys. At least my mother was Irish.'

'Today,' said George, who had dyed the beer green with creme de menthe, 'Everybody's mother is Irish.' And to Steve Primero he said: 'And there's a special rule for getting into the party tonight, Steve.'

'Oh yeah - what's that?'

'You have to dye your hair green. Mike is going to dye his moustache green and Irish Tony said he'd dye his beard green, but I don't think he will. I think he's got his own secret party going on somewhere and a few secreted bottles of Bushmills and Paddy whiskey...'

'Steve won't do it...' said Mike

'Oh yeah - wanna bet?

'Yeah - a bottle of Bushmills says you won't do it.'

'You're on.'

Tristan Jones arrived sporting a small thin leek attached by a safety pin to his seaman's jersey. He was also sporting a big black eye.

'And I'm flying a sweeping brush from my mainmast,' said Jones as they all stared at his shiner. 'One of those crafty Ibbo fishermen caught me by surprise in the dark last night and knocked me straight into the 'oggin. So I've advanced St. David's day and I'm going to sweep the sea clean. When Van Trompe flew a whip from his mast to whip the British fleet, Drake attached a broom to his and swept the seas clean for the Royal Navy.'

'Lookout - here comes Paul the Bubble,' said George.

'Bubble?' said Mike.

'Bubble and Squeak - Greek. Rhyming slang,' George explained to the American.

'Hey - look at you guys,' said Paul George entering the bar. 'I forgot it was Saint Paddy's day - and I'm part Irish...'

'Yeah, ' said Mike, 'part Irish, part Scotch and part Bourbon.'

'When are you going to England to get that Jaguar for me, George? I just gotta get back to racin' again...'

'Can you imagine him in a Jaguar?' Doreen asked, sarcastically, then burst into song:

'Oh. what a Fag-you-are, in your Jag-you-are.'

'Jag-you-were when he wraps it round a bloody tree,' said Tristan. who resented Paul's enormous dollar remittance from his brother in Hollywood when his own Royal Navy pension had been reduced from £6 a week to £2 a week, because, he believed, someone had reported him chartering and therefore physically fit after his medical discharge.

'Here comes Rick the Prick, back from Barcelona,' said Doreen. He was wearing his motor cycle leathers and had a plaster dildo in his back pocket, as usual (he presented it to girls who turned him down, offering to lend it to them). On his arm was a beautiful Flower Child.

'Jeez - the Wearing of the Green in here. Allow me to present the future Mrs. Rick the Prick, Cokespoon Kathy. That's what she does - she manufactures coke spoons in silver and they go like a bomb in London and Paris. Anybody wanna buy a coke spoon?'

He pointed to the tiny silver cocaine spoon that Cokespoon Kathy wore, attached to a silver chain around her neck.

'I'll stick to San Miguel,' said Tristan.

'Got any snow to go with it? asked Frank.

'Negative, sir,' said Rick, who respected ex-officers, having pulled down five years in the U. S. Navy.

'Goddamn junkies - you give me a pain in the ass. George - gimme a gin *con gel*,' said Steve.

'We just left the fishermen's bar,' said Rick, 'and there was an English guy in there, who used to be an officer in the Grenadier Guards. Seems this long drink of water had been put on pills by his doctor to stop him drinking, but he fell off the wagon at a party in Santa Eulalia and got on a bike and rode down the hill and fell off in the dark into a ditch. He decided to wait till morning because he'd heard his money scatter out of his pocket. When he woke up, with the sun out, all his money was there, but his shoes were gone, a wedding present made by the famous bootmaker in London called Lobb, cost a fortune, with gold buckles and crocodile skin, from his wife. He's been going all over the island trying to find an Ibicenco fisherman wearing a pair of Lobb's shoes - hey, Steve, get your hands off my girlfriend's ass, will you...'

Steve Primero took his hand away quickly, laughing.

'You're too old for that. Stop dreaming old man,' said Rick.

'Oh yeah? Some people are beginning to wonder about you, old man, walking around with that stoopid plaster dick in your back pocket.'

'What you need, Steve, is an aphrodisiac,' said George.

'Don't I know it! I've tried them all, and they don't work. As Errol Flynn used to say, the only aphrodisiac is another woman, and he should know. Hey, I just remembered that somebody wrote a poem about me and Nescafe Jack discussing the ageing process. It went something like this:

Said Steve to Jack, 'what is an aphrodisiac?'
Said Jack to Steve, 'To tell the truth,
The only aphrodisiac is YOUTH!'

So how about that for truth? And talking about youth, my goddamn daughter hasn't written to me yet... people don't write letters any more. What happened to the American love of letters, for Chrissake, and all those famous letter writers: Gertrude Stein, Ernest Hemingstein, F. Scott Fitzglitter, T.S.E., the tse-tse fly Elliot, and William Faulkener, Dixie's Dostoyevsky, and those two English men of letters, Florence of Arabia and Alfred Lawn Tennison... '

'The curse has come upon me, cried the Lady of Shallot...' called Doreen.

'Here - you're supposed to be barred from here,' said George.

'Don't I get a dispensation for St. Patrick's day?'

'Oh, all right then, but just you behave yourself in this bar.'

'What's that supposed to mean?'

'Just keep a civil tongue in my arse,' said George, smiling.

'It's a bit vulgar in here, isn't it?' said Cherokee Frank

'No place for an officer and a gentleman, no sir,' said Rick.

'Hey Gawge - gimme that gin, will you? I haven't got all day...' shouted Steve.

He paused for a moment, and looked thoughtful, a little smile breaking out at the corners of his mouth as he looked around and said, shyly: 'Come to think of it - I *have*!'

Grimes the old cartoonist came into the bar, a little silver haired artist. who had lived for years in the old town. 'I'm leaving Spain,' he said woefully, 'I've just been refused a *residencia* because they say I haven't paid tax on the portraits I sold here. I'm eighty years of age, for

God's sake. I was in the first World War. They only want people with money here. Look at me, I'm shaking...' He showed his trembIing hands.

'Isn't that what they call the D.D.T's?' said Cyril's wife, having come into the bar quietly with her husband, having discarded their orange capes (the gas butano bottle look) knowing it might cause offence on this day.

'No, dear, that's what you spray on your fly buttons,' said Cyril.

'This place is boring,' said Cokespoon Kathy. 'I'm going to Wauna's bar...'

George looked at Steve who looked at Kathy's flowing Indian robes as she flounced out. 'Check the bar sign outside, will you, Steve - maybe I'm serving in the wrong bar.'

'Goddamn Junkies - they don't know their ass from a hole in the ground,' said Steve, glaring at Rick, clearly jealous of him and Kathy.

'Anybody want to order an Irish coffee?' asked George.

'Irish coffee? You make that with fake ingrediants,' said Doreen. 'Brendan Behan said businessmen were only crooks with an office, and I say British bar owners in Spain are boa-constrictors - B.O.A., the British bar owners association. Time, gentlemen, please. Watch your language. Behave yourselves. We've got homes to go to if you haven't. No sex in the bar - we're British. And they make the so-called Irish coffee out of *hierbas*, Nescafe and margarine and milk whisked up in the mixer to con the tourists.'

'That's slander,' said George. 'Wauna doesn't use margarine, she uses Tulipan.'

'You're not allowed to bar people in Spain. It's a public bar. These little fascist pricks come over from England and inflict their own standards on us here, their own mean-minded puritanism and their ridiculous licensing laws. Some of them even have the nerve to close on Sundays...'

'Darling, stop worrying about it. Have another drink,' said Fortune. 'It'll be party time soon.'

A Spanish waiter came into the bar and called out to Steve Primero: *'Hola, Esteve! Telegrama para te - bar Estrella.'*

Steve, looking flustered, hurried out of Wauna's bar to pick up his telegram. He returned two minutes later waving the telegram and calling: 'It's from my daughter, Rebecca. She's coming to Ibiza, arriving today. Frank, can you give me a lift to the airport?'

CHAPTER 25

Party Time

FAR Out Phyllis rented an enormous old farmhouse on the hillside above the village of Jesus, with a magnificent view of the old town of Ibiza, especially at night, with its lights flickering and winking in the distance like the decorations on a Christmas tree. In the living room was an enormous fireplace with a rack of a hundred assorted hashish pipes and chillums from many parts of the world. On the terrace below the house were set out several tables groaning with ham and beef and French, Russian and German salads, and three barrels of wine, red, white and rose, and two barrels of beer and cases of bottled beer and wine.

Most of the island's stars and celebrities were there, mixing with American navy, army and air force ex-servicemen, a few British colonials from Santa Eulalia, painters, poets, writers, sculptors, photographers, dancers, ex-jail birds and nickel-and-dime dope dealers, forgers, pimps, confidence tricksters, car thieves, singers, waiters and barmen, bar owners, bar flies, poker players, card-sharpers, roulette players and croupiers, journalists, cooks, cleaners and kleptomaniacs, all milling around the food and drink tables as the conversations of a dozen or more nationalities floated in the afternoon air.

Terry Thomas said: 'Have I told you my favourite drunk story? A drunk went into a restaurant and said: 'Waiter - bring me some fish and chips,' and the waiter said: 'Sorry, sir, but I'm the wine waiter,' and the drunk said: 'All right, then, bring me some wine and chips.'

George, having escaped the bar for an hour or two, was telling one of his London salesman stories: 'I asked her out from the typing pool and we went to a cocktail bar and she said she'd never had a cocktail before, so I ordered a Tom Collins for her, and another and another and next morning when we woke up I went back with her for an eye-opener, a light ale, in the same bar and I asked her what she wanted. "Oh, I'll have the same as I had last night, George," she said, "A John Thomas..."'

A former Royal Navy commander, retired, said: 'Back in the fifties, four British chaps climbed Vedra and planted a Union Jack on the summit. The Spanish were furious, of course, but it took their navy four days to shoot it off doing a target practice.'

Fortune, in an Yves St. Laurent dress and pearl necklace, was saying: 'I like my small, comfortable, flat in Figueretas, darling. I couldn't live in a place as big as this. It's Cold Comfort Farm with central heating.'

Steve Primero, about to leave for the airport with Cherokee Frank, noticed Nick's washed-out blue denim navy-issue workshirt, and said: 'Can you get me a couple of workshirts like that Nick next time the Fleet comes in?'

Rick the Prick said: 'Why? Are you planning to do some work?'

Chelsea Elsie's friend from London, Edna, known as Dreadna, was being told by Pot Peggy: 'Don't you ask my kids to translate at the pharmacy again, Edna. They're only six and seven years old. How would they know the Spanish for "speed"?'

George, asked who Edna was, explained: 'She sleeps in the car park opposite the French pub in Soho. Francis Bacon paid her holiday here. She was supposed to clean Dora's house, and she asked how to get I.T.V. on the gas butano fire. She asked me: "'Ow big's your bird, then, Gawge?" and I said she was pretty big, why? "Cos I tried some of 'er gear on an' I fought I was wearin' a bleedin' parachute."'

Hairy Pat was saying: 'Steve Segundo, you know, Steve Erickson, invited Doreen for Christmas last year in a flat in Figueretas and she got the wrong flat and thought they were late, so she fell asleep and woke up on Boxing night, and missing Christmas altogether.'

Doreen was saying: 'Manchester Dave sent a kid from his bar to buy a *tortilla boccadilla* from Mariano's snack bar opposite, you know, the big omelette sandwich, and when he came back Dave bit into it and said: Wot's this? I asked for a torfookintillioboccafookindillio. This is hard-boiled egg.'

'I hear Jaime, the black sheep of that rich Bilbao family, got thrown out of his flat at Salinas. Every time he killed a mosquito with his flip-flop he put a pornographic stamp over the blood mark on the whitewashed wall. and the cleaning woman brought the priest to him and the priest made the landlord order him to leave.'

'Is that right, he's been everywhere in the world?' a young man asked.

'Sure. He disgraced his family, getting involved with bombers from E.T.A. so they paid him to stay away from the Basque country. For ten years he went to airports and just took the first flight out, no matter where it was going, stayed in a city till he got bored, then went to the airport and took the first flight out. He's quite a character, used to supply dope to Barbara Hutton in Tangiers, and he supplied dope to Tallulah Bankhead and her sister and pulled gypsy boys for them.'

The sea shimmered in the distance and some young ones decided to go for a swim off Talamanca lighthouse rocks. Others passed the chillum and said: 'Wow, man'. The girls wore transparent coloured cheesecloth robes, showing their breasts, badge of the bra-burning generation, and they wore silver and gold slippers from Calcutta and Kashmir, and earrings and bracelets from Goa.

Far Out Phyllis wore a silver silk dress with tassels, a regurgitated fashion from the '20s and the Gatsby era, and smoked a joint through a long jade holder as she discussed and compared home comforts in America and Spain with Gordon the Flute who had managed to get the two halves of his sports coat expertly sewn together by a seamstress and wore neat, pressed grey flannels in the style of an off-duty serviceman, and he was insisting to Phyllis that his finger went through the Spanish toilet paper every time.

Tristan Jones said: 'Marlika, the Dutch teacher in the village school in Jesus, asked me to give a little talk to the kids about the sea and fishing and boats and navigation etcetera. I said they'd heard of Commander Topp, the teacher at the posh school in Santa Eulalia, well I was Captain Bottom from the harbour, which got a laugh, and I talked about the fishing boats they'd seen with their teacher there. Afterwards Marlika asked the children to write a composition. What do *marineros* do? One little boy wrote: '*Marineros* kiss ladies at the top of their legs. I know because when I went home for lunch I saw a *marinero* kissing my mummy there.'

'Ten out of ten for observation,' said Doreen.

* * *

At the airport, people meeting the flight from Madrid looked curiously at Steve Primero with his dyed hair, bright green on the greying strands. He held a photograph of Rebecca in his hand as the passengers came through Customs and the exit barrier.

'Rebecca?' he asked a dark-haired girl in blue jeans and wearing a black leather jacket

'Who are you?' she snapped.

'I'm Steve, your long-lost father.`

'You're my what?'

'I'm your father, Rebecca. Don't you recognise me from my photograph on my books?'

'Your goddamn hair is GREEN!'

'My what?'

'Your HAIR is GREEN, for Chrissake.'

'It is?' said Steve, a little smile playing around his mouth, glancing sideways at Cherokee Frank who stood patiently waiting.

'Let me have a look-see,' said Steve with a wink at Frank.

He walked over to a mirror and yelled: 'HOLY SHIT - my hair's turned green. It must have been that green beer George was selling in Wauna's bar. I'll sue the sonofabitch.'

'He's only kidding,' said Frank to Rebecca. 'Steve did it for a St. Patrick's day bet. It'll grow out.'

'Grow out? What - in two years time? You think I'm going around with a guy with green hair telling people he's my father. And who the fuck are you, anyway?'

'Hey, watch it there, Rebecca, you ain't in New York now. This is Cherokee Frank, invalided out of the Marines with a bad heart, so stop the yelling, OK?'

'Yeah, he's got a bad heart and you've got no heart, right, but you've got two livers, right? That's what Mom told me she said to you, and what your wives said to you. Anyway, what are you doing, a Jew and an Indian celebrating St. Patrick's day? Who was he anyway?'

'Well, if you really want to know,' said Frank, 'I'm told he was the son of a Roman consul who had a villa on the coast of Wales and he went to Ireland and drove the snakes out and sent them to the city of London.'

'So he was Italian?'

'Roman.'

'Same thing. And my so-called father is Jewish, and I was so proud when Mom told me my father was not only Jewish but a literary man and a college man, and I come all the way here to meet a circus freak and...'

'Hey, hold on there now,' said Steve. 'Frank told you I did it for a bet. Don't you have a sense of humour? I might go *blonde* tomorrow, who knows? What's wrong with the younger generation - don't they know how to laugh any more? Don't take life so seriously. Come on, let's have one drink at the bar and then shoot back. There's a great party going on today. You can meet everyone...'

'I don't drink alcohol, *Dad*, but I hear there's some good shit on this island.'

'Doping up at your age? You haven't finished college yet.'

'Get real. You've been living in a cave here...'

'I hope you're not going to do anything here to make me ashamed of you... er... dear...'

'Ashamed? You, ashamed of me? I know all about you guys in New York where they say this is the grooviest place on earth, right? The Indian who chases all the girls. Down to the she in sips, right, Frank? Pony soldier speak with forked tongue, and my Dad with his list of conquests like a teenager counting scalps. And they talk about this open-air lunatic asylum as if it's the greatest thing since sliced bread. And you think *you* might be ashamed of *me*? Put that bottle down, for Chrissake. You're killing yourself with that stuff.'

Steve had taken a bottle of vodka from his pocket and was tilting it back.

'And furthermore, I heard about you, Daddy-o, during Holy Week when they were carrying the cross up the hill to where you live and you were bitching that they were denying you access to your house and you shouted out: 'Only a dumb goy would worship a dead Jew.' It's a good thing they didn't understand or they'd have lynched you. My father - a juice-head yet! Look at yourself - cast-off clothes, old shoes, green hair. What the hell are you doing celebrating St. Patrick's day like all those Micks in the Apple? An Eye-tralian, as they say in the Bronx, a goddamn Guinea. Well how's about this, phrasemaker: Only A Dumb Mick Would Worship A Dead Wop!'

Steve put the bottle in his coat pocket, lifted his eyes heavenwards and said: 'Oi, Oi, Oi. May God forgive me. I have given birth to a RACIST.'

After a silent and uncomfortable journey back to the party, Rebecca turned her back on Steve and joined the group of hippies with the chillums. As a parting shot she turned her head and yelled: 'And I'll tell you something else - one screw on Bleecker Street doesn't make a Daddy.'

* * *

Bodies lay in various stages of undress in the many rooms of Far Out Phyllis's house; a group of four bare girls in one double bed like an erotic Indian fresco, young men in cowboy boots and tight blue jeans and bomber jackets stretched out on mattresses. Rick the Prick and Cokespoon Kathy were entwined between the fridge and the gas cooker; the former naval Commander was sleeping rigidly at attention on top of the dining room table; Chelsea Elsie, Dreadna and Pot Peggy were asleep sitting up on a sofa; an Argentinian anarchist-on-the-run wearing Gordon the Flute's sports coat and flannels and highly polished brogue shoes slept on a kitchen chair, and, on the first terrace, swaying gently in a string hammock, Gordon the Flute slept, wearing Far Out Phyllis's silver silk shimmy dress and silver high-heeled shoes, snoring gently in the morning air.

Doreen held her head in her hands, then searched, painfully, for something to cure her monumental hangover, a drink of any sort, a hair of the dog, but there was nothing to be found, for Too Much Tommy had taken the last drop of gin after Sarah Churchill had taken one big goblet from the pretty litre bottle with the juniper berries on the label.

Sarah had come to Ibiza for sun, starved of it in London, but she did like a drink, as her famous father loved his whisky and his brandy. She had discarded her layers of woollens from the long English winter and stripped, stark naked, in order to sunbathe in the garden where roses grew between cement footpaths, there to stretch out, large gin at hand, to catch the first rays of the sun on her marmoreal skin, for, like most actresses, she never missed the opportunity of getting a sun-tan.

Too Much Tommy raised his miniscule drink with trembling hand.

Suddenly, there was a piercing scream from the garden and a white naked body appeared in the doorway, holding the large goblet that contained the last drink in the house.

'Tommy, that old swine of a Spanish gardener just raped me. I was lying there sunbathing and he jumped out of the rose bed and gave me one, the horrible old ...'

Tommy began to stutter, and when he managed to synchronise the stutter with the trembling of his hand he gasped: 'Bloody hell, Sarah, that's terrible. What are you going to do? How can I help? He actually raped you?'

'Jumped right out of the rose-bed. Talk about Speedy Gonzalez, darling. It was daylight rape. Can you believe it? He must be seventy if he's a day. The nerve of it!'

'Well. what do you want me to do, Sarah? Shall I call the police? It'll cause a terrible scandal, of course. I speak Spanish well enough to phone them. Shall I call the cops?'

Tommy's hand was now shaking at twice the rate it had before the naked aparition had appeared in the doorway clutching her drink.

She made a deep frown, mulling it over, and looked with a myopic stare at the tiny drink in Tommy's hand and at her own glass, held high out of harm's way, at shoulder level, then she said.. 'No, never mind, Tommy. Forget it.' She turned to go back into the garden, and called over her shoulder: `At least he didn't spill the gin.'

* * *

Fortune and her boyfriend Jaime the milkman managed to get their weekend away in Barcelona. In the morning sunshine, while walking up the Ramblas, Fortune spied two lovely white pigeons in a cage for sale and said: 'Wouldn't they look marvellous on my terrace, with the red geraniums, darling? I must buy them.'

'No,' said Jaime gallantly, 'You have paid for the tickets, the hotel, and dinner at the Caracoles last night. It's my turn.'

He then bargained with the crone with the stall, saying he was not a tourist but an Ibicenco, and beat her down to two hundred pesetas for the pair, whereupon she reached into the cage, swiftly wrung their necks and, wrapping them in a page of Il Mondo, handed them to Fortune, who let out a shriek that was heard down the Ramblas as far as the statue of Christopher Columbus. 'She's killed them!' she cried while the crone explained that they were good in an *estofado* or stew, with chick peas.

In Formentera that Sunday morning, a Swedish resident dressed in his best suit and walked into the sea, lay down, and drowned himself after a bout of depression. The Chief of Police raged at the fishermen and others who sat on the sea wall and watched it happen, asking why they had not saved him. But it was explained to the Chief that they did not know he was drowning himself because all foreigners can breathe under water – unlike Spaniards who can't – and did not think he would die in the shallow water. They had seen scuba divers and snorkellers in the bay many times before.

On the Monday morning following this incident, Dutch Katey, who had been away from the island for some years, went to try and renew her resident's permit at the police headquarters. As she passed an open door on the second floor, she heard a call: 'Hello, Katey,' and looked at the title on the door which said the occupant was an assistant Chief of Police, Ibiza. Inside, at a large desk was the former waiter from the Balear cafe, the notorious Rapido. 'Hello, Rapido, what are doing here?' she asked. 'Look on the door, Katey,' Rapido said in perfect English. 'I work here. I was a very bad waiter, but a very good secret policeman. Your residence has been approved, so good luck, and thanks for those tips you gave me.'

The news came that little Mimi had been given ten years in Beirut jail. She formed a committee of murderers, prostitutes, and thieves and soon had them whitewashing the cells. Visited by a couple from Ibiza who asked what conditions were like for a 70-year-old pensioner in an Arab jail in the heat of summer and with eight years to go, she replied with her strong Lancashire accent: 'Oh, it's not too bad, you know. I'll tell you what – it's better than one of those Old Folks Homes in Eastbourne.'

George and McGinn finally managed to capture the little dog on the harbour that had evaded outstretched hands for years. The little leather collar was worn and the brass plate on it had clearly come from a Royal Navy ship, for, engraved on the plate were the words, 'Captain's Toilet.'

'I always thought the little toe-rag was a snob,' said George.

CHAPTER 26

Chaos

THEN there was the summer, the long, scorching Spanish summer when the only breeze came off the seashore and the elderly died of heat-stroke in Seville and Cordoba, and the best place to go was Salinas beach, or for a drink in the cool little bar in La Canal and watch the salt boats at anchor in the beautiful bay, or to swim underwater off Talamanca lighthouse, with the surface of the sea covered with golden date flowers and palm fronds and a thousand startled eyes of a shoal of fish turning in the sea the colour of the blue grotto in Capri.

To awake on bright, fresh mornings with the contrast of the purple and red bougainvillea against the light blue of the sea, and go fishing for *raons* off Formentera, the prehistoric small red fish with pirhana teeth that lived in the sand, and had the best taste of any fish in the Mediterranean, and were rarely seen on sale in a market. The unforgettable sight of flying fish with splayed diaphanous wings, racing between two speedboats and keeping pace, like glistening aluminium models of fish; and the playful dolphins around the keel of Cresswell then, or Banjo or Barbara now, sailing off Es Palmador; and the beach picnics with chicken and salad and cold beer and iced rose wine; and the beautiful girls, daring to go topless and defy the ancient laws of Spain, still slumbering in the 19th century.

The police, however, thought differently. Spanish soldiers strolling by the dunes of Salinas were amazed to see the naked brown bodies of girls on one beach, and further along towards the Martello tower, where a hermit lived, naked men stretching out in the sun. The police rounded them all up and kept them shivering in blankets while they took details, then fined them, and in some cases, deported them.

There were scandals that turned the local people against the hard drug users and the hippies: children ate sugar lumps coated with L.S.D. they had found in a car and went into a coma in hospital; two men jumped from the battlements of the old town, thinking they could fly; two hippie girls in Formentera dug up the bones from graves in the cemetery and settled them around in their hotel room with lighted candles in the eye sockets; a young American girl who dropped too much acid reverted to childhood and was kept hidden down a well and fed from above by her friends until they could ship her back to the United States for treatment; an unpopular backpacker from Canada, aggressive with the locals, was killed and buried in Formentera, and his body was never found.

The little men in black suits and white shirts, carrying briefcases, were beginning to make headway as the new hotels and blocks of flats rose all over the once-primitive paradise.

On the narrow terrace of the bar Estrella which was, in fact, the pavement, Steve Segundo sat quietly reading the Paris edition of the New York Herald Tribune. In the distance, along the Mole, a skull and crossbones and a sweeping brush fluttered and jigged on the mast of Tristan Jones's yacht. At the corner of the Mole, the first work was beginning to turn that picturesque fisherman's working place into a container-ship unloading depot. A merchant vessel was unloading refrigerators and television sets in crates on the harbour.

Four Swiss teenagers, smartly dressed in the latest expensive Paris fashion, went to the boot of their polished Mercedes, opened a suitcase, and changed into hippie shirts, pants, sandals and beads, locked the boot of the car and strolled into town. hoping to blend in and not be charged double because they were Swiss.

Steve Primero, whose hair was now back to normal, changed, free of charge, by Tipperary, for old times' sake, turned to Steve Segundo and said: 'The artists took nothing from this island. Greed will ruin it. I could live for a year on what they pay for a TV set.'

Gordon the Flute, his Daily Express shaking at the corners as he contemplated the city page and realise that the value of his Sterling pension had halved overnight said: 'It's the consumer society, Steve. And they're inhabiting this *Paradiso Perdido.*'

'Did you see those kids getting out of that car?' Steve Segundo asked.

'Phonies,' said Steve Primero. 'With Daddy's or Mummy's travellers' cheques stitched into their tailor-made rags.'

'The bourgeoisie have won,' said Gordon the Flute.

'Well,' said Steve Perimero, 'All I can say is that the artists saw the very best years of this island, as an artist sees a tree or a flower, or a sunset, instead of a balance sheet or a bank statement...'

'If artists ran the world, it would be chaos,' said Gordon the Flute.

'It's chaos now,' said McGinn.